PROGRESS IN

Nucleic Acid Research and Molecular Biology

Volume 42

PROGRESS IN
Nucleic Acid Research and Molecular Biology

edited by

WALDO E. COHN

Biology Division
Oak Ridge National Laboratory
Oak Ridge, Tennessee

KIVIE MOLDAVE

Department of Biology
University of California
Santa Cruz, California

Volume 42

ACADEMIC PRESS, INC.

Harcourt Brace Jovanovich, Publishers

San Diego   New York   Boston
London   Sydney   Tokyo   Toronto

Academic Press, Inc.
1250 Sixth Avenue, San Diego, California 92101

United Kingdom Edition published by
Academic Press Limited
24–28 Oval Road, London NW1 7DX

Library of Congress Catalog Number: 63-15847

International Standard Book Number: 0-12-540042-X

PRINTED IN THE UNITED STATES OF AMERICA
92 93 94 95 96 97   BC   9 8 7 6 5 4 3 2 1

Contents

The Trp Repressor, A Ligand-Activated Regulatory Protein

Ronald Somerville

Immunochemical Analyses of Nucleic Acids

B. David Stollar

Oligodeoxynucleotides as Antisense Inhibitors of Gene Expression

Mridul K. Ghosh and Jack S. Cohen

5,6-Dihydropyrimidine Adducts in the Reactions and Interactions of Pyrimidines with Proteins

Kathryn M. Ivanetich and Daniel V. Santi

RNA Replication of Plant Viruses Containing an RNA Genome

Chantal David, Radhia Gargouri-Bouzid and Anne-Lise Haenni

Intron Splicing and Intron-mediated Enhanced Expression in Monocots

Ralph M. Sinibaldi and Irvin J. Mettler

De Novo Purine Nucleotide Biosynthesis

Howard Zalkin and Jack E. Dixon

Abbreviations and Symbols

All contributors to this Series are asked to use the terminology (abbreviations and symbols) recommended by the IUPAC-IUB Commission on Biochemical Nomenclature (CBN) and approved by IUPAC and IUB, and the Editors endeavor to assure conformity. These Recommendations have been published in many journals (*1, 2*) and compendia (*3*) and are available in reprint form from the Office of Biochemical Nomenclature (OBN); they are therefore considered to be generally known. Those used in nucleic acid work, originally set out in section 5 of the first Recommendations (*1*) and subsequently revised and expanded (*2, 3*), are given in condensed form in the frontmatter of Volumes 9–33 of this series. A recent expansion of the one-letter system (*5*) follows.

SINGLE-LETTER CODE RECOMMENDATIONS[a] (*5*)

Symbol	Meaning	Origin of symbol
G	G	Guanosine
A	A	Adenosine
T(U)	T(U)	(ribo)Thymidine (Uridine)
C	C	Cytidine
R	G or A	puRine
Y	T(U) or C	pYrimidine
M	A or C	aMino
K	G or T(U)	Keto
S	G or C	Strong interaction (3 H-bonds)
W[b]	A or T(U)	Weak interaction (2 H-bonds)
H	A or C or T(U)	not G; H follows G in the alphabet
B	G or T(U) or C	not A; B follows A
V	G or C or A	not T (not U); V follows U
D[c]	G or A or T(U)	not C; D follows C
N	G or A or T(U) or C	aNy nucleoside (i.e., unspecified)
Q	Q	Queuosine (nucleoside of queuine)

[a]Modified from *Proc. Natl. Acad. Sci. U.S.A.* **83**, 4 (1986).
[b]W has been used for wyosine, the nucleoside of "base Y" (wye).
[c]D has been used for dihydrouridine (hU or H_2 Urd).

Enzymes

In naming enzymes, the 1984 recommendations of the IUB Commission on Biochemical Nomenclature (*4*) are followed as far as possible. At first mention, each enzyme is described *either* by its systematic name *or* by the equation for the reaction catalyzed *or* by the recommended trivial name, followed by its EC number in parentheses. Thereafter, a trivial name may be used. Enzyme names are not to be abbreviated except when the substrate has an approved abbreviation (e.g., ATPase, but not LDH, is acceptable).

REFERENCES

1. *JBC* **241**, 527 (1966); *Bchem* **5**, 1445 (1966); *BJ* **101**, 1 (1966); *ABB* **115**, 1 (1966), **129**, 1 (1969); and elsewhere.† General.
2. *EJB* **15**, 203 (1970); *JBC* **245**, 5171 (1970); *JMB* **55**, 299 (1971); and elsewhere.†
3. "Handbook of Biochemistry" (G. Fasman, ed.), 3rd ed. Chemical Rubber Co., Cleveland, Ohio, 1970, 1975, Nucleic Acids, Vols. I and II, pp. 3–59. Nucleic acids.
4. "Enzyme Nomenclature" [Recommendations (1984) of the Nomenclature Committee of the IUB]. Academic Press, New York, 1984.
5. *EJB* **150**, 1 (1985). Nucleic Acids (One-letter system).†

Abbreviations of Journal Titles

Journals	*Abbreviations used*
Annu. Rev. Biochem.	ARB
Annu. Rev. Genet.	ARGen
Arch. Biochem. Biophys.	ABB
Biochem. Biophys. Res. Commun.	BBRC
Biochemistry	Bchem
Biochem. J.	BJ
Biochim. Biophys. Acta	BBA
Cold Spring Harbor	CSH
Cold Spring Harbor Lab	CSHLab
Cold Spring Harbor Symp. Quant. Biol.	CSHSQB
Eur. J. Biochem.	EJB
Fed. Proc.	FP
Hoppe-Seyler's Z. Physiol. Chem.	ZpChem
J. Amer. Chem. Soc.	JACS
J. Bacteriol.	J. Bact.
J. Biol. Chem.	JBC
J. Chem. Soc.	JCS
J. Mol. Biol.	JMB
J. Nat. Cancer Inst.	JNCI
Mol. Cell. Biol.	MCBiol
Mol. Cell. Biochem.	MCBchem
Mol. Gen. Genet.	MGG
Nature, New Biology	Nature NB
Nucleic Acid Research	NARes
Proc. Natl. Acad. Sci. U.S.A.	PNAS
Proc. Soc. Exp. Biol. Med.	PSEBM
Progr. Nucl. Acid. Res. Mol. Biol.	This Series

†Reprints available from the Office of Biochemical Nomenclature (W. E. Cohn, Director).

Some Articles Planned for Future Volumes

Regulation of Gene Expression by Steroid Hormones
ANDREW C. B. CATO, H. PONTA AND P. HERRLICH

Developmental Regulation of Nuclear Gene Expression in *Trypanosoma brucei*
CHRISTINE CLAYTON

The DNA Binding Domain of the Zn(II)-containing Transcription Factors
JOSEPH E. COLMAN AND T. PAN

Latent Viruses and Mutated Oncogenes: No Evidence for Pathogenicity
PETER DUESBERG AND JODY SCHWARTZ

Specific Hormonal and Neoplastic Transcriptional Control of the Alpha 2u Globulin Gene Family
PHILIP FEIGELSON

Cellular Transcriptional Factors Involved in the Regulation of HIV Gene Expression
RICHARD GAYNOR AND C. MUCHARDT

Two Prokaryotic Transcriptional Enhancer Systems
E. PETER GEIDUSCHEK

Correlation between tRNA Structure and Efficient Aminoacylation
RICHARD GIEGE, C. FLORENTZ AND J. PUGLISI

Structure, Function, Evolution of Transcription Factor IIIA
JAY S. HANAS, C. J. GASKINS, J. F. SMITH AND M. K. OGILVIE

snRNA Genes: Transcription by RNA Polymerase II and RNA Polymerase III
NOURIA HERNANDEZ AND S. LOBO

Regulation of mRNA Stability in Yeast
ALLAN JACOBSON

Cell Delivery and Mechanisms of Action of Antisense Oligonucleotides
J. P. LEONETTI, G. DEGOLS, J. P. CLARENC, N. MECHTI AND B. LEBLEU

Signal-transducing G Proteins: Basic and Clinical Implications
MICHAEL A. LEVINE

Synthesis of Ribosomes
LASSE LINDAHL AND J. M. ZENGEL

The Trp Repressor, A Ligand-Activated Regulatory Protein[1]

RONALD SOMERVILLE

Department of Biochemistry
Purdue University
West Lafayette, Indiana 47907

The Trp repressor (protein) of *Escherichia coli* is one of the most exhaustively studied DNA-binding regulatory macromolecules. Its physiological role is to reduce or eliminate transcription from certain regulatable promoters through the formation of RNA-polymerase-preemptive non-

---

[1] In this review, mutant bacterial genes or genotypes are designated according to standard convention in lower-case italics (e.g., *trpR*). Wild-type alleles are indicated with a superscript plus sign (e.g., *trpR*+). Phenotypes and proper names for the protein products of genes are indicated by capitalized roman letters (e.g., Lac, Trp repressor). "Trp repressor" connotes a structurally and functionally characterized protein entity; "*trp* repressor" connotes any factor (and there may be several) having the ability to modify the expression of some gene of the *trp* regulon.

1

Progress in Nucleic Acid Research
and Molecular Biology, Vol. 42

covalent complexes between protein and DNA. The structure–function analyses carried out on the Trp repressor place this system in the top rank in
terms of the breadth and detail of the information that is available. It seems
timely to review the existing body of knowledge about the Trp repressor with
the goal of distinguishing general structure–function principles as well as
specific features that might also apply to other amino-acid-activated proteins
able to form complexes with duplex DNA.

The Trp repressor shares with a number of other activator and repressor
proteins an important structural element, namely, a helix–turn–helix motif
(1, 2). The importance of this structure is supported by its presence in a
number of well-studied DNA-binding proteins (3) and by polypeptide sequence alignments that suggest the presence of similar recognition elements
in other operator-binding proteins (3–7).

The Trp repressor engages appropriate operator targets within DNA only
if the protein has first undergone a tryptophan-mediated conformational
change. The geometry of several complexes involving the Trp repressor is
now well understood at the atomic level, from X-ray crystallographic comparisons of liganded and unliganded species and from the analysis of a
crystalline Trp-holorepressor–operator complex. The crystallographic results have recently been summarized and discussed (2, 8). This aspect of the
system is therefore reviewed in less detail than other aspects of Trp repressor
research.

I. Early (Pre-cloning) Research on the Trp Repressor, 1959–1980

The *trpR* gene was first described in 1959 (9). Classical *E. coli trpR*
mutants, in an otherwise wild-type background, display the phenotype of
resistance to high levels (>1 mg/mL) of 5-methyltryptophan (5MeTrp). Mutations at other loci in *E. coli* also confer resistance to such tryptophan
analogs (10). A range of phenotypic and genetic tests have been used to
classify collections of 5MeTrp-resistant mutants. Of particular utility in identifying *trpR* mutants is to score the effect of phenylalanine (20–50 mg/ml) on
analog resistance. Resistance to 5MeTrp attributable to lesions in *trpR* is
reversed in the presence of phenylalanine (11) via effects on *mtr*, which
encodes a tryptophan-specific permease. Phenylalanine stimulates the expression of this integral membrane permease, thereby elevating the capacity
for 5MeTrp uptake. This in turn overrides the elevation in tryptophan biosynthetic capacity brought about by genetic elimination of the Trp repressor.
The phenotypic result is restoration of 5MeTrp sensitivity.

On physiological and genetic grounds, it was concluded that the role of
the *trpR* gene is to specify a protein that acts to negatively modulate the

levels of the five terminal enzymes of tryptophan biosynthesis (9). On the *E. coli* genetic map, *trpR* is 70% co-transducible by phage P1 with *thr*, i.e., at about minute 99.7 (*12*, *13*), or at coordinate 4710 according to the most recently adopted system of mapping (*14*). Genetically speaking, the TrpR phenotype is recessive in most *trpR*/*trpR*⁺ merodiploids, as expected for a *trans*-acting control element that negatively affects transcription. However (see Section IX), there are certain *trpR* missense mutants wherein *trpR*/*trpR*⁺ merodiploids exhibit a TrpR⁻ (analog-resistant) phenotype. Such *trans*-dominant mutations are of particular relevance to an understanding of the details of protein–DNA interaction. That the product of the *trpR* gene is truly a protein was conclusively established by the isolation of amber (*15*) and temperature-sensitive mutants within *trpR* (*16*, *17*).

The number of Trp repressor molecules per cell is low (*18*). This fact, plus the lack of a convenient assay, frustrated early efforts to obtain quantities of protein sufficient for direct physicochemical study. The first efforts at Trp repressor purification demonstrated (*19*) a repressing activity attributable to the *trpR*⁺ gene product in a test system where *in vitro* β-galactosidase synthesis depended on transcription and translation events driven by a phage-borne *trp–lac* operon fusion. These workers (*19*) were able to purify the Trp repressor about 55-fold by phosphocellulose chromatography. Later, two other groups also accomplished partial purification of the Trp repressor. One used an assay system based on the *in vitro* synthesis of *trp* mRNA programmed by DNA from a specialized transducing phage (*20*). This group showed that the Trp repressor can be separated from tryptophanyl-tRNA synthetase on Bio-Gel P-60 columns, and estimated a mol wt for the Trp repressor of 60,000. Similar procedures yielded preparations of Trp repressor estimated to be 550-fold enriched over crude extracts (but still only about 1% pure) (*21*, *22*). This work ruled out the involvement of tryptophanyl-tRNA synthetase and tRNA^Trp in repressor-mediated control, and further showed that *trpO*ᶜ mutations eliminated repressor–operator interaction. The estimated mol wt for the Trp repressor was 58,000.

The magnitude of the task of Trp repressor purification from ordinary haploid strains of *E. coli* deserves some comment. We now know (see Section VII) that the monomer mol wt of Trp repressor is about 12,000. If a cell contained 100 monomers of repressor protein, this would amount to 2×10^{-15} mg per cell, or about 0.0005% of the total extractable protein. Obtaining homogeneous material would require about a 200,000-fold purification. Assuming no losses during purification, one could obtain 1 mg of pure repressor from 2 kg of wet-cell paste. The advantages of engineered production strains capable of overproducing the Trp repressor are obvious. It is unrealistic to contemplate detailed physicochemical studies of the Trp repressor unless there exist highly enriched sources of starting material for protein purification. Molecular cloning and gene regulation technology has effectively surmounted this problem (see Section VIII).

Substantial information about the mode of action of the Trp repressor has nonetheless been obtained through work with partially purified protein (22, 23). By quantitating *trp* mRNA production in a system composed of *trp* DNA, RNA-polymerase, and partially purified repressor, the Trp repressor–*trpO* dissociation constant (0.2 μM) and the half-life of the repressor–operator complex (less than 2 min) have been estimated (23). The question of affinity between the Trp repressor and low mol wt effectors such as L-tryptophan or its analogs has been addressed (24). The tryptophan concentration required for half-maximal repression was 3 μM, a value well below any other subsequently determined. The binding of tryptophan to repressor was antagonized by indolepropionic acid, a gratuitous inducer of the *trp* system, whose mode of action had been anticipated from earlier *in vivo* studies (25) and which is now understood in great detail from crystallographic work (26).

These studies produced the first direct evidence that the Trp repressor acts by physically blocking the access of RNA-polymerase to the *trp* promoter (22), implying functional overlap between *trpO* and *trpP*. That there are points of close contact in DNA shared by RNA-polymerase and the Trp repressor was shown (27) by use of an older technique (28) that exploits the reactivity toward dimethyl sulfate of guanine and adenine residues protruding into the major and minor grooves, respectively, of double-helical DNA. The structure of the *trp* promoter–operator and the particular residues whose alkylation by dimethyl sulfate are modified by bound protein are shown in Fig. 1.

The methylation protection studies confirmed and extended earlier work (29, 30) wherein the Trp holorepressor was shown to protect *trp*-promoter–operator DNA from hydrolysis by restriction endonuclease *Hpa*I. The cleavage site for this enzyme is the hexanucleotide palindrome GTTAAC, found upstream from the transcription start-point of *trpP* at positions −9 through −14, directly astride the axis of symmetry of *trpO* (Fig. 1). Such "protection

$$
\begin{array}{ccc}
-20 & -10 & +1 \\
\bullet & \bullet & \bullet
\end{array}
$$

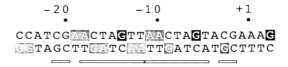

FIG. 1. Residues within a 28-residue stretch of the *trp* promoter–operator region of *Salmonella typhimurium* protected from chemical attack by dimethyl sulfate when complexed with the *E. coli* Trp holorepressor. Residues in stippled boxes are protected by the Trp holorepressor. Residues shown in black boxes are also protected by bound *E. coli* RNA-polymerase holoenzyme. Also shown are an axis of dyad symmetry (open boxes, below) and the transcription start-point (+1). [Redrawn from (27).]

assays" for the Trp repressor offer a convenient semiquantitative method for monitoring the course of repressor purification.

Methylation protection studies (27), plus others of a similar nature involving promoter–operator regions of bacteriophage λ and the *lac* operon (31), enable one to compare the binding of repressors and RNA-polymerase to the same stretch of DNA. Whereas bound Trp repressor protected 16 different purines from attack by dimethyl sulfate, only three were rendered inaccessible to methylation by RNA-polymerase (Fig. 1). This points to marked differences in the nature and/or strength of binding of these two proteins. Certain experiments (32) suggest that RNA-polymerase can undergo conformational changes upon binding small molecules such as ppGpp, an effector that stimulates transcription from the *trp* promoter (33). Perhaps the observed differences in the accessibility to methylation of certain purine residues within the *trp* promoter–operator region reflect the fact that RNA-polymerase frequently assumes a conformational state relatively unfavorable for the formation of open complexes with *trp* promoter–operator DNA. It is regrettable that methylation protection and/or other types of "footprinting" studies have not been conducted using *trp* promoter–operator DNA simultaneously exposed to the Trp holorepressor and the RNA-polymerase holoenzyme. Recent work with the *lac* system has shown that the repressor and RNA-polymerase interact cooperatively at the *lac* promoter–operator (34). It would be of interest to establish whether repressor–polymerase interactions occur in the *trp* system.

An independent approach to the problem of defining which regions of DNA are critical for Trp repressor binding involved the selection and structural analysis of *trpO*ᶜ mutants. In such *cis*-acting mutants, one or more changes in *trpO* lead to some degree of constitutivity in the expression of the *trp* operon. This approach (see Section X) has yielded a large body of information that is in general accord with the aforementioned chemical protection studies. One limitation to the early mutational analysis of *trpO* is the underlying requirement that any O^c mutation not diminish *trp* promoter function below the threshold needed for operon expression, i.e., scoring and selection are carried out in living cells, an approach with inherent constraints. Moreover, some O^c mutations might only partially affect the binding of repressor to operator, yielding an "O^c" event only marginally more constitutive than wild-type.

II. The Molecular Cloning of *trpR*⁺ DNA Opened the Floodgates to Structure–Function Analysis

By the mid-1970s, it was clear that further progress in the understanding of Trp repressor biochemistry would require cloned *trpR* DNA. Because the major TrpR phenotype (resistance to the analog 5MeTrp) offered nothing in the way of selective possibilities that could be exploited in the available cloning schemes, it became necessary to screen collections of cloned fragments harboring nearby genes, either $serB^+$ or thr^+, for the presence of $trpR^+$ DNA. Such screens required stable E. coli tester strains doubly mutant in trpR and/or thr/serB. We devised a procedure for isolating rare λ lysogens in which prophage formation proceeded via the insertional inactivation of deoD, a gene situated in close proximity to serB and trpR (35). From such lysogens, a family of deletions with end-points throughout the serB–thr sector of the E. coli genome were isolated. Several of these deletions proved to be useful tester strains in subsequent cloning experiments. Abnormal excision events from deoD::λ lysogens generated a series of specialized transducing phages defective in gene N, all of which replicated intracellularly as plasmids. Many of these phages carried the chromosomal $serB^+$ gene; about 7% also carried $trpR^+$ DNA, detected by virtue of the 5MeTrp sensitivity of serB–trpR deletions harboring such phages. By restriction endonuclease mapping and subcloning experiments, the trpR gene was localized within a BamHI fragment of about 1.25 kb. The trpR gene lay astride a region of DNA having a site susceptible to cleavage by restriction endonuclease SalI. This cloning scheme is presented in Fig. 2.

This result was independently confirmed by Gunsalus et al. (36), who cocloned thr^+–$trpR^+$ DNA in a different specialized transducing phage, then subcloned an identical BamHI fragment into a plasmid. On the basis of in vitro transcription–translation studies with plasmids harboring $trpR^+$ DNA, these workers judged the Trp repressor monomer to have a mass of 24,000 Da (36). The actual mass of this protein is now established to be 12,356 Da, based on extensive DNA sequencing studies as well as protein purification (37, 38).

III. Nucleotide Sequence of trpR DNA

Two groups independently determined the sequence of DNA segments containing the trpR gene. In one case (37), 1041 nucleotides were determined. In the other study, 558 nucleotides were determined (38). Each reported sequence contained errors, which were subsequently reconciled. A low-resolution summary of the structural studies is shown in Fig. 3. In the analysis of the sequence information, particular weight was given to open reading frames interrupted by the unique SalI site (Fig. 3) because this hexanucleotide lies within the trpR gene or its promoter (41). Although the complete sequence of the BamHI fragment containing trpR is now known, connecting sequence information to other nearby genes within this region of the E. coli chromosome is also not yet available (13).

The elucidation of the nucleotide sequence of the trpR gene made it

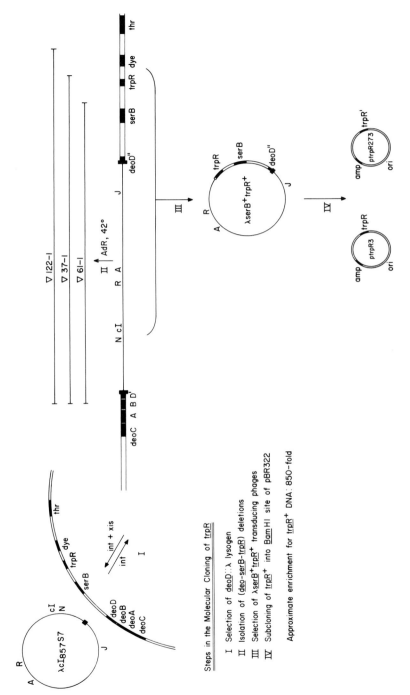

Steps in the Molecular Cloning of trpR

I   Selection of deoD::λ lysogen

II   Isolation of (deo-serB-trpR) deletions

III Selection of λserB⁺trpR⁺ transducing phages

IV   Subcloning of trpR⁺ into BamHI site of pBR322

Approximate enrichment for trpR⁺ DNA: 850-fold

Fig. 2. Scheme for the cloning of trpR⁺ DNA from the chromosome of E. coli into the general-purpose cloning vector pBR322. [Adapted from Roeder and Somerville (35).]

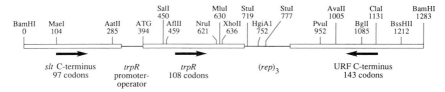

FIG. 3. The *trpR* gene of *E. coli* K-12 and its immediate environment. Shown is a selectively annotated map of a 1283-bp *Bam*HI fragment located at coordinate 4711 of the physical map (*14*). Only a few restriction endonuclease cleavage sites, all of which have been experimentally demonstrated, are shown. The map is based on the DNA sequencing studies of Singleton *et al.* (*37*), Gunsalus and Yanofsky (*38*), and G. Bogosian (personal communication). The presence of partial coding information for *slt* (approximately 590 codons total) was reported by Betzner and Keck (*39*). The trimeric *rep* (repetitive extragenic palindromic) sequences downstream from *trpR* were identified by Stern *et al.* (*40*). The unknown reading frame (URF) of opposite orientation to *slt* and *trpR* was identified by Bogosian (personal communication). Nucleotide sequences on which this map is based are deposited in the GENBANK and EMBL data libraries under the headings ECOTRPR (Accession No. V00369) and ECTRPR, respectively. The GENBANK Accession No. for the URF is M59771. Coordinate 0 is on the *serB* side of the map, while coordinate 1283 is on the *thr* side.

possible to predict the amino-acid sequence of the Trp repressor. The primary translation product of *trpR* mRNA is a polypeptide of 108 amino acids (*38*). This is proteolytically processed, which removes an N-terminal methionine residue. Knowledge of the nucleotide sequence of the upstream punctuation elements of *trpR* (*37*) not only laid the foundation for studies of how *trpR* expression is controlled, but also guided the design of systems for overproduction of the Trp repressor.

IV. Autogenous Transcriptional Regulation of the *trpR* Gene

The expression of the *trpR* gene and its regulation have been experimentally addressed in several laboratories. By chemical procedures (*38*), the *in vitro* transcriptional start-point was found to be an adenylate residue at coordinate 328 (Fig. 4). The resulting transcript contains an untranslated leader sequence of 56 nucleotides with strong potential for the formation of a stable G·C-rich stem–loop structure. During *in vitro* transcription from the *trpR* promoter, termination just downstream from the G·C-rich stem–loop occurs frequently (*38*), to yield an abortive transcript of about 40 nucleotides. Whether this secondary structure also forms *in vivo*, or whether premature termination is relevant to the regulation of *trpR*, is unclear.

Within the *trpR* promoter lies a 22-bp block of nucleotides with extensive homology to other known targets of the Trp repressor (*37, 38*) (Fig. 5).

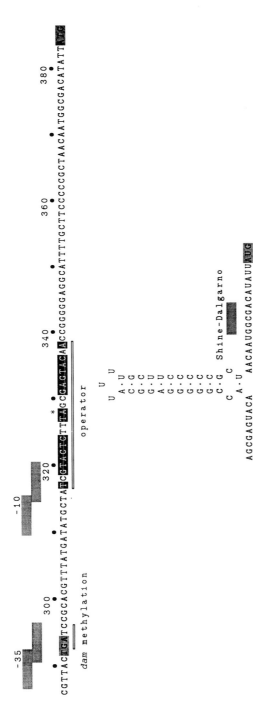

FIG. 4. Intergenic region between the presumed termination codon (TGA) of *slt* (39) and the initiation codon (ATG) of *trpR* (37, 38). For simplicity, only the mRNA-equivalent strand is depicted. The translation elements are shown in stippled boxes at or near the ends of the sequence. The coordinate system is that of Fig. 3. The experimentally determined transcriptional start-point (asterisk) is coordinate 328. Shown in black boxes are operator targets, known to interact with the Trp holorepressor (see Section X and Fig. 5). The operator lies astride the transcriptional start-point. The lower set of −10 and −35 hexamers was determined experimentally (38); the upper set of hexamers was inferred on the basis of a promoter homology index algorithm (42) (see Section V). The GATC sequence at −35 is a substrate for the *dam* methylase of *E. coli* (see Section V).

Location

trpO   ATCGA**ACTAG**TTAA**CTAGT**ACGCA   -10

aroH   AATGT**ACTAG**AGAA**CTAGT**GCATT   -35

trpR   ATCGT**ACTCT**TTAG**CGAGT**ACAAC   startpoint

mtr   TTTGT**ACTCG**TGTA**CTGGT**ACAGT   -35}{-10

FIG. 5. Nucleotide sequences of the four major operator regions recognized by the Trp holorepressor, and their locations within their respective promoters. The characters in black boxes refer to residue locations where changes in nucleotide composition lead to reductions in affinity for the repressor (30, 43) (see Section X). Characters shown in stippled boxes refer to deviations from the consensus sequence, whose effect on repressor binding varies from mild to inconsequential. The open boxed areas above each operator emphasize the palindromic nature of each operator. Only one sequence (the "top" or "mRNA-equivalent" strand) is shown for each operator.

This suggests that autogenous regulation is the mechanistic basis for an earlier finding (35) that "super-repression" of the trp operon does not occur in cells harboring a multicopy trpR+ plasmid. Trp repressor levels are evidently optimized by various means that enable the cell to control the expression of the tryptophan biosynthetic operon and other genes, such as aroH (44) and mtr (11). Although autogenous control at the transcriptional level may not be the only mechanism used by E. coli to optimize Trp-repressor levels, the evidence strongly favors it.

The earliest experimental support for autogenous regulation in the trpR system came from an in vitro study (38). When the Trp holorepressor was present, neither normal nor prematurely terminated trpR mRNA was generated in a purified transcription system. This result was supported by direct in vivo measurements of the levels of trpR mRNA extracted from cells cultivated under a variety of physiological conditions (45). Cells with normal haploid levels of the Trp repressor, grown in the presence of tryptophan, contain approximately one-half the amount of trpR mRNA present in mutant cells unable to make functional Trp repressor. Nearly the same amplitude of regulation (about 3-fold) of the trpR gene was observed in parallel studies in which the production of β-galactosidase from single-copy trpR–lacZ transcriptional fusions was used to evaluate rates of transcription from the trpR promoter (46, 47). Severe (about 37-fold) repression at the trpR promoter took effect in strains engineered to produce elevated levels of the Trp repressor. A similar in vivo study several years later (48) gave an identical result.

That the Trp repressor autogenously controls expression of the *trpR* gene in a negative manner *in vivo* by influencing transcription at the *trpR* promoter was also confirmed by Kelley and Yanofsky (49). These workers used a reporter system based on a chimeric enzyme having the N terminus of the Trp repressor and the C terminus of β-galactosidase, whose expression depended jointly on transcription initiation at the *trpR* promoter and translation at the natural *trpR* ribosome-binding site within mRNA (Fig. 4). In terms of the amplitude of *trpR* regulation, the effect of the Trp repressor (4- to 5-fold tryptophan-dependent decrease) and the effect of engineered overproduction of the Trp repressor (245-fold repression) agreed with earlier studies. Because the ribosome-binding signal of *trpR* mRNA is remarkably weak (50), the absolute levels of reporter enzyme in these studies were substantially lower than the levels observed when the *lacZ* ribosome-binding site is available to support translation.

The Trp repressor also controls the expression of *aroH*. In a careful study of how *aroH* is regulated, it was noted (51) that the translational signals for this gene are quite weak (about 1/17th that of *lacZ*). However, the amplitude of transcriptional regulation of *aroH* by the Trp repressor (3- to 5-fold) was the same whether the *aroH* or *lacZ* ribosome-binding site was part of the reporter system.

V. Signal Strength of the *trpR* Promoter Relative to Other σ⁷⁰ Promoters of *E. coli*

Attempts to determine the strength of the *trpR* promoter have involved two approaches. First, with transcriptional fusions to an efficiently translated reporter gene, the levels of reporter enzyme can be compared to other well-characterized systems. Second, the nucleotide sequence of the *trpR* promoter can be compared to known promoters through the use of computer algorithms. Both approaches yield the same answer: The *trpR* promoter is a surprisingly effective punctuation element. In the absence of autogenous regulation, transcription initiates about 10% as often as the primary *trp* promoter, which is one of the most efficient in *E. coli* (33, 47, 52). The efficiency of the *trpR* promoter doubles in *dam* strains of *E. coli*, which cannot methylate adenines in the sequence GATC (53). Such a sequence is situated in the recognition hexamer at −35 of the *trpR* promoter (37, 38) (Fig. 4).

Thanks to the early availability of its sequence, the *trpR* promoter has been included in almost every computer-based survey of promoter structure–function relationships (42, 54–59). The structural features that have dominated the computer comparison of promoters are the degree of concordance with two canonical recognition hexamers centered at 35 and 10 bp upstream from the transcriptional start point, and the number of base-pairs between these hexamers. The locations of these recognition elements for RNA-polymerase in the *trpR* promoter are shown in Fig. 4. Because there is partial overlap between the recognition element at -10 and an operator target for binding of the Trp repressor, there must be certain constraints on the sequence of the *trpR* promoter in this region. For the -35 recognition element, 3 out of 6 bp match the consensus sequence that has been derived by tabulating conserved homologies among a large set of σ^{70} promoters. For the -10 recognition element, 4 out of 6 bp match (54).

There is a direct relationship between the ability of a given segment of duplex DNA to function effectively as a promoter and the extent of agreement of its sequence with the consensus. Statistically derived weighting factors yielded numerical values (homology scores) for the RNA-polymerase selectivity of a series of promoters (55). These values are proportional to the rate at which RNA chains are initiated. There are strong correlations between computationally derived homology scores and the experimentally determined second-order rate constants for the formation of open complexes between the σ^{70} form of RNA-polymerase and promoters (55). From DNA sequence information alone, RNA-polymerase selectivity can be predicted to within a factor of ± 4 over a range of selectivity of 10^4. In terms of homology score, promoter function increases 10-fold for each increase of 10 points in the homology score. The homology scores for the *trpR* promoter (51.5) and the *trp* promoter (61.5) are in excellent agreement with the 10-fold difference in the strengths of these two promoters, measured *in vivo* (47). According to this analysis, the *trpR* promoter is slightly superior to the well-studied *lacP1* promoter (homology score, 49.7).

As the number of known *E. coli* promoter sequences in the data base grew, further computational analysis, using reiterative alignments to optimize homology to an expanded reference set, were carried out (42). The algorithm that was used selected the statistically best -35 and -10 regions for each promoter, which were then matched against the consensus sequence TTGACA . . . 17 . . . TATAAT and rank-ordered statistically. Because promoter strength and promoter homology index are correlated, rough comparisons between promoters can be made according to the homology index values, which lie along a logarithmic scale. Two homology indices were computed for the *trpR* promoter (42). The lowest (-4.3) corresponded to the -35 and -10 hexamers used by Mulligan *et al.* (55), while the other (-2.8) corresponded to different -35 and -10 hexamers displaced upstream from the "standard" hexamers by four and five nucleotides, respectively. The latter value, which places the *trpR* promoter in the same relative range as the *lacP1* promoter (-2.0), is more compatible with the observed 10-fold difference between the *trpR* promoter and the *trp* promoter (homology index, -1.7). A reinvestigation of the 5′ end of *trpR* mRNA generated *in vivo* might resolve this apparent discrepancy.

Because promoter mutations and regions of contact between promoters and RNA-polymerase tend to lie within the well-conserved -10 and -35 hexamers, there is a widespread misconception that these two recognition elements define a promoter. In a lucid and sophisticated analysis, O'Neill (59) showed that the σ^{70} promoters of *E. coli* actually fall into three major classes, distinguishable on the basis of the distance (16, 17, or 18 bp) between the -10 and -35 recognition hexamers. For each class, there is a characteristic set of less strongly conserved base-pairs outside the recognition hexamers. The weakly conserved bases supposedly contribute to the specificity of RNA-polymerase binding by determining the conformation of the highly conserved -10 and -35 hexamers. Promoter structures thus involve a degree of compromise between optimal contacts (a property of the recognition hexamers) and optimal conformation (a property of the weakly conserved "framework" nucleotides).

The *trpR* promoter was classified among the 18-bp spacing group (59). Promoters of this class tend to have an additional 44 weakly conserved base-pairs whose role is presumed to be conformational in nature. Computerized search protocols (58) effectively identify members of the known promoter data base. However, the *trpR* promoter failed this test, a result that either calls into question the eligibility of this promoter for membership in the 18-bp spacing group or suggests that the true *trpR* promoter has not been precisely identified.

In this connection, it should be noted that the supporting data for the *trpR* transcription start-point have never been published, and that the computer algorithm of Harley and Reynolds (42), applied to the *trpR* promoter, signaled a possible discrepancy in the choice of the -35 and -10 recognition hexamers. The Harley–Reynolds analysis could place the *trpR* promoter in the 17-bp spacing group of O'Neill (59). The only experimental evidence that bears on this point comes from the work (53) showing that transcription from the *trpR* promoter *in vivo* increases 2- to 3-fold when an adenine residue of a GATC sequence within the *trpR* promoter (see Fig. 4) cannot be methylated as a result of a mutation in the *dam* (DNA-adenine methylase) gene. The GATC sequence in question lies within the traditionally accepted -35 region for the *trpR* promoter, but outside the -35 hexamer that turned up during the computer search by Harley and Reynolds (Fig. 4).

Two other structural features of *E. coli* promoters in general, and of the *trpR* promoter in particular, have been addressed through computational analysis. The upstream regions of promoters having distributions of nucleotides associated with curved DNA structures have been examined (56). Promoters with high transcription rates tend to have high curvature scores;

the converse is true for weak promoters. Neither the upstream nor the downstream regions of the *trpR* gene were predicted to contain regions of curvature, scoring zero according to the algorithm used. Tung and Harvey (57) examined the local helix geometry of a number of *E. coli* promoters, using algorithms based on nucleotide sequence to predict helix twist angles, and by focusing on hexanucleotide sequences, detected a common helix twist motif in 58 out of 61 promoters studied. The structurally synonymous motif, which is not highly sequence-dependent, was located 127 times within the promoter data set. The structures in question were largely absent from genes and from random DNA in general. One such structure was found within the *trpR* promoter, just upstream from the −35 hexamer. Its functional role, if any, has not been established.

There have been no systematic studies of the relationship between the nucleotide sequence of the *trpR* promoter and its strength or susceptibility to regulation. With present technology (60–62) it is feasible to examine in detail which base-pairs within a promoter determine how RNA-polymerase engages such segments of duplex DNA and initiates transcription. With respect to *trpR*, such analyses remain for the future.

VI. Translation of *trpR* mRNA and the Effect of Temperature on Regulation in the *trp* System

Much is known about the factors that are important in the translation of prokaryotic mRNA (reviewed in 63 and 64). The critical steps are the formation of a 70-S ribosomal initiation complex, which requires structural information from the 5′ end of an mRNA and the plentiful availability of aminoacyl-tRNAs having anticodons complementary to those of the mRNA (reviewed in 65 and 66).

That one or more of these factors might affect the rate of Trp repressor synthesis is suggested by several structural features of *trpR* mRNA, both in the untranslated leader region and in the polypeptide coding segment. In the leader region of *trpR* mRNA (57 nucleotides), from 11 through 39, lies a stretch of nucleotides with strong potential for the formation of a stable secondary structure (Fig. 4) with a calculated net ΔG of −27 kcal/mol (67). The ribosome-binding site (68) has the distinction of being less homologous to the punctuation elements of this class than any other ribosome-binding site analyzed (68). The patterns of codon usage and of codon context are strongly biased, as expected (69–71) for a nonabundant protein. Ten *trpR* codons (9.3% of the total) are rarely used in *E. coli*. These are CCC (Pro; used twice), ACG (Thr; used thrice), CAA (Glu; used thrice), and AAT (Asn; used twice).

Whether the presence of rare codons or the codon context is a rate-determining feature in the synthesis of the Trp repressor has not been experimentally established. By analogy to other systems (66), this would be predicted to occur, particularly in engineered production strains designed to overproduce the Trp repressor. However, there is suggestive evidence that the 5' end of *trpR* mRNA presents a somewhat inefficient template to the translational apparatus of the cell. In three separate studies, a range of issues pertaining to the regulation of *trpR* expression were addressed (47–49). In one study (47), β-galactosidase levels were controlled by the *trpR* promoter and the highly efficient *lacZ* ribosome-binding site; in the others, β-galactosidase production depended on the same promoter and the native ribosome-binding site of the *trpR* message. To a first approximation, the nonrepressed levels of reporter enzyme were one-third to one-fifth in the latter situation, suggesting that the expression of the reporter enzyme was proceeding inefficiently.

Another way of addressing translational efficiency in the *trpR* system is to measure mRNA and protein levels directly for a Trp repressor-specific expression system. Parallel measurements in a reference system permit one to compare translational efficiency directly. Two studies of this sort (49, 72) suggest that the translatability of *trpR* mRNA is only one-quarter to one-fifth that of the efficiently translated *trp* operon leader mRNA or *lacZ* mRNA.

The possible regulatory role of the G·C-rich palindrome situated near the 5' end of *trpR* mRNA (Fig. 4) was addressed experimentally by means of a set of β-galactosidase reporter systems having the *lac*UV5 promoter–operator region driving the production of mRNA with the Shine–Dalgarno sequence of *trpR* (73). The mRNA either had the G·C-rich palindrome or was deleted for this structural element. The *lacZ* genes of these constructs were weakly expressed and unaffected by growth in the presence of tryptophan, by genetic elimination of the Trp repressor, or by removal of the G·C-rich palindrome. The physiological role in the translation process, if any, of the G·C-rich palindrome therefore seems tenuous. It is possible that this structural feature of *trpR* message is related to mRNA stability, an issue that has not been studied. Because of its highly inefficient Shine–Dalgarno sequence, *trpR* mRNA might tend to remain unattached to ribosomes for relatively long periods, thereby offering an opportunity for the formation of extended secondary structures such as pseudoknots.

In a tryptophan-dependent manner, the steady-state levels of the Trp repressor respond to the temperature at which cells are grown. At 40°C, the Trp repressor content was approximately four times that at 30°C (18). There were no temperature-dependent changes in Trp repressor levels in cells cultivated in tryptophan-free medium. One interpretation of this result is to assume either that the affinity of the Trp holorepressor for the *trpR* operator diminishes at the higher temperature, or that the stability of the holorepressor–operator complex is lowered at the elevated temperature. It may be relevant to note that repression at the *trp* promoter also diminished by about a factor of 2 in cells grown at elevated temperatures (*74*), that conformational changes within the -10 region of the *trp* promoter take place in response to shifts in temperature (*75, 76*), and that the affinity of the Trp aporepressor for L-tryptophan falls to approximately one-half between 30°C and 40°C (*77*). The Trp repressor itself is extremely stable over this range of temperatures (*78*). Direct *in vitro* measurements of holorepressor–operator affinity as a function of temperature have not yet been made, so it is not possible to propose a mechanism for the effect of temperature change on Trp repressor function. The gene products of promoters subject to regulation by the Trp repressor are not normally considered to be heat-shock proteins (*79*).

VII. The Primary Amino-acid Sequence of the Trp Repressor: General Overview

The amino-acid sequence of the Trp repressor (Fig. 6), originally deduced from the nucleotide sequence of *trpR* DNA (*38*), is fully supported by structural studies on the purified protein (*82*) and by crystallographic analysis (*83–85*), and has been confirmed by gene synthesis (*86*). The predicted molecular weight of the Trp repressor, from the amino-acid sequence, is 12,356. This value has been confirmed by sodium dodecyl sulfate/polyacrylamide-gel electrophoresis (*87, 88*). The size of the Trp repressor thus supports the contention (*89*) that many of the proteins of *E. coli* have molecular masses that are multiples of $14,000 \pm 2,500$. As shown by chemical cross-linking, the Trp repressor exists in solution in the form of a dimer (*87, 88*) of considerable stability (*77*). The apparent molecular weight by gel filtration is 30,000, suggesting that the Trp-repressor dimer has an ellipsoidal shape (*77*). This inference and the dimeric state of the Trp repressor were both subsequently borne out by crystallographic analysis (*83*).

In terms of amino-acid composition and sequence, the Trp repressor has many unusual features that may be functionally significant (Table I). The possible uniqueness of these features can be evaluated either statistically, by comparison to other prokaryotic proteins of similar size, or experimentally, by site-directed mutation.

In terms of ionizable side chains, the Trp repressor has 15 proton-accepting amino-acid residues (2 His, 9 Arg, and 4 Lys) and 16 proton-donating ones (4 Asp and 12 Glu), plus one of each at either terminus. The theoretical isoelectric point (*90*) for the Trp repressor is 5.45; the experimentally determined isoelectric point (*88*) was 5.9. The reason for this discrepancy is not apparent.

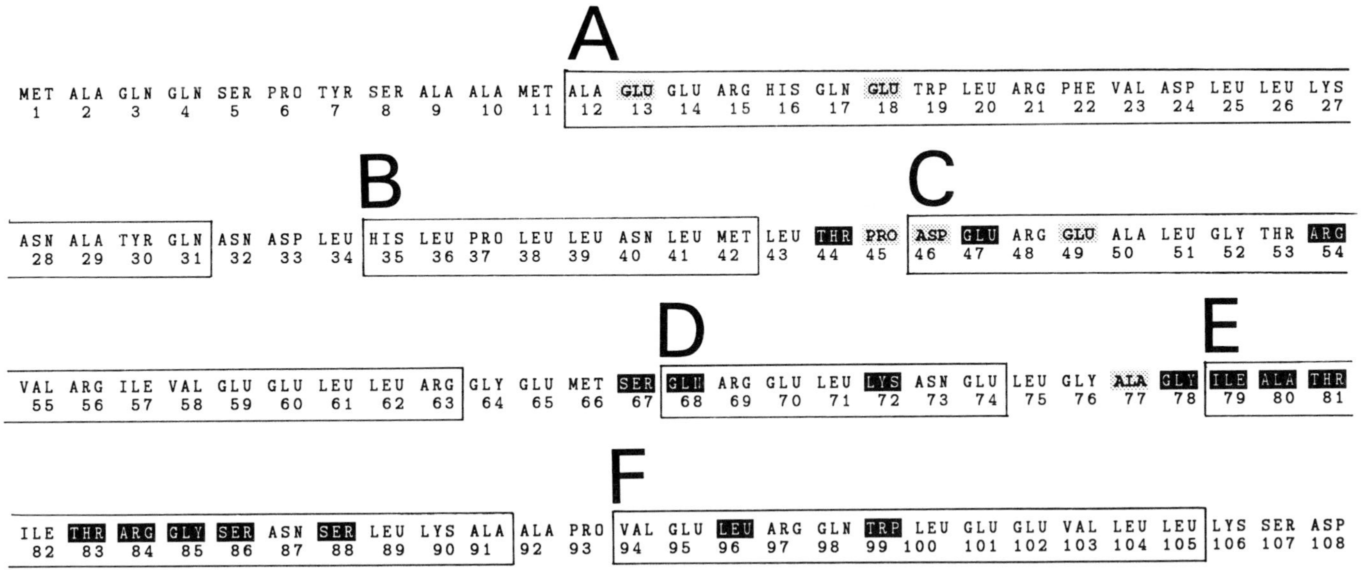

Fig. 6. Amino-acid sequence of the Trp repressor. The N-terminal methionine is proteolytically removed *in vivo* during or shortly after translation, as expected for proteins having an alanine residue at the penultimate position of the polypeptide chain (80, 81). The boxed segments correspond to α-helical regions, as determined crystallographically (see also Fig. 7). The residues shown in black boxes, when altered by mutation, lead to proteins with diminished affinity for *trpO*. The residues in stippled boxes, when altered by mutation, lead to proteins with enhanced operator affinity ("super-repressors").

TABLE I
POSSIBLE COMPOSITIONAL IDIOSYNCRASIES OF THE Trp REPRESSOR

1. No cysteine residues
2. There are nine homodipeptide pairs (17% of total sequence; Leu–Leu recurs four times)
3. Several heterodipeptide sequences recur:

Twice	Three times	Four times
Lys–Asn	Leu–Arg	Glu–Leu
Trp–Leu		Leu–Lys
Met–Ala		
Val–Glu		
Thr–Glu		
Arg–Gly		
Leu–Gly		

By establishing the structure of the Trp repressor and its corresponding gene and mRNA, the stage was set for the development of systems for the high-level production of this previously inaccessible protein. In turn, the availability in quantity of pure Trp repressor made possible a range of physicochemical studies. These included questions as to how L-tryptophan and its analogs are bound and lead to conformational change, how the holorepressor engages operator targets in duplex DNA, and how the Trp repressor monomers self-associate to form functionally active homodimers. The answers (complete and partial) to these questions have come from multidisciplinary studies involving conventional and site-directed mutagenesis, microbial physiology, protein biochemistry and biophysics, computer-aided model-building, and X-ray crystallography. For the most part, there is a high degree of concordance among researchers who have adopted these different approaches. But there are also a few discrepancies and paradoxes that offer useful points of departure for future studies.

VIII. Engineered Systems for Overproduction of the Trp Repressor; Protein Purification Schemes

Because the Trp repressor autogenously regulates transcription at the *trpR* promoter (35, 46, 47, 49), the stratagem of using *E. coli* strains harboring multicopy *trpR*⁺ plasmids as starting material for protein purification offers no advantage over ordinary *trpR*⁺ haploid cells. The most fruitful approaches have involved disengaging the *trpR* autogenous regulatory circuit through the use of a strong promoter whose regulation is distinct from that of the *trp* system. In addition, it has usually been necessary to engineer Trp repressor production strains in which the expression of the desired protein is prevented throughout most of the growth cycle. This approach is necessary to prevent uncontrolled overproduction of the Trp repressor, which is frequently deleterious to normal *E. coli* physiology *(91)* and imposes selective pressures that invariably lead to the accumulation of *trpR* mutations.

The successful *E. coli* production systems for the Trp repressor have involved use of the promoters for *lac*UV5, λP$_L$, *tac*, and T7. A number of these production systems are listed in Table II. The merits and drawbacks of some of these schemes, based in part on the experience of this laboratory, are as follows. For the production of wild-type Trp repressor, it is essential that *trpR* expression remain silent during routine cultivation. This is because even slight levels of overproduction of Trp repressor create a selective pressure that quickly leads to the emergence of bacteria with a mutationally altered and usually inactive form of Trp repressor. For systems in which the *lac* or *tac* promoter–operator is to drive transcription of *trpR*, this means that the cell must have adequate levels of Lac repressor to prevent *trpR* expression. Usually a single copy of *lacI* or *lacI^q* is not sufficient to "tame" a *lac* promoter on a multicopy plasmid. The same is true for F' *lacI^q* production strains.

In recent years, workers using a *lac* or *tac* promoter-driven system have introduced a multicopy lacI$^+$ plasmid, pMS421, as an additional means to avoid strain degradation during production runs *(95)*. For the production of mutationally altered forms of the Trp repressor, it is desirable that the host strain contain a *trpR* deletion mutation, so that no wild-type protein will be present *(72, 93, 95)*.

More sophisticated systems for holding the production of unwanted proteins in check during the growth of cells involve the construction of ex-

TABLE II
ENGINEERED PRODUCTION SYSTEMS FOR THE Trp REPRESSOR

Host/plasmid	Promoter	Production level	Reference
W3110 SRT4/pRPG12	λP$_L$	Not stated	38
W3110 (ptrpR 99-7)	*trp*	0.1%	82
SP-361 (λGB2) (pLtrpR)	λP$_L$	0.1%	82
W3110 *trpL75 leu* (pRLK18)	*trp*	1.6%	88
JM 101 SRT4/F' *lacI^q* (pJPR2)	*tac*	25–50%	72
LE 392 (pRPG47)	*lac*UV5	0.75%	77, 92
BL-21 (λDE3) (pLySE) (ptrpRT7)	T7 gene 10	5–10%	93
DC 41-3 (pWB101)	Unregulated	Not stated	94

pression cassettes having the powerful φ10-S10 expression signals of phage T7 (96). Production of the Trp repressor is inefficient in cells bearing such constructs unless T7 RNA-polymerase is provided. This is done either by infecting cells with a phage λ derivative carrying the T7 RNA-polymerase structural gene, or by inducing the production of T7 RNA-polymerase from a second T7 RNA-polymerase expression cassette that is itself under the control of the *lac* promoter. The inactivation of any T7 RNA-polymerase that may accidentally appear by escape from *lac* repression during the handling of the culture is ensured by the presence of a compatible plasmid that specifies T7 lysozyme, a known inhibitor of T7 RNA-polymerase (96).

In this laboratory, such production systems have proved to be quite stable and to yield reproducibly high levels of mutant and wild-type Trp repressor for biochemical work. Although it is, in principle, desirable to start with crude extracts highly enriched with respect to Trp repressor, the starting material need not contain more than 5–10% Trp repressor to yield suitable amounts of purified material. This is because a very efficient heat step (92) used batchwise early in purification effectively removes all but a few contaminating proteins. These are easily separated by various column chromatographic procedures (92, 93, 97).

IX. Interaction of Tryptophan and Its Analogs with the Trp Repressor; Effects of Ligand Binding on Operator Affinity

The binding of L-tryptophan and a host of tryptophan analogs to the Trp repressor has been studied quantitatively in a number of laboratories. The techniques used include standard equilibrium dialysis, flow dialysis, spectroscopy, and direct measurements of effects on *trp* operon mRNA production *in vitro* (Table III). The aspects of ligand binding receiving attention include: stoichiometry; dissociation constant; effects of pH, salt, and temperature; and the binding consequences of changing various functional groups of the ligand. The genetic and crystallographic analyses of the Trp repressor and Trp holorepressor (Sections XI and XII) provide a satisfying and consistent model for how L-tryptophan precipitates conformational change within the protein, as well as revealing which side-chains of amino-acid residues are critical for ligand binding.

L-Tryptophan binds in a noncooperative manner to identical and independent sites on the Trp aporepressor, with a stoichiometry of two molecules per dimer. The observed dissociation constants (Table III) fall reproducibly in the 1–5×10^{-5} M range. Estimates of the intracellular concentration of free tryptophan in *E. coli* cells growing in minimal media range from 7×10^{-5} M (*102*) to 15×10^{-5} M (*103*). Thus, a substantial fraction of the intracellular Trp repressor might be expected to be in the liganded (oper-

TABLE III
BINDING PARAMETERS FOR THE INTERACTION OF L-TRYPTOPHAN WITH THE Trp
REPRESSOR IN THE ABSENCE OF THE *trp* OPERATOR

Dissociation constant (K_D)	Experimental conditions	Additional comments	Reference
$1 \times 10^{-5}\ M$ (est.)	*In vitro* transcription: pH 7.9, 100-mM KCl	37°C	98
$1.6 \times 10^{-5}\ M$	Equilibrium dialysis: pH 7.5, 6-mM MgCl$_2$, 50-mM NaCl; BSA at 100 μg/ml	24 hr, 25°C	88
$1.8 \pm 2 \times 10^{-5}\ M$	Difference spectroscopy: pH 7.6	25°C	99
$4.6 \times 10^{-5}\ M$	Equilibrium dialysis: pH 7.4, 0.1-mM EDTA, 200-mM KCl, 5% glycerol	6 hr, 25°C	77
$4.9 \times 10^{-5}\ M$	Flow dialysis: pH 7.4, 0.1-mM EDTA, 200-mM KCl, 5% glycerol	25°C	77
$1.46 \times 10^{-5}\ M$	Equilibrium dialysis: pH 8.1, 250-mM KCl	16 hr, 4°C	100
$3.7 \pm 1.2 \times 10^{-5}\ M$	Fluorescence spectroscopy; displacement of ANS[a]: pH 7.5, 100-mM KCl, 1-mM EDTA	25°C	101
$1 \times 10^{-5}\ M$	0.15 M salt, 0.25 M glutamate, 5% Me$_2$SO, pH 7.5	25°C	95

[a]ANS, 8-Anilino-1-naphthalenesulfonate.

ator-binding) state in cells grown under standard laboratory conditions. The other major tryptophan-binding protein of the *E. coli* cytoplasm is tryptophanyl-tRNA synthetase, whose K_M for tryptophan ($3 \times 10^{-5}\ M$) falls within the same range (*104*).

Although the affinity of tryptophan for the Trp repressor is almost unaffected by variations in salt concentration and pH (Table III), there is substantial temperature dependence for tryptophan binding. At 40°C, the K_D for tryptophan binding increases about 8-fold over the K_D at 6.5°C (*77*). There is a similar effect of temperature on the binding of effector ligand to the Lac repressor (*105*). On thermodynamic grounds, it was concluded from these studies that hydrophobic interactions between L-tryptophan and its binding pocket cause the conformational changes necessary to convert the Trp repressor to an operator-binding species (*77*). Ionic interactions and/or the formation of hydrogen-bonds appear not to play important roles in ligand binding to the Trp repressor.

A displacement method using 8-anilino-1-naphthalenesulfonate (ANS) (*101*) to study ligand binding to the Trp repressor has been used to quantitate the kinetics of tryptophan binding and dissociation. The association and dissociation rate constants, K_a and K_D, are 4×10^{-6} $M^{-1}sec^{-1}$ and 60 sec^{-1}, respectively, in agreement with the experimentally measured K_D values.

The role of tryptophan binding is to generate a species with high affinity for *trp*-operator DNA. This comes about via conformational change that involves amino-acid residues 67–86 within the "helix–turn–helix" motif of the protein (*84*). The Trp aporepressor has relatively weak affinity for *trpO* [reported K_D values, 4×10^{-8} M (*106*) and 6×10^{-7} M (*95*)]. In one study, *trpO* DNA reduced the K_D of tryptophan for the aporepressor to about one-sixth that of control systems without *trpO* DNA (*101*). In other studies, the effect, if any, was marginal (*95, 107*). Since the measurements involved the use of different operator-bearing DNA fragments, no firm conclusions about the role of DNA in tryptophan binding can be drawn at the present time.

The nature of the functional groups within tryptophan that are important to the formation of stable binary complexes has been explored in detail by studying the binding to the Trp repressor of a large number of tryptophan analogs, and by quantitative studies of the interaction of analog-liganded repressors with operator DNA (*8, 100, 108*). The use of tryptophan analogs to address structure–function issues in the *trp* system is a time-honored experimental approach (*10*). The indole nucleus and the α-carboxyl group of tryptophan are chiefly responsible for determining repressor–ligand affinity. The α-amino group does not enhance ligand binding. Instead, the amino group properly orients the tryptophan molecule within its binding pocket, thereby creating a high-affinity interface between the holorepressor and the operator (*8*).

X. Operator Targets Recognized by the Trp Holorepressor

Four promoters of *E. coli* contain high-affinity targets important in the negative regulation of transcription by the Trp repressor (Fig. 5). These are: the *trp* promoter, which drives the production of the enzymes of tryptophan biosynthesis (reviewed in *33*); the *aroH* promoter, which drives the production of the tryptophan-inhibitable isoenzyme of 3-deoxy-D-*arabino*-heptulosonate 7-phosphate synthetase (*44, 51*); the *trpR* promoter, a key punctuation element in the autogenous transcriptional regulation of cytoplasmic Trp-repressor levels (*37, 38, 46, 47, 49*); and the *mtr* promoter, whose availability is essential for the production of an L-tryptophan-specific integral membrane permease (*11, 109*). There are also a number of promoters having secondary operator targets of lower affinity, whose interaction with the Trp

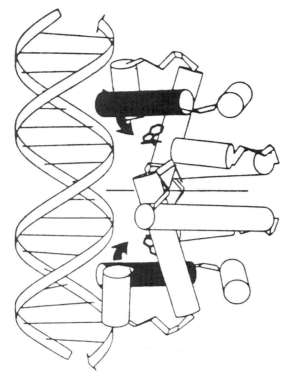

FIG. 7. Schematic representation of how the Trp holorepressor engages an operator target in duplex DNA. The recognition helices (black cylinders) bind noncovalently to residues in duplex DNA, whose position in space is determined by the operator sequence. Sometimes water molecules are important in the interface between protein and DNA. In the absence of ligand, the recognition helices collapse, taking up spatial locations unfavorable for engagement with DNA. [Reprinted with permission of the editors of *Nature* and Paul Sigler (see *83*).] (For additional information on this topic see refs. *84*, *85*.)

repressor can be demonstrated *in vivo* when high levels of protein are provided (*91*, *110*). A model showing how the Trp holorepressor engages operator targets appears in Fig. 7.

In common with a number of other systems of protein–DNA interaction (*2*), Trp repressor homodimers function by forming complexes with symmetrically disposed arrays of purine·pyrimidine base-pairs whose edges lie in the major groove of duplex DNA. The structure of those operator targets efficiently engaged by the Trp repressor, and their general locations within the relevant promoters, are presented in Fig. 5. As expected for systems of protein–DNA interaction involving dimeric proteins, the operator targets are palindromic. However, the disposition of equivalent residues about each axis of symmetry in the known targets differ from one operator to another.

TABLE IV
DISSOCIATION CONSTANTS GOVERNING THE INTERACTION OF WILD-TYPE Trp
HOLOREPRESSOR WITH ITS OPERATORS

Measured K_D (nM)	Experimental conditions	Assay method	Reference
0.2	0.2-M salt, pH 7.9, 37°C	*In vitro* transcription of φ80-*trp* DNA; impure Trp repressor	23
2.0	0.05-M salt, pH 7.5, 20°C	Restriction endonuclease protection	88
6.7	0.05-M salt, pH 7.4, 20°C	Gel retardation	112
<100	0.1-M salt, pH 7.5, 25°C	Circular dichroism	113
2.6	1.5-M salt, pH 7.6, 25°C	Nitrocellulose filter binding	107
7.0	0.24-M salt, pH 7.6, 25°C	Nitrocellulose filter binding	114
0.5	0.025-M salt, pH 6.0, 25°C	Gel retardation; *Serratia marcescens trpO*	106
0.5	0.025-M salt, pH 6.0, 25°C	Gel retardation: same K_D's for *trpP1*, *trpR*, and *aroH* operators	48
5.9	0.25-M salt, pH 8.1, 4°C	Negative nitrocellulose filter binding	108
2.0	0.25-M salt, pH 7.4, 22°C	Alkaline phosphatase protection	115
0.2	0.15-M salt, 0.25-M glutamate, 5% Me$_2$SO, pH 7.5, 25°C	Filter binding	95
0.33 ± 0.16	0.25-M salt, pH 6.0, 25°C	Gel retardation	101

The locations of each operator with respect to the start-points of transcription are also different.

The solution structures of synthetic oligonucleotides containing wild-type and mutant *trpO* sites have been investigated by one- and two-dimensional NMR methods (75, 76, 111). The data are consistent with a B-DNA structure, with variations of local geometry from step to step (111). From NMR studies over a range of temperatures, two conformational transitions, localized to a TTAA sequence at the center of a *trpO* sequence, were detected. The conformational changes affected the propeller twist of the two central T–A base-pairs (76).

There have been many quantitative *in vitro* studies of the interaction between the Trp holorepressor and its operator targets (Table IV). One objective of these analyses has been to determine the parameters for protein–DNA binding, thereby establishing a basis for rationalizing the effects on transcription of mutational alterations within operators and amino-acid switches in mutant repressors. It is difficult to compare the published results directly to one another because a range of different natural or synthetic duplex DNA fragments of varying length and composition were studied. With respect to how closely the experimental arrangement approximated *in vivo* reality, each study had certain flaws. Nonetheless, the equilibrium dissociation constants for holorepressor–operator interaction all fell within the 0.2–7.0 nM range. The Trp repressor–operator binding appears not to be driven by cation release, because K_D's varied only slightly when salt concentrations were changed (*113, 116*). In the average *E. coli* cell, the "concentration" of palindromic Trp repressor targets in the genome is about 4 nM, so a first approximation about operator occupancy might be that one-half of the possible protein–DNA interactions of this specificity class could exist within cells under laboratory conditions.

The relative *in vitro* affinities of the Trp repressor for three of the four known operators (Fig. 5) were essentially identical, as expected for a set of targets having such a large number of structural identities (*48*). Paradoxically, the amplitude of regulation *in vivo* from the promoters bearing internal *trpO*$^+$ sequences falls into two widely disparate classes. The *trpR* and *aroH* promoters were stimulated weakly (3- to 6-fold) by genetic elimination of the Trp repressor from the cell (*47–49, 51*), whereas the *trp* and *mtr* promoters show elevations in signal strength of 100- to 300-fold when analyzed using similar experimental arrangements (*47, 49, 109*).

Two hypotheses have been offered to explain the differential susceptibility to *in vivo* shutdown of the known Trp repressor-regulated promoters. On the basis of DNase-I footprinting and methylation protection studies (*117*), it was suggested that the *trp* promoter contains three helically stacked Trp repressor-binding sites, that the *aroH* promoter has two such sites, and that the *trpR* promoter has a single site. The binding of two or more dimeric Trp holorepressor molecules to promoters with multiple operators was invoked (*117*) as an explanation for the strong repressibility of the *trp* promoter. Although the multiple-protein-binding model is appealing, it is contradicted by two independent kinds of observation: First, the only Trp-repressor–*trpO* complexes observed *in vitro* have a 1:1 protein–DNA stoichiometry (*106, 112*); and second, mutational changes in *trpO* that diminish affinity for the holorepressor are found mainly within two mutually symmetrical 5-bp clusters equidistant from the primary center of symmetry (*30, 43*) (Fig. 5).

An alternative hypothesis to explain the exquisite susceptibility to repression of the *trp* and *mtr* promoters would be to assign a major role to the position of *trpO* within these promoters. By virtue of its ability to prevent the formation of open complexes between RNA-polymerase and the *trp* promoter (22), the Trp repressor might be better able to block transcription from the *trp* promoter than from others having *trpO* sites. In some ill-defined way, DNA in the vicinity of the −10 hexamer of the *trp* promoter appears to be rendered particularly refractile to RNA-polymerase-mediated melting by complexed Trp holorepressor. The same situation could presumably hold true for the *mtr* promoter, where the *trpO* site lies between the −35 and −10 recognition hexamers.

There is one experimental test for the "operator position" model of Trp-repressor effectiveness (*118*). Operator targets positioned downstream from the transcription start-point were less effective than an operator situated over the −10 hexamer. The mutational elimination of the proposed (*117*) secondary operator targets had, at most, a 4-fold effect in diminishing repression. Although this result is consistent with the multiple-repressor-binding model, the principal targets for repression are those nucleotide pairs that lie astride the central operator (Fig. 5). With present technology, it is feasible to construct synthetic promoters containing more than one operator target. For example, *trpO–aroH* or *trpR–aroH* promoters could readily be assembled. Such promoters would be predicted to be hyper-repressible and to give rise to O^c derivatives at low frequencies.

There are a number of additional plausible explanations, drawn from analogies to other systems, for the fact that the *trp* and *mtr* promoters are particularly susceptible to repression, in comparison to the *aroH* and *trpR* promoters. It is possible that the high signal strength *in vivo* of the *trp* and *mtr* promoters is due to some form of positive stimulation, epistatic to the Trp repressor, that does not prevail for the *aroH* and *trpR* promoters. This is certainly the case for the *mtr* promoter (*109*), whose rate of transcription is enhanced about 10-fold by the product of the *tyrR* gene.

In this connection, it is worth noting that two independent studies suggest that regions upstream from the −35 hexamer of the *trp* promoter constitute low-level upstream activating sequences (*119, 120*). Equally plausible is the possibility that an undefined protein, absent from highly purified *in vitro* systems, increases in a selective fashion the affinity of the Trp holorepressor for the *trp* and *mtr* promoters or decreases the affinity of the Trp repressor for the *trpR* and *aroH* promoters. In the absence of such a factor(s), the observed Trp-holorepressor-binding affinity would be identical for each promoter. The major chromosome-associated protein of *E. coli* (HU) is an example of a protein that negatively affects binding of the Trp repressor to the *aroH* operator (*121*).

In the binding of dimeric proteins such as the Trp repressor to palindromic operators, the fundamental units of recognition consist of two complementary surfaces. The first is that of a protein monomer; the second is that of a DNA half-operator (*122, 123*). The multiplicative effect of two pairs of closely spaced complementary surfaces plays a large role in determining the overall binding affinity of such systems, although conformational changes in protein and DNA are also important steps in the pathway to the final stable complex (124). The Trp holorepressor, both *in vivo* and *in vitro*, interacts with DNA segments containing *trp*-system half-operator sequences (125). This result has been confirmed and extended, and it was also proposed that two Trp-repressor dimers can bind simultaneously to each full *trp* operator (i.e., one dimer for each half-operator). As yet, however, there have been no convincing demonstrations of the formation of such complexes *in vitro*.

Approximately one-third of the nucleotide sequence of the *E. coli* genome has been determined and is accessible in the data bases. A recent search (126) for DNA segments with homology to authentic *trp* half-operators turned up more than 80 statistically significant matches. Whether any of these "pseudo-half-operators" interact with the Trp holorepressor in a physiologically meaningful fashion remains to be established. By extrapolation, the number of target sequences having the potential to form complexes with the Trp repressor could be as high as 200–300.

XI. Structural Alterations in the Trp Repressor Generated by Mutation or Proteolysis

Several groups of investigators have addressed the relationship between the identity of a particular amino-acid residue at a given location within the Trp repressor and some functional property of the system. The literature includes descriptions of mutagen-induced amino-acid switches that produced dominant negative changes in operator binding (127), and changes that produced so-called "super-repressors," able to bind operator when intracellular tryptophan levels are low (95, 114, 127, 128). A number of structurally altered Trp repressors generated by site-directed mutagenesis have also been described (97, 129, 130). The amino-acid residues of the Trp repressor where mutational alterations have been described are shown in Fig. 6.

Of particular interest in such studies is the identity of residues important in ligand binding [recall the L-tryptophan, the corepressor, must precipitate a conformational change in the protein for operator binding to occur (see Fig. 7)]. In high-resolution X-ray crystallography (83, 84), the tryptophan-binding pocket was one where the indole ring of tryptophan was flanked on either side by the aliphatic arms of Arg-54 and Arg-84, plus the α-carbon of Gly-85. The side-chain hydroxyl of Thr-44, on a different subunit, was hydrogen-bonded with the α-carboxyl of tryptophan. Other interactions important to tryptophan binding involved three hydrogen-bonds between the α-amino group of tryptophan on the one hand and the hydroxyl of Ser-88 and the backbone carbonyls of residues 41 and 43 on the other (*84*). Purified mutant proteins altered in residues 44, 54, 84, 85, and 88 (*97, 130, 131*) disrupted the specific binding of tryptophan and diminished the affinity for operator DNA, by factors of up to 10^4. Amino-acid substitutions that affected the tryptophan-binding pocket (and therefore operator affinity) altered neither the secondary or quaternary structures of the mutant proteins nor their ability to form heterodimers with wild-type Trp-repressor monomers (*130, 131*).

Amino-acid substitutions at positions not considered to be part of the tryptophan pocket (Ser-67 and Ser-86) diminish both tryptophan binding and operator affinity (*97*). These effects were attributed to distortions in the binding region.

That distortions in the tryptophan-binding region (but outside the ligand-binding pocket) may affect the functional behavior of the Trp repressor is supported by studies of a particular super-repressor mutant involving a change at codon 77 from Ala to Val. Residues 75–78 of the Trp repressor comprise the "turn" portion of the DNA-binding helix–turn–helix motif (*83*). The Ala-77 side-chain of wild-type protein permits the collapse of un-liganded repressor into a conformation with minimal operator-binding capability (*115*). In one study, the α-methyl groups of Val-77, in the absence of tryptophan, were reported to force the protein into a conformation capable of engaging *trpO* in a specific manner (*8, 115*). This result conflicts with an independent analysis of the Ala-77→Val mutant protein, where it was not possible to distinguish the behavior of this mutant protein from that of wild-type (*95*).

The role of charged amino-acid residues in binding of the Trp repressor to operator targets has been investigated in studies of four different super-repressor mutants (*95, 127, 128*). The charge-modified repressors (Glu-13→Lys, Glu-18→Lys, Asp-46→Asn, and Glu-49→Lys) all bound operator DNA more tightly than the wild-type Trp repressor, primarily because of a reduced rate of dissociation of the protein–DNA complexes. Several of the super-repressor–operator complexes had half-lives of 1 hr or more. It was argued (*95*) that the relatively short (3 min) half-life of the wild-type Trp-repressor–operator complex would be most appropriate for the optimal control of the promoters of the *trp* regulon.

A number of amino-acid switches that diminish operator binding and that lie mainly in the helix–turn–helix operator-binding motif (Fig. 6) have been described (*127, 129*). Our understanding of these mutant proteins is some-what superficial, since few have either been purified or otherwise studied in detail. Only one mutant Trp repressor of the thermosensitive class (Trp-99→Arg) has been characterized (*132*).

The N-terminal segments of λ repressor (*133*) and *Eco*RI restriction endonuclease (134) are critically important in the formation of specific DNA–protein complexes. The possibility that the N-terminal "arms" of the Trp repressor might play a similar role in DNA binding has been investigated (135, 136). The Trp repressor is remarkably resistant to chymotrypsin digestion (82), presumably because of its tightly folded structure. It is therefore possible to establish conditions under which the only peptide bond cleaved on exposure to this protease is that connecting Tyr-7 and Ser-8. The resulting "des-7" form of the Trp repressor was purified and found by gel-mobility-shift assay to engage in tryptophan-dependent operator binding at pH 6.0, about 1/50 as efficiently as the full-length Trp repressor. Using a different assay, at pH 7.4, the binding of des-7 Trp repressor to the operator was nearly identical to wild-type (115). A similar result has been reported elsewhere (129).

Clearly, the mutational analysis of the Trp repressor has not progressed as far as have parallel systems of protein–DNA interaction, such as λ repressor (137). Little attention has been paid to the characterization of trpR mutations that are neutral in effect; that involve in-frame deletions or insertions of integral numbers of codons; or that affect folding, subunit assembly, binding to nonstandard operators, or susceptibility to intracellular proteolysis. There are likewise no reports on the cloning and/or characterization of trpR genes from related enteric organisms, despite longstanding evidence (138) that such genes exist. If even a small number of homologous trpR genes were characterized, this would be beneficial in guiding the course of future structure–function analyses in this system.

XII. The Trp Repressor as a Prototypical Member of the Helix–turn–helix Family of DNA-Binding Proteins

A common structural feature shared by the Trp repressor and many other DNA-binding proteins is a stretch of 20–22 amino acids whose organization in three-dimensional space is that of two α-helical segments joined by a short turn: the helix–turn–helix motif (reviews in 1, 2 and 139). The helix–turn–helix motif is a recurring substructure embedded within many DNA-binding proteins, but is not a stably folded independent domain. The segment of the Trp repressor that constitutes (83) this DNA-binding motif is given in Fig. 8, aligned with selected sequences from other well-studied regulatory proteins of the same class. The main features of this motif appear to be (1) an absence of proline residues from internal positions within the helices; (2) residue 9 is almost always glycine; (3) residue 5 (usually Gly or Ala) is Lys in the Trp repressor, a situation that perturbs the geometry of the helix–turn–helix in a specific way (83); and (4) hydrophobic residues tend to predominate at positions 4, 8, 10, 16, and 18.

There is no universal "recognition code" that determines which arrays of

		-2	-1	1	2	3	4	5	6	7	8	9	10	11	12	13	14	15	16	17	18	19	20
TrpR	66	Met	Ser	Gln	Arg	Glu	Leu	Lys	Asn	Glu	Leu	Gly	Ala	Gly	Ile	Ala	Thr	Ile	Thr	Arg	Gly	Ser	Asn
REP434	16	Leu	Asn	Gln	Ala	Glu	Leu	Ala	Gln	Lys	Val	Gly	Thr	Thr	Gln	Gln	Ser	Ile	Glu	Gln	Leu	Glu	Asn
CRO434	16	Met	Thr	Gln	Thr	Glu	Leu	Ala	Thr	Lys	Ala	Gly	Val	Lys	Gln	Gln	Ser	Ile	Gln	Leu	Ile	Glu	Ala
Rep	31	Leu	Ser	Gln	Glu	Ser	Val	Ala	Asp	Lys	Met	Gly	Met	Gly	Gln	Ser	Gly	Val	Gly	Ala	Leu	Phe	Asn
CRO	14	Phe	Gly	Gln	Thr	Lys	Thr	Ala	Lys	Asp	Leu	Gly	Val	Tyr	Gln	Ser	Ala	Ile	Asn	Lys	Ala	Ile	His
CAP	167	Ile	Thr	Arg	Gln	Glu	Ile	Gly	Ile	Ile	Gly	Gly	Cys	Ser	Arg	Glu	Thr	Val	Gly	Arg	Ile	Leu	Lys
LAC	4	Val	Thr	Leu	Tyr	Asp	Val	Ala	Glu	Tyr	Ala	Gly	Val	Ser	Tyr	Gln	Thr	Val	Ser	Arg	Val	Val	Asn

Helix   Turn   Helix

FIG. 8. The helix–turn–helix motif of the Trp repressor (top line) compared to a group of other prokaryotic regulatory proteins that use the same general principle for protein–DNA recognition. The numbering convention is that of Pabo and Sauer (1). The number on the left refers to the position in each protein of the first residue in the motif. Residues characteristic of this DNA-binding motif are shown in black boxes.

amino-acid side-chains are most appropriate for interaction with the edges of purine·pyrimidine base-pairs that are exposed within the major groove of duplex DNA (140). Protein–DNA recognition is the result of many factors, including specific hydrogen-bonds, van der Waals contacts between amino-acid side-chains and parts of base-pairs, and appropriately positioned water molecules that lie on the protein–DNA interface. Conformational changes in both interacting macromolecules are also likely to be important in the pathway to stable complex formation (124). In the Trp repressor and other proteins of this class, the helix–turn–helix motif appears to provide a framework for the recognition elements of the protein, but the final geometry of the protein–DNA interaction surface is governed by the subtle interplay of functional groups.

Within the limitations imposed by this perspective, there are a number of quite successful attempts to use primary amino-acid sequence information to identify helix–turn–helix motifs in proteins of unknown structure. The Trp repressor is, in fact, a protein in which such a prediction has been verified by subsequent structural determination (83, 87). The availability of a reasonable number of authentic representative helix–turn–helix motifs has facilitated the development of statistical algorithms for comparing newly established amino-acid sequences with known data sets. Brennan and Matthews (3) statistically compared the primary sequences of a master set of 10 known helix–turn–helix motifs (including the Trp repressor) and developed criteria for judging prospective DNA-binding proteins. Their algorithm successfully predicted all known examples of helix–turn–helix motifs in sequence-specific DNA-binding proteins. Dodd and Egan used master sets of 37 (4) and 91 (5) sequences to develop and calibrate weight-matrix methods for scoring potential helix–turn–helix motifs.

In the initial work (4), the Trp repressor failed to meet the similarity criterion for a helix–turn–helix protein. Later, when a mutant super-repressor form of Trp repressor, having an Ala-77→Val switch, was tested statistically, the Trp repressor met the test for inclusion. The failure of the earlier detection algorithm was attributed to the fact that the Trp repressor is a special case: The helix–turn–helix motif of this protein does not form properly unless tryptophan is bound. Moreover, atypical amino-acid residues, present in the Trp repressor's helix–turn–helix motif, introduced penalties in the weight-matrix analysis.

From stereochemical considerations, Shestopalov (7) devised a sequence template approach to predict which amino acids would be allowed within helix–turn–helix motifs. As expected, proline was forbidden in most positions; the other locations predicted to have large numbers of forbidden residues were 4, 5, 8, 9, 11, and 15 (see Fig. 8 for the numbering convention). The first rounds of mutational analysis of the Trp repressor (Fig. 6) do not offer conclusive tests of the validity of the predictions of Shestopalov. In some cases, amino-acid switches at locations other than those mentioned above either abolished repressor binding or created new binding specificities (43); in other cases, amino-acid switches either generated a super-repressor (Ala-77→Val: Pabo–Sauer position 11) or brought about the predicted abolition of operator binding (43, 127). Clearly, much additional work, both theoretical and practical, is required to reconcile the predicted and observed effects of amino-acid switches within the helix–turn–helix region of the Trp repressor and other proteins of the same class.

XIII. Concluding Comments and Perspectives for Future Research on the Trp Repressor

More than 30 years have passed since the original observations (9) that eventually led to our current view of how the *trp* system of *E. coli* is negatively controlled. It was the hope of many researchers studying the transcriptional control of gene expression that the Trp repressor system would turn out to be a paradigm strongly representative of other cases of gene control in the area of amino-acid biosynthesis and metabolism. However, the regulation of amino-acid metabolism in bacteria at the DNA level has turned out to be highly idiosyncratic. At the present time, there are no generally applicable molecular models that explain all cases satisfactorily. Amino-acid biosynthetic repressors differ greatly in size, subunit organization, cellular location, nature of the corepressor, and in the ways they interact with operator targets in DNA. In some cases, positive control of transcription initiation plays a key role in determining the rates of expression of amino-acid biosynthetic genes. For several amino acids, systems of global control can impose subtle and often unpredictable effects on gene expression. In the following paragraphs, I mention a few of the better-studied systems, comparing, when possible, their molecular physiology to that of the Trp repressor.

The regulatory gene for arginine biosynthesis, *argR*, has been known almost as long as has *trpR* (141, 142). Recently, the *argR* gene and its protein product have been characterized structurally (143). The Arg repressor, a hexamer composed of six identical subunits of molecular weight 16,500, not only controls a number of *arg* promoters (144), but also functions as an accessory factor in a site-specific recombination system of plasmid Col E1 (145). One should thus remain alert to the possibility that any protein of the *E. coli* cytoplasm, particularly those with DNA-binding capability, may have been recruited during evolution to participate in the life cycle of some other replicon. Such alternative roles for DNA-binding proteins may offer particular technical advantages in the study of structure–function relationships. There are at present no known effects of the Trp repressor on the behavior of other replicons in *E. coli*.

Repressor-mediated control of methionine biosynthesis was recognized as early as repression in the tryptophan system (9). The methionine biosynthetic genes, like those of the *trp* and *arg* regulons, are dispersed throughout the *E. coli* genome (146). Negative regulation at *met*-specific promoters involves the protein product of *metJ*, which contains two intertwined identical subunits of molecular weight 12,000. The corepressor is S-adenosylmethionine. The three-dimensional structures of the Met repressor, with and without S-adenosylmethionine, are known (147). The Met repressor utilizes an antiparallel β-sheet as the DNA-binding motif. The β-strands become inserted, on one side of the DNA helix, into successive major grooves. It appears that several dimeric Met repressors bind in cooperative fashion to tandemly repeated 8-bp targets, forming a left-handed superhelix around the DNA (148, 149).

It should be recalled that a structural model involving the binding of Trp-repressor dimers to tandem overlapping operators has also been proposed (117). The *trp* operators contain as consensus elements the sequence AGN_4CT, which happens to match the *met* operator (148). Although there have been no experimental tests of possible interactions between the Met repressor and *trpO*, such experiments deserve to be carried out, particularly in view of the fact that promoters with $trpO^+$ sequences appear to have a certain degree of plasticity, in that they can be engaged by at least one other repressor type encoded by phage 434 (150).

One of the most enigmatic prokaryotic regulatory proteins is the Tyr repressor, a polypeptide of 513 amino acids (151). A group of genes, known as the TyrR regulon, encoding enzymes and proteins important in the biosynthesis and transport of aromatic amino acids, are controlled by the Tyr repressor (152). By unknown mechanisms, in response to the individual aromatic amino acids, the Tyr repressor is able differentially to inhibit or stimulate promoters bearing TYR boxes. The binding of the Tyr repressor to operator targets requires ATP (153). Although the Tyr repressor contains a large block of polypeptide sequences with identities to proteins that activate σ^{54} promoters (154), attempts to demonstrate such promoters among Tyr regulon genes have failed (126).

A number of homologous activator proteins important in amino-acid biosynthesis in prokaryotes have been characterized structurally. These include: LysR (311 codons), activated by diaminopimelate (155); CysB (324 codons), activated by O-acetylserine (156); IlvY (297 codons), activated by acetohydroxybutyrate or acetolactate (157); MetR (276 codons), activated by vitamin B_{12} (158); and LeuO (290 codons), whose mode of action has not been established. The relevant genes, on the basis of homology comparisons, encode a set of regulatory proteins, all of which were predicted to contain a helix–turn–helix motif (159).

Several interesting examples of transcriptional regulatory proteins that contain independently functioning DNA-binding and catalytic domains have recently been described. PutA, a membrane-associated proline dehydrogenase of 130 kDa, ordinarily functions as a repressor of the divergent *put* operon. This protein undergoes a proline-induced conformational change that sequesters it in the membrane, where it is unable to function as a repressor *(160)*. Other examples of bifunctional regulatory proteins with clearly distinguished roles either in catalysis or as modifiers of a transport process are the BirA protein of *E. coli (161–163)* and the NadR regulator of *Salmonella typhimurium (164–166).*[2] Given the multiplicity of covalent and noncovalent modes of association already established for the tryptophan biosynthetic enzymes *(167)*, it would not be surprising to encounter examples of naturally occurring Trp repressor chimeras having domains with extra functional capabilities. Nor would it be unexpected to encounter cases of noncovalent association between the Trp repressor and other proteins of the *E. coli* cytoplasm or cytoplasmic membrane. There is strong suggestive evidence that protein–protein complexes involving the Trp repressor can form *(168)*. One challenge for the future will be to characterize biochemically and genetically the participating macromolecules, then rationalize these interactions in terms of cellular physiology.

ACKNOWLEDGMENTS

Work in the author's laboratory was supported by USPHS Grant GM22131 from the National Institute of General Medicine Sciences. The work at Purdue University would not have been possible without the dedicated efforts of William Roeder, Stuart Kuhstoss, Gregg Bogosian, Michael Tsapakos, Paul Haydock, Kathleen Brechling, Jill Zeilstra-Ryalls, Byron Hagewood, Linda Eades, Barbara Nicodemus, and Tiee-Leou Shieh.

REFERENCES

1. C. O. Pabo and R. T. Sauer, *ARB* **53**, 293 (1984).
2. S. C. Harrison and A. K. Aggarwal, *ARB* **59**, 933 (1990).
3. R. G. Brennan and B. W. Matthews, *JBC* **264**, 1903 (1989).
4. I. B. Dodd and J. B. Egan, *JMB* **194**, 557 (1987).
5. I. B. Dodd and J. B. Egan, *NARes* **18**, 5019 (1990).
6. B. Gicquel-Sanzey and P. Cossart, *EMBO J.* **1**, 591 (1982).
7. B. V. Shestopalov, *FEBS Lett.* **233**, 105 (1988).
8. R. Q. Marmorstein and P. B. Sigler, *in* "Nucleic Acids and Molecular Biology" (F. Eckstein and D. M. J. Lilley, eds.), Vol. 3, pp. 56–78. Springer-Verlag, Berlin, 1989.
9. G. Cohen and F. Jacob, *C. R. Hebd. Seances Acad. Sci.* **248**, 3490 (1959).
10. R. L. Somerville, *in* "Amino Acids: Biosynthesis and Genetic Regulation" (K. M. Herrmann and R. L. Somerville, eds.), pp. 351–378. Addison-Wesley, Reading, Massachusetts, 1983.

[2] NadR is a bifunctional protein of *S. typhimurium* that regulates the *de novo* biosynthesis of NAD as well as the cellular uptake of NMN.

11. V. M. Heatwole and R. L. Somerville, *J. Bact.* **173**, 108 (1991).
12. B. J. Bachmann, *Bact. Rev.* **54**, 130 (1990).
13. M. Kröger, R. Wahl and P. Rice, *NARes* **18** (Suppl.), 2549 (1990).
14. Y. Kohara, K. Akiyama and K. Isono, *Cell* **50**, 495 (1987).
15. D. E. Morse and C. Yanofsky, *JMB* **44**, 185 (1969).
16. J. Ito, S. Hiraga and T. Yura, *J. Bact.* **99**, 279 (1969).
17. W. Reznikoff and K. P. Thornton, *J. Bact.* **109**, 526 (1972).
18. R. P. Gunsalus, A. Gunsalus-Miguel and G. L. Gunsalus, *J. Bact.* **167**, 272 (1986).
19. G. Zubay, D. E. Morse, W. J. Schrenk and J. H. M. Miller, *PNAS* **69**, 1100 (1972).
20. Y. Shimizu, N. Shimizu and M. Hayaishi, *PNAS* **70**, 1990 (1973).
21. C. L. Squires, J. K. Rose, C. Yanofsky, H.-L. Yang and G. Zubay, *Nature NB* **245**, 133 (1973).
22. C. L. Squires, F. D. Lee and C. Yanofsky, *JMB* **92**, 93 (1975).
23. J. K. Rose and C. Yanofsky, *PNAS* **71**, 3134 (1974).
24. D. McGeoch, J. McGeoch and D. Morse, *Nature NB* **245**, 137 (1973).
25. D. E. Morse, R. D. Mosteller, and C. Yanofsky, *CSHSQB* **34**, 725 (1969).
26. C. L. Lawson and P. B. Sigler, *Nature* **333**, 869 (1988).
27. D. S. Oppenheim, G. N. Bennett and C. Yanofsky, *JMB* **144**, 133 (1980).
28. L. Johnsrud, *PNAS* **75**, 5324 (1978).
29. G. N. Bennett, M. E. Schweingruber, K. D. Brown, C. Squires and C. Yanofsky, *PNAS* **73**, 2351 (1976).
30. G. N. Bennett and C. Yanofsky, *JMB* **121**, 179 (1978).
31. M. Ptashne, A. Jeffrey, A. D. Johnson, R. Maurer, B. Meyer and C. Pabo, *Cell* **19**, 1 (1980).
32. A. Travers, *FEBS Lett.* **69**, 195 (1976).
33. R. L. Somerville, *in* "Biochemistry and Genetic Engineering Reviews" (G. E. Russell, ed.), Vol. 6, p. 1. Intercept, Wimborne, Dorset, England, 1988.
34. S. B. Straney and D. M. Crothers, *Cell* **51**, 699 (1987).
35. W. D. Roeder and R. L. Somerville, *MGG* **176**, 361 (1979).
36. R. P. Gunsalus, G. Zurawski and C. Yanofsky, *J. Bact.* **140**, 106 (1979).
37. C. K. Singleton, W. D. Roeder, G. Bogosian, R. L. Somerville and H. L. Weith, *NARes* **8**, 1551 (1980).
38. R. P. Gunsalus and C. Yanofsky, *PNAS* **77**, 7117 (1980).
39. A. S. Betzner and W. Keck, *MGG* **219**, 489 (1989).
40. M. J. Stern, G. F.-L. Ames, N. H. Smith, E. C. Robinson and C. F. Higgins, *Cell* **37**, 1015 (1984).
41. W. Roeder and R. L. Somerville, *FP* **38**, 396 (1979).
42. C. B. Harley and R. P. Reynolds, *NARes* **15**, 2343 (1987).
43. S. Bass, P. Sugiono, D. N. Arvidson, R. P. Gunsalus and P. Youderian, *Genes Dev.* **1**, 565 (1987).
44. G. Zurawski, R. P. Gunsalus, K. D. Brown and C. Yanofsky, *JMB* **145**, 47 (1981).
45. G. Bogosian, R. L. Somerville, K. Nishi, Y. Kano and F. Imamoto, *MGG* **193**, 244 (1984).
46. G. Bogosian, K. Bertrand and R. L. Somerville, *JMB* **149**, 821 (1981).
47. G. Bogosian and R. L. Somerville, *MGG* **193**, 110 (1984).
48. L. S. Klig, J. Carey and C. Yanofsky, *JMB* **202**, 769 (1988).
49. R. L. Kelley and C. Yanofsky, *PNAS* **79**, 3120 (1982).
50. G. D. Stormo, T. D. Schneider and L. M. Gold, *NARes* **10**, 2971 (1982).
51. C. L. Grove and R. P. Gunsalus, *J. Bact.* **169**, 2158 (1987).
52. K.-O. Cho and C. Yanofsky, *JMB* **204**, 41 (1988).
53. M. G. Marinus, *MGG* **200**, 185 (1985).

54. D. K. Hawley and W. R. McClure, *NARes* **11**, 2237 (1983).
55. M. E. Mulligan, D. K. Hawley, R. Entriken and W. R. McClure, *NARes* **12**, 789 (1984).
56. R. R. Plaskon and R. M. Wartell, *NARes* **15**, 785 (1987).
57. C.-S. Tung and S. C. Harvey, *NARes* **15**, 4973 (1987).
58. M. O'Neill and F. Chiafari, *JBC* **264**, 5531 (1989).
59. M. O'Neill, *JBC* **264**, 5522 (1989).
60. M. S. Z. Horwitz and L. A. Loeb, *PNAS* **83**, 7405 (1986).
61. A. R. Oliphant and K. Strubb, *NARes* **16**, 7673 (1988).
62. M. Kobayashi, K. Nagata and A. Ishihama, *NARes* **18**, 7367 (1990).
63. G. D. Stormo, *in* "Maximizing Gene Expression" (W. Reznikoff and L. Gold, eds.), p. 195. Butterworths, Stoneham, Massachusetts, 1986.
64. P. H. van Knippenberg, *in* "The Ribosome Structure, Function, and Evolution" (W. E. Hill, P. B. Moore, A. Dahlberg, D. Schlessinger, R. A. Garrett and J. R. Warner, eds.), p. 265. American Society for Microbiology, Washington, D.C., 1990.
65. H. A. de Boer and R. A. Kastelein, *in* "Maximizing Gene Expression" (W. Reznikoff and L. Gold, eds.), p. 225. Butterworths, Stoneham, Massachusetts, 1986.
66. D. B. Dix, L. K. Thomas and R. C. Thompson, *in* "The Ribosome Structure, Function and Evolution" (W. E. Hill, P. B. Moore, A. Dahlberg, D. Schlessinger, R. A. Garrett and J. R. Warner, eds.), p. 527. American Society for Microbiology, Washington, D.C., 1990.
67. I. Tonoco, Jr., P. N. Borer, B. Dengler, M. D. Levine, O. C. Uhlenbeck, D. M. Crothers and J. Gralla, *Nature NB* **246**, 40 (1973).
68. J. Shine and L. Dalgarno, *Nature* **254**, 34 (1975).
69. M. Gouy and C. Gautier, *NARes* **10**, 7055 (1982).
70. E. S. Shpaer, *JMB* **188**, 555 (1988).
71. L. S. Folley and M. Yarus, *JMB* **209**, 359 (1989).
72. J. L. Paluh and C. Yanofsky, *NARes* **14**, 7851 (1986).
73. J. H. Zeilstra-Ryalls, Ph.D. thesis. Purdue University, West Lafayette, Indiana, 1990.
74. C. Yanofsky, *in* "The Molecular Biology of Bacterial Growth" (M. Schaechter, F. C. Neidhardt, J. L. Ingraham and N. O. Kjelgaard, eds.), p. 165. Jones and Bartlett, Portole Valley, California, 1985.
75. J.-F. Lefèvre, A. N. Lane and O. Jandetzky, *Bchem* **27**, 1086 (1988).
76. A. N. Lane, *BJ* **259**, 715 (1989).
77. D. N. Arvidson, C. Bruse and R. P. Gunsalus, *JBC* **261**, 238 (1986).
78. S.-J. Bae, W.-Y. Chou, K. Matthews and J. M. Sturtevant, *PNAS* **85**, 6731 (1988).
79. F. C. Neidhardt and R. A. van Bogelen, *in* "*Escherichia coli* and *Salmonella typhimurium* Cellular and Molecular Biology" (F. C. Neidhardt, J. L. Ingraham, K. B. Low, B. Magasanik, M. Schaechter and H. E. Umbarger, eds.), Vol. 2, p. 1335. American Society for Microbiology, Washington, D.C., 1987.
80. P.-H. Hirel, J.-M. Schmitter, P. Dessen, G. Fayat and S. Blanquet, *PNAS* **86**, 8247 (1989).
81. H. Dalboge, S. Bayne and J. Pedersen, *FEBS Lett.* **266**, 1 (1990).
82. M. J. Tsapakos, P. V. Haydock, M. Hermodson and R. L. Somerville, *JBC* **260**, 16383 (1985).
83. R. W. Schevitz, Z. Otwinowski, A. Joachimiak, C. L. Lawson and P. B. Sigler, *Nature* **317**, 782 (1985).
84. R.-G. Zhang, A. Joachimiak, C. L. Lawson, R. W. Schevitz, Z. Otwinowski and P. B. Sigler, *Nature* **327**, 591 (1987).
85. Z. Otwinowski, R. W. Schevitz, R.-G. Zhang, C. L. Lawson, A. Joachimiak, R. Q. Marmorstein, B. F. Luisi and P. B. Sigler, *Nature* **335**, 321 (1988).
86. D. D. Moore, *in* "Current Protocols in Molecular Biology" (F. A. Ausubel, R. Brent, R. E. Kingston, D. D. Moore, J. G. Seidman, J. A. Smith and K. Struhl, eds.), pp. 8.2.8–8.2.13. Greene and Wiley (Interscience), New York, 1989.

87. P. V. Haydock, Ph.D. dissertation. Purdue University, West Lafayette, Indiana, 1983.
88. A. Joachimiak, R. L. Kelley, R. P. Gunsalus, C. Yanofsky and P. B. Sigler, *PNAS* **80**, 668 (1983).
89. M. Savageau, *PNAS* **83**, 1198 (1986).
90. A. Sillero and J. M. Ribeiro, *Anal. Biochem.* **179**, 319 (1989).
91. G. Bogosian and R. Somerville, *MGG* **191**, 51 (1983).
92. D. N. Arvidson, A. A. Kumamoto and R. P. Gunsalus, *UCLA Symp. Mol. Cell. Biol., New Ser.* **68**, 401 (1987).
93. B. Hagewood, T.-L. Shieh, W.-P. Yang and R. L. Somerville, unpublished observations, 1991.
94. S. Stacke, B. Walter, B. Kisters-Woicke, B. v. Wilcken-Bergmann and B. Müller-Hill, *EMBO J.* **9**, 1963 (1990).
95. B. K. Hurlburt and C. Yanofsky, *JBC* **265**, 7853 (1990).
96. F. W. Studier, A. H. Rosenberg, J. J. Dunn and J. W. Dubendorf, *in* "Methods in Enzymology" (D. V. Goeddel, ed.), Vol. 185, p. 60. Academic Press, San Diego, California, 1990.
97. W.-Y. Chou and K. S. Matthews, *JBC* **264**, 18314 (1989).
98. J. K. Rose, C. L. Squires, C. Yanofsky, H.-L. Yang and G. Zubay, *Nature NB* **245**, 133 (1973).
99. A. N. Lane, *EJB* **157**, 405 (1986).
100. R. Q. Marmostein, A. Joachimiak, M. Sprinzl and P. B. Sigler, *JBC* **262**, 4911 (1987).
101. W.-Y. Chou, C. Bieber and K. S. Matthews, *JBC* **264**, 18309 (1989).
102. J. L. Ingraham, O. Maaloe and F. C. Neidhardt, "Growth of the Bacterial Cell." Sinauer, Sunderland, Massachusetts, 1983.
103. R. D. Bliss, *Anal. Biochem.* **93**, 390 (1979).
104. D. R. Joseph and K. H. Muench, *JBC* **246**, 7602 (1971).
105. Y. Oshima, T. Mizokoshi and T. Horiuchi, *JMB* **89**, 127 (1984).
106. J. Carey, *PNAS* **85**, 975 (1988).
107. L. S. Klig, I. P. Crawford and C. Yanofsky, *NARes* **15**, 5339 (1987).
108. R. Q. Marmostein and P. B. Sigler, *JBC* **264**, 9149 (1989).
109. V. M. Heatwole and R. L. Somerville, *J. Bact.* **173**, 3601 (1991).
110. D. I. Johnson and R. L. Somerville, *J. Bact.* **155**, 49 (1983).
111. J.-F. Lefèvre, A. N. Lane and O. Jardetzky, *Bchem* **26**, 5076 (1987).
112. P. V. Haydock and R. L. Somerville, *BBRC* **119**, 926 (1984).
113. A. N. Lane, J.-F. Lefèvre and O. Jardetzky, *BBA* **909**, 58 (1987).
114. L. S. Klig and C. Yanofsky, *JBC* **263**, 243 (1988).
115. R. W. Marmorstein, M. Sprinzl and P. B. Sigler, *Bchem* **30**, 1141 (1991).
116. L. R. Chandler and A. N. Lane, *BJ* **250**, 925 (1988).
117. A. A. Kumamoto, W. G. Miller and R. P. Gunsalus, *Genes Dev.* **1**, 556 (1987).
118. S. J. Elledge and R. W. Davis, *Genes Dev.* **3**, 185 (1989).
119. T. Nishi and S. Itol, *Gene* **44**, 29 (1986).
120. M. Latta, M. Philit, I. Maury, F. Soubrier, P. Denefle and J.-F. Mayaux, *DNA Cell Biol.* **9**, 129 (1990).
121. Y. Flashner and J. D. Gralla, *Cell* **54**, 713 (1988).
122. M. Hollis, D. Valenzuela, D. Pioli, R. Wharton and M. Ptashne, *PNAS* **85**, 5834 (1988).
123. A. M. Dranginis, *Nature* **347**, 682 (1990).
124. R. G. Brennan, S. L. Roderick, Y. Takeda and B. W. Matthews, *PNAS* **87**, 8165 (1990).
125. P. V. Haydock, G. Bogosian, K. Brechling and R. L. Somerville, *JMB* **170**, 1019 (1983).
126. V. M. Heatwole, unpublished observations, 1991.
127. R. L. Kelley and C. Yanofsky, *PNAS* **82**, 483 (1985).
128. L. S. Klig, D. L. Oxender and C. Yanofsky, *Genetics* **120**, 651 (1988).

129. S. Bass, V. Sorrells and P. Youderian, *Science* **242**, 240 (1988).
130. J.-J. He and K. S. Matthews, *JBC* **265**, 731 (1990).
131. T. J. Graddis, L. S. Klig, C. Yanofsky and D. L. Oxender, *Proteins, Struct., Funct., Genet.* **4**, 173 (1988).
132. B. Hagewood and R. L. Somerville, unpublished results, 1991.
133. J. L. Eliason, M. A. Weiss and M. Ptashne, *PNAS* **82**, 2339 (1985).
134. L. Jen-Jacobsen, D. Lessen and M. Kurpiewski, *Cell* **45**, 619 (1986).
135. J. Carey, *JBC* **264**, 1941 (1989).
136. C. H. Arrowsmith, J. Carey, L. Treat-Clemons and O. Jardetsky, *Bchem* **28**, 3875 (1989).
137. R. T. Sauer, S. R. Jordan and C. Pabo, *Adv. Protein Chem* **40**, 1 (1990).
138. R. L. Somerville, *Science* **154**, 1585 (1966).
139. R. G. Brennan and B. W. Matthews, *JBC* **264**, 1903 (1989).
140. B. W. Matthews, *Nature* **355**, 294 (1988).
141. L. Gorini, W. Gundersen and M. Burger, *CSHSQB* **26**, 173 (1961).
142. W. K. Maas, *CSHSQB* **26**, 183 (1961).
143. D. Lim, J. D. Oppenheim, T. Eckhardt and W. K. Maas, *PNAS* **84**, 6697 (1987).
144. R. Cunin, N. Glansdorff, N. Pierard and V. Stalon, *Microbiol. Rev.* **50**, 314 (1986).
145. C. J. Stirling, G. Szatmani, C. M. Smith, G. Stewart and D. J. Sherratt, *EMBO J.* **7**, 4389 (1988).
146. I. Saint-Girous, C. Parsot, M. M. Zakin, O. Bârzu and G. N. Cohen, *CRC Crit. Rev. Biochem.* **23** (Suppl. 1), 1 (1988).
147. J. B. Rafferty, W. S. Somers, I. Saint-Girous and S. E. V. Phillips, *Nature* **341**, 705 (1989).
148. S. E. V. Phillips, I. Manfield, I. Parson, B. E. Davidson, J. B. Rafferty, W. S. Somers, D. Margarita, G. N. Cohen, I. Saint-Girous and P. G. Stockley, *Nature* **341**, 711 (1989).
149. B. E. Davidson and I. Saint-Girous, *Mol. Microbiol.* **3**, 1639 (1989).
150. R. L. Somerville, G. Bogosian and J. H. Zeilstra-Ryalls, *JMB* **217**, 599 (1991).
151. E. C. Cornish, V. P. Argyropoulos, J. Pittard and B. E. Davidson, *JBC* **261**, 403 (1986).
152. A. J. Pittard, in "*Escherichia coli* and *Salmonella typhimurium* Cellular and Molecular Biology" (F. C. Neidhardt, J. L. Ingraham, K. B. Low, B. Magasanik, M. Schaechter and H. E. Umbarger, eds.), Vol. 1, pp. 368–394. American Society for Microbiology, Washington, D.C., 1987.
153. T. Triglia, V. P. Argyropoulos, B. E. Davidson and D. J. Kemp, *NARes* **18**, 1080 (1990).
154. J. B. Stock, A. J. Ninfa and A. N. Stock, *Microbiol. Rev.* **53**, 450 (1989).
155. P. Stragier and J.-C. Patti, *JMB* **168**, 333 (1983).
156. J. Ostrowski, G. Jagura-Burdzy and N. M. Kredich, *JBC* **262**, 5999 (1987).
157. R. C. Wek and G. W. Hatfield, *JBC* **261**, 2441 (1986).
158. L. S. Plamann and G. V. Stauffer, *J. Bact.* **169**, 3932 (1987).
159. S. Henikoff, G. W. Haughn, J. M. Calvo and J. C. Wallace, *PNAS* **85**, 6602 (1988).
160. D. R. Hahn, R. S. Myers, C. R. Kent and S. R. Maloy, *MGG* **213**, 125 (1988).
161. D. F. Barker and A. M. Campbell, *JMB* **146**, 451 (1981).
162. D. F. Barker and A. M. Campbell, *JMB* **146**, 469 (1981).
163. M. R. Buoncristani and A. J. Ohtsuka, *JBC* **263**, 1013 (1988).
164. J. W. Foster, Y. K. Park, T. Penfound, T. Fenger and M. P. Spector, *J. Bact.* **172**, 4187 (1990).
165. N. Zhu and J. R. Roth, *J. Bact.* **173**, 1302 (1991).
166. N. Zhu, B. M. Olivera and J. R. Roth, *J. Bact.* **173**, 1311 (1991).
167. I. D. Crawford, *CRC Crit. Rev. Biochem.* **8**, 175 (1980).
168. R. L. Somerville, J. H. Zielstra-Ryalls and T.-L. Shieh, *UCLA Symp. Mol. Cell. Biol., New Ser.* **133**, 181 (1990).

Immunochemical Analyses of Nucleic Acids

B. David Stollar

Department of Biochemistry
Tufts University Schools of Medicine,
    Dental Medicine and Veterinary
    Medicine
and the Sackler School of Graduate
    Biomedical Sciences
Boston, Massachusetts 02111

Antibodies to nucleic acids, which may arise in autoimmune disease or be induced by experimental immunization, can serve as reagents for the detection of specific nucleic-acid structures and structural transitions. Studies of antibodies to nucleic acids contribute to and benefit from burgeoning research on interactions between proteins and nucleic acids, a field that is growing with the increasing number of proteins recognized to be of fundamental importance in the processes of replication, recombination, chromatin assembly, transcription, RNA processing, and regulation. Analyses of pro-

Progress in Nucleic Acid Research
and Molecular Biology, Vol. 42

teins involved in these processes have led to identification of certain structural motifs, such as the helix–turn–helix or zinc-finger structures, in DNA-binding proteins (1, 2). Antigen-binding sites of immunoglobulins do not contain these motifs (3).

The specific interactions of antibodies with nucleic acids, as with other antigen–antibody systems, probably involve considerable diversity. The binding of antibodies depends on the amino-acid sequences of the six hypervariable regions, also known as the *complementarity-determining regions* (CDRs) (3), in the amino-terminal domains of the immunoglobulin heavy and light chains. Many different amino-acid sequences are known to occur in the CDRs of anti-DNA antibodies for which the primary structure is known (4–13). Additional sequences are beginning to be discovered for experimentally induced antibodies to nucleic acids (14). This diversity is both a challenge and an opportunity. The challenge is to define multiple specific interactions, which may be unique for each antibody. The opportunity is in the rich supply of naturally occurring immunoglobulin structures that could be modified by protein engineering to provide specifically desired interactions.

Although the amino-acid sequences and particular assembly of protein interactions with nucleic acids are diverse and individual for each antibody, the basic kinds of interactions are probably similar to those already known from crystallographic studies of DNA-binding proteins. They include: van der Waals complementarity; hydrogen bonding of amino-acid side-chains (Arg, Asn, Ser, Gln, Thr, His, Asp, and Glu) to purines and pyrimidines, and to nonesterified oxygens in the phosphate backbone; and ionic interactions of positively charged amino-acid side-chains with the negatively charged oxygens of the phosphate backbone (1, 2). A few antibodies to nucleic acids have been crystallized (15, 16), bringing some investigators to the verge of being able to examine these antibody/nucleic-acid interactions at high resolution. Previous reviews have summarized the methods for induction of antibodies to nucleic acids, the chemistry of antibody/nucleic-acid interaction, the antibodies associated with autoimmune disease, and the genes that encode antibodies to nucleic acids (6, 17–23). This article emphasizes recent developments in the production and assay of antibodies to nucleic acids, structural analyses of specific antibody/nucleic-acid interactions, and applications of the antibodies as biochemical reagents.

I. Sources and Assays of Antibodies to Nucleic Acids

A. Immunogenicity

As discussed in previous reviews (17–24), two kinds of immunogens have been used widely for the experimental induction of polyclonal or monoclonal antibodies to nucleic acids. For one class of immunogen, nucleosides or nucleotides are conjugated covalently to protein carriers to serve as haptens and to induce antibodies directed mainly against the purines or pyrimidines. The second kind of immunogen is a noncovalent complex of polynucleotide with a positively charged carrier-protein, such as methylated bovine serum albumin (MBSA). Apart from experimental immunization, the sera of humans or animals with autoimmune disease provide other sources of antibodies to nucleic acids. Patients with systemic lupus erythematosus (SLE) and related autoimmune diseases make antibodies to native and denatured DNA, Z-DNA, double-stranded helical RNA, tRNA, and rRNA (reviewed in 18, 21a and 23). The immunogenic stimuli for production of these autoantibodies have not been identified.

Complexes of nucleic acids with MBSA have been useful for the production of antibodies to denatured DNA, single-stranded synthetic polyribonucleotides and polydeoxyribonucleotides, double-stranded RNA, RNA·DNA hybrids, left-handed Z-DNA, triple-helical polynucleotides, cruciform structures, and chemically modified DNA. MBSA complexes have been much less useful for immunizing animals with tRNA or B-helical eukaryotic DNA or synthetic polynucleotides that are very close in structure to B-DNA.

The low immunological response to injected native B-helical DNA poses a particular challenge: Why do MBSA complexes of native DNA, unlike MBSA complexes of certain other helical nucleic acids, form a poor immunogen in experimental animals even though DNA is a prominent target of certain autoantibodies? This challenge has stimulated efforts to re-examine previously used immunogens and to identify other carriers or stimuli for the preparation of immunological reagents for native DNA. Some examples of experimentally induced antibodies that do react with native DNA have been reported in recent years. An IgM monoclonal antibody that reacts well with native DNA was obtained from a mouse immunized several times with MBSA complexes of DNA and several different double-stranded synthetic polydeoxynucleotides (25). In evaluating the immunogenic stimulus for induction of this and other anti-DNA antibodies, one must consider that adjuvant alone increases the production of autoantibodies, including some that react with native and denatured DNA (26–28).

A second useful IgM monoclonal antibody that reacts with both native and denatured DNA was obtained from a BALB/c mouse immunized with a preparation of cytoskeletal proteins (29). The cytoskeletal preparation used for immunization did contain some DNA; again, it was not clear whether the antibody was part of an enhanced autoantibody background or was specifically induced by the DNA content of the preparation.

Other antibodies against native DNA have been identified as a small fraction of the total antibody population induced by nucleotide–protein conjugates (30) or denatured DNA–MBSA complexes (31), even though the majority of the antibodies in such sera react only with denatured DNA.

Further, immunization with *Escherichia coli* DNA complexed to MBSA has induced antibodies to the native bacterial DNA, even though parallel immunization with mammalian DNA–MBSA complexes did not yield anti-DNA antibodies (32); the antibodies induced by bacterial DNA did not react with mammalian DNA.

Another approach used for experimental induction of anti-native DNA antibodies was the immunization of rabbits with BK virus, a polyoma-like virus that infects human cells (33, 34). The immunized rabbits produced antibodies that reacted with native and denatured DNA and histone. The viral protein may be a more effective antigen-presenting carrier than MBSA. Protection against degradation by nucleases might also enhance immunogenicity; when several double-helical synthetic polynucleotides were tested as immunogens, nuclease-resistant polymers [such as poly(rG)·poly(rC)] were immunogenic, whereas nuclease-sensitive polymers [such as poly(dG–dC)] were not (35).

These findings may encourage a search for other appropriate carriers for the presentation of nucleic-acid antigens to responding cells in the immune system. Nothing is known of the mechanisms of nucleic-acid antigen processing and presentation in the immune system, but T cells are involved in production of both IgG anti-DNA autoantibodies and IgG experimentally induced antibodies (36–38).

B. Assays

Numerous assay methods have been used for measuring and characterizing anti-nucleic-acid antibodies. The solid-phase ELISA (enzyme-linked immunosorbent assay) (39) has become most widely used for the primary screening of either serum or monoclonal antibodies. For this assay, *denatured* DNA readily adsorbs to plastic surfaces such as polystyrene (or to nitrocellulose for an equivalent solid-phase assay of blotted nucleic acid). However, the adsorption of *native* DNA or double-stranded synthetic polynucleotides is much less effective, or at least more variable (40). One approach to overcoming this problem with native DNA has been to pre-coat the wells of polystyrene microtiter plates with a basic polypeptide, such as poly(L-lysine), protamine, or methylated BSA (41–43), to provide a positively charged surface to which native DNA subsequently binds well. This pre-coating procedure sometimes gives rise to a background of non-specific antibody binding and could measure coexisting antibody to basic protein as well.

A more specific preparation for solid-phase detection of anti-native DNA antibodies involves coating the solid phase with streptavidin, and use of biotin-labeled DNA as the coating antigen (44). A simpler procedure is to expose the polystyrene microtiter plates to UV light in a tissue-culture hood overnight and then coat the wells of the plate directly with nucleic acid (45). Such irradiated plates have been useful for assays of both native and denatured DNA, as well as single-stranded and double-stranded synthetic polynucleotides. The basis for the effect of UV light has not been established. The irradiation may alter the surface properties of the plastic to favor physical adsorption, or it may generate chemically reactive radicals that can bind the nucleic acid covalently to the plastic (46).

Although assay by binding to immobilized nucleic acid provides a convenient method for identifying antibodies, it does not allow a precise comparison of the binding of a given antibody to different nuclei-acid antigens. One limitation to precision is the uncertainty as to whether different nucleic acids adsorb to a similar extent to the solid phase and present the same number of binding sites to the antibodies. Also, adsorption to the solid phase itself may cause conformational changes in the nucleic acids, as it does with proteins. For example, in the initial screening of anti-Z-DNA monoclonal antibodies, wells of plastic microtiter plates were coated with polylysine and then with either brominated poly(dG–dC) (Z-DNA) or untreated poly(dG–dC) (B-DNA) (47). At low concentration, the monoclonal antibodies bound only to Z-DNA; but, at about a 25-fold higher protein concentration, they also bound to immobilized poly(dG–dC). When the reactions of these antibodies were tested with soluble antigens, the reaction with untreated poly(dG–dC) in physiological ionic strength was negligible at both antibody concentrations, indicating that the selectivity of the antibodies for Z-DNA was very much higher than was apparent on the solid-phase binding. For these reasons, the reactions of a given antibody with various nucleic acids are best compared by a competitive assay. In the competitive assay, the interactions with various antigens occur in solution, and a single solid-phase antigen is used simply as a detector of available soluble antibody. The determination of antibody affinity also requires measurement of a reaction in solution, in a homogeneous phase.

Radioimmunoassay is another method applied widely to measure reactions of antibodies with nucleic acids. Labeled antigen–antibody complexes are separated from free nucleic acid by precipitation with ammonium sulfate (48) or anti-immunoglobulin (49), by binding of complexes to membranes (50, 51), or by electrophoresis (52). As in assays of other DNA-binding proteins, the retardation in electrophoresis of labeled nucleic acid by antibody provides significant advantages. In particular, electrophoresis allows one to identify which components of a nucleic-acid mixture (e.g., DNA minicircles with varying degrees of supercoiling) are bound (52) (Fig. 1).

Specialized applications of anti-nucleic-acid antibodies are: identification of intracellular antigen by immunofluorescence (53) or immunoelectron mi-

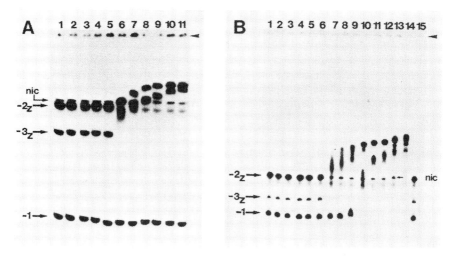

FIG. 1. Titration of monoclonal anti-Z-DNA antibody Z22 binding to topoisomeric minicircles. The minicircles were generated from the end-labeled DNA fragments AN701–*Eco*RI (A) and LP14–*Taq* (B), both of which contain d(C–G)$_7$ insertions. The amounts (in nanograms) of protein added in (A) were: 0 (lanes 1 and 2); 0.65 (lane 3); 1.3 (lane 4); 2.6 (lane 5); 5.2 (lane 6); 10.5 (lane 7); 21 (lane 8); 45 (lane 9); 90 (lane 10); and 180 (lane 11). The amounts (in nanograms) of protein added in (B) were: 0 (lane 1); 1.83 (lane 2); 3.65 (lane 3); 7.3 (lane 4); 11 (lane 5); 14.6 (lane 6); 18.25 (lane 7); 27.5 (lane 8); 36.5 (lane 9); 73 (lane 10); 145 (lane 11); 182 (lane 12); 365 (lane 13); 730 (lane 14); and 0 (lane 15). Identification of topoisomers is given in the margins. The arrowheads point toward the origins of the gels. The −1 topoisomer of the AN701 minicircle is not bound specifically by antibody (A), whereas the −1 topoisomer of the LP14 minicircle is bound (B). Different amounts of antibody are required for binding of the −1, −2, and −3 topoisomers. The electrophoretic assay allows one to see which of the components of a mixture is bound. [Reprinted with permission from *Nucleic Acids Research* (52).]

croscopy (29); NMR spectroscopy (54); and protection of specific sites from nuclease digestion or chemical modification (55).

II. Antibodies to B-DNA

Although some encouraging approaches to the experimental induction of antibodies to native DNA are being explored, as noted above, anti-DNA antibodies of human patients with SLE and lupus mice are the most available immunological anti-B-DNA reagents. Some anti-native DNA autoantibodies can distinguish among polynucleotides of differing base sequence, whereas others cannot. Some of the sequence-selective antibodies have a strong preference for poly(dG–dC) (56, 57), whereas others have a strong preference for poly(dA–dT) (58, 59).

A. Estimation of Affinity

It has been difficult to estimate the affinities of antibodies to native DNA, because most assays measure interactions of multivalent DNA of high molecular weight with bivalent antibody. In some cases, the affinity for native DNA is high enough to allow measurement of reactions of these antibodies with small double-stranded DNA fragments (60) or synthetic helical oligonucleotides that are likely to be monovalent antigens (57). The affinities of such monoclonal anti-native DNA antibodies, measured by competitive radioimmunoassay with helical oligonucleotides, were estimated to be 10^6 to 10^7 M^{-1} (60).

Two additional methods of analysis were applied to a monoclonal anti-DNA autoantibody from an NZB/NZW lupus mouse, which bound mammalian DNA and poly(dA–dT). This antibody, JEL-241, stabilized the double helix, so that the T_m of the polynucleotide was increased by up to 18°C at a high ratio of IgG to DNA (61). From these experiments, performed with varying amounts of IgG and subjected to an analysis described by McGhee (62), it was calculated that one IgG molecule occluded approximately 12 bp, and that the affinity for a double-helical structure was 10^4 that of the single-stranded polynucleotide. A gel filtration technique originally applied to other DNA-binding proteins (63) was used to estimate actual affinities, rather than the relative affinities of antibody JEL-241 under varying conditions of ionic strength (61). Scatchard analysis yielded K_a values of 1.49×10^6 M^{-1}, 1.83×10^5 M^{-1}, and 4.4×10^4 M^{-1} for the binding of calf-thymus DNA by Fab fragments of JEL-241 in solutions of 50 mM, 100 mM, and 150 mM NaCl, respectively. From the ionic strength dependence, it was estimated that four ion-pairs are involved in the interaction. The K_a for intact IgG was estimated to be 60-fold higher than that for the Fab fragment, i.e., 2.79×10^6 M^{-1} in 150 mM NaCl, a value similar to that estimated for a different anti-DNA autoantibody from radioimmunoassay, as described above.

B. DNA Epitopes for Antibodies to B-DNA

The epitope of helical DNA for H241, a monoclonal anti-DNA autoantibody from an MRL–*lpr* lupus mouse was defined with synthetic helical oligonucleotides of various sequences (57) (Table I). Antibody H241 bound poly(dG–dC) much more strongly than native calf DNA, but did not bind poly(dA–dT). It bound a soluble 18-bp oligonucleotide, d(ATATAGCGC-GCGCTATAT). This self-complementary oligonucleotide forms a duplex structure with a central core of 8 bp of alternating G·C sequence, flanked by five A·T base-pairs on each side. Modification of the flanking A·T base-pairs did not affect binding, suggesting that the recognition site was in the G·C

TABLE I

Inhibition of the Binding of Labeled Native DNA by MRL–1pr
Monoclonal Anti-DNA Autoantibody H241

Competitor[a]	Concentration of competitor required for 50% inhibition of the binding of labeled native DNA (μM)
gatgaGCGCGCGCtcatc	0.23
atataGCGCGCGCtatat	0.54
atataGsCsGsCsGsCsGsCstatat	1.5
atataGCGCsGCGCtatat	2.9
atataGCGmCGCGCtatat	3.0
atataGCGCHCGCtatat	3.1
atataHCHCHCHCtatat	3.9
atataGmCGmCGmCGmCtatat	n^b
atataGCGATCGCtatat	n^b
atataGCGCGTGCtatat	n^b

[a]In the listing of structures, bases in the target region for antibody binding are in upper-case letters, and bases that flank the target region are in
lower-case letters. The phosphorothioate internucleotide link is designated by
"s," 5-methylcytosine by "mC," and hypoxanthine by "H." [Data are from
Stollar *et al.* (57).]

[b]n, Less than 10% inhibition at 10^{-5} M.

central region. Confirming this suggestion, replacement of a single G·C base-
pair in the center with an A·T pair eliminated the binding.

Modifications that reduced binding by antibody H241 to the central core
included: a methyl group on the C5 of cytosine; replacement of the N7 of
guanine with C (yielding 7-deazaguanine); phosphorothioate substitution or
isopropyl ester formation with the backbone phosphate in the center of the
target; and replacement of the central guanine with hypoxanthine. A central
core of at least six G·C base-pairs was required to form an effective binding
site.

These findings defined an epitope encompassing the major groove (accounting for the base-sequence selectivity of this antibody), a portion of the
backbone [perhaps accounting for cross-reactions of this antibody with phos-
pholipids (64)], and a small portion of the minor groove. Binding to this
epitope could be achieved if the antibody binding site straddles the backbone of a single chain, with portions of the antibody extending into the major
groove and, to a lesser extent, into the minor groove. Such a binding site
could also account for the ability of this antibody to cross-react with single-
stranded DNA (although it reacts more strongly with the native form).

A similar analysis has been applied to a second MRL–*lpr* antibody, 2C10,
which binds to poly(dA–dT) but not to poly(dG–dC) (65). Assignment of an

epitope from reactions with oligonucleotides has been more difficult with this antibody, because sequences of alternating (dA–dT)·(dA–dT) base-pairs or (dG–dA)·(dT–dC) base-pairs form a reactive antigenic site (unpublished).

C. Binding Sites on Antibodies to B-DNA

The primary structures of the variable regions of some mouse autoan-tibodies to native DNA have been determined from the mRNA base se-quences (4–14). From comparisons of the sequences in different antibodies, certain amino-acid side-chains have been predicted to interact with DNA. It has been suggested that the binding of native DNA is related to the presence of arginine and asparagine residues in the CDRs, and that the heavy-chain CDR3 is particularly important for this activity (6, 10).

The role of certain light- and heavy-chain regions in DNA binding was tested by use of UV-induced cross-linking of antibody–oligonucleotide com-plexes (66). The oligonucleotides d(ATATAGCGCGCGCTATAT) and (dG–dC)$_5$ were cross-linked to both heavy and light chains of MRL–*lpr* autoan-tibody H241. On the other hand, (dG–dA)$_{10}$·(dT–dC)$_{10}$ and several other oligonucleotides were cross-linked only to the heavy chain of MRL–*lpr* auto-antibody 2C10. Sites cross-linked by UV irradiation must be very close to each other in a protein–nucleic-acid complex (67).[1] Most of the amino acids and each purine and pyrimidine can participate in UV-induced cross-linking (68, 69). As the most reactive sites of the bases are exposed in the major groove, the cross-linking results support the notions that portions of these two antibodies do make contact with the bases in the major groove and that considerable diversity will be found in the interactions of different anti-bodies with DNA.

D. Reagent Applications of Antibodies to B-DNA

Antibodies that react with native DNA are valuable reagents for immu-nohistochemical analysis of cellular DNA (29, 70, 71). Because the epitopes of unmodified native DNA are virtually universal (72), the antibodies can be applied to cells of mammalian, avian, amphibian, algal, and mycoplasma (29) as well as higher plant sources (71). Antibodies to native DNA stain both nuclear and mitochondrial DNA (29). Nucleoli generally remain unstained, except for a ring at the periphery of the organelle. Some staining of amplified nucleoli may identify rDNA. IgM anti-native DNA antibody microinjected into dividing epithelial cells of rat kangaroo kidney becomes localized in nuclei of the daughter cells (29), indicating that intracellular DNA is accessi-ble to the large IgM molecule during cell division, and that the presence of antibody does not arrest the mitotic process. On the other hand, injection of

---

[1] See Budowsky and Abdurashidova in Vol. 37 (1989) of this series. [Eds.]

the antibody into oocytes of *Pleurodeles* does interfere with transcription, causing a retraction of the lateral loops of lampbrush chromosomes into the central axis (29).

III. Antibodies to Single-stranded DNA

The characterization of both autoantibodies and experimentally induced antibodies to denatured DNA has been discussed in earlier reviews (18–21a). In recent years, pictures of specificity have been refined by extending the use of oligonucleotides to investigate reactions of autoantibodies (73), crystallographic analyses of antibodies to nucleic acids (15, 16, 22), and application of NMR spectroscopy to study an antibody to a nucleoside (74).

A. Binding Sites and Affinity

Affinity chromatography with denatured DNA–agarose and mono-nucleotide–BSA–agarose columns was used in a recent study to fractionate autoantibodies to denatured DNA from pooled MRL–*lpr* mouse serum (73). As in earlier experiments with lupus sera (75, 76) and myeloma proteins (77), anti-GMP reactivity was most prominent and anti-dTMP reactivity was second most common. Antibodies isolated from pooled MRL–*lpr* lupus mouse serum with GMP–BSA–agarose or TMP–BSA–agarose columns comprised distinct populations, both of which reacted with denatured DNA (73).

Oligonucleotides were much more effective competitors than mono-nucleotides for binding the affinity-purified antibodies. Oligonucleotides of various sizes were compared. For antibodies isolated with the GMP–BSA column, $(dG)_{10}$ was optimal, reacting with a K_a of 1×10^7 M^{-1}. For antibodies isolated with the TMP–BSA column, $(dT)_{15}$ was still more effective a competitor than $(dT)_{10}$. A similar size dependence had been observed with NZB/NZW mouse monoclonal autoantibodies to denatured DNA (78). These findings recall that the first identified determinant for antibodies to denatured DNA in serum of an SLE patient was oligo(dT) (72), and that very strong reactions with poly(dT) were characteristic of many human and mouse monoclonal autoantibodies (79–81). An NZB/NZW mouse monoclonal auto-antibody, HED-10, bound poly(dT) with a K_a of 1.2×10^7 (81), and a mouse monoclonal autoantibody E-1-4 bound the dinucleoside GpG with a K_a of 1.7×10^6 (82). There have been few other precise measurements of the affinities of antibodies to DNA.

B. Antibody Crystals

Crystallographic analysis of autoantibodies with bound oligonucleotide gives valuable pictures of the interactions involved in antibody recognition of nucleic acids. Fab fragments of two monoclonal mouse autoantibodies to denatured DNA have been crystallized. Both antibodies, HED-10 (15) and BV04-01 (16) bind oligo(dT). The structure of HED-10, an IgG$_\lambda$ antibody, has been solved to a resolution of 3.0 Å, aided by molecular replacement modeling on the known structure of the Fab fragment of myeloma protein McPC603 (15). Purification of the Fab fragment by isoelectric focusing was considered to be important for the success of crystallization. The crystal did not contain an antigen fragment, and the heavy- and light-chain CDR1 loops were not completely resolved. A prominent structural feature of HED-10 is an angle of 162° between the two domains of the Fab; there is less bending at the elbow between the domains than in the Fab of the mouse myeloma protein McPC603, which has an angle of 132° between the domains.

The structure of the IgG2b$_\lambda$ antibody BV04-01 has been determined at 2.7-Å resolution (16). Like HED-10, the Fab structure of BV04-01 is extended, with little bend between the variable domain (Fv) and the first constant domain (Fd). There is a large irregular groove at the probable antigen-binding site. All three hypervariable loops of the light chain and the second and third hypervariable loops of the heavy chain are prominent in the formation of the groove. Some amino-acid side-chains appear to hinder access to the binding groove, and several positively charged residues and aromatic residues are observed in the probable binding region: light-chain Lys-55, His-31, His-98, Tyr-37, and Tyr-54; and heavy-chain Arg-50, Arg-52, Arg-100, and Trp-107.

The structure of BV04-01 was also solved after hexanucleotide had been diffused into the crystal. Widely distributed conformational changes, beyond the binding site, were observed in comparison of the free Fab and the oligonucleotide-containing crystal, so that specific binding-site changes could not be assigned. For further study, complexes of the Fab with oligonucleotides have also been prepared by co-crystallization rather than by diffusion of oligonucleotide into the pre-existing protein crystal.

C. Epitope Analysis by NMR Spectrometry

As a model for application of NMR spectroscopy to analysis of the interaction of antibody and DNA, a monoclonal anti-GMP antibody was prepared from a BALB/c mouse immunized with a GMP–hemocyanin conjugate (74). The Fab of this purified antibody bound to denatured DNA, and this reaction was inhibited by free guanosine, deoxyguanosine, GMP, or dGMP. Binding of GMP by the Fab fragment caused a broadening of the ^{31}P-NMR spectrum peak of GMP. However, antibody binding did not alter the titration of the phosphate, as measured by changes in chemical shifts. This indicates that the phosphate itself is probably not involved in the antibody–nucleotide interaction. This conclusion is consistent with the fact that guanosine is a more effective competitor than GMP for binding by this antibody. As with the ^{31}P peak, the NMR spectrum for the C8 proton of the guanosine was also broadened by antibody binding. A saturation transfer experiment identified a second C8 proton peak when the nucleotide was bound, indicating that the C8 proton is involved in the antibody/nucleotide interaction. This finding is consistent with the fact that 8-bromoguanosine is one-fiftieth as effective as guanosine in competition for antibody binding. The N7 of the base is probably even more centrally involved in binding, as a substitution on that position had a much more marked effect on binding.

D. Reagent Applications of Antibodies to Single-stranded DNA

Many applications of antibodies to denatured DNA as biochemical reagents have been discussed in previous reviews (17–20, 21a). These applications included the use of antibodies specific for individual bases and for such modified bases as 5-methylcytosine (19, 20, 21a). In more recent studies, antibodies to individual nucleosides, which detect single-stranded regions, were used to measure the local unwinding of DNA caused by reaction of calf DNA with cis-diamminedichloroplatinum(II (cisplatin) (83). Antibodies to single-stranded DNA induced with chemically modified DNA–MBSA complexes were used to measure denatured regions, considered to be regions of damage, in the DNA of cells exposed to ionizing radiation (84).

IV. Antibodies to Z-DNA

A. Immunological Recognition of Z-DNA

Previous reviews have discussed the structure and biology of "left-handed" Z-DNA (85–87) and the characterization and application of experimentally induced antibodies to Z-DNA (21a, 23, 86). Autoantibodies of SLE and rheumatoid arthritis patients and lupus mice also include immunoglobulins that react with Z-DNA (88, 89). Some of the autoantibodies react with both single-stranded denatured DNA and double-helical Z-DNA, but others are more selective for Z-DNA and remain in SLE serum after antibodies to denatured and native DNA have been removed (88). The SLE autoantibodies react with brominated poly(dG–dC) in 150-mM NaCl, but not in 4-M NaCl, whereas the antibodies induced by immunization with Z-DNA do bind antigen in 4-M NaCl. Monoclonal autoantibodies to Z-DNA have been obtained from MRL–lpr/lpr mice (89). I emphasize here recent advances in the definition of the sites on Z-DNA recognized by experimentally induced antibodies, and recent applications of antibodies to Z-DNA as biochemical reagents.

Earlier research defined the Z-DNA recognition sites mainly by comparison of antibody binding to Z-DNA polymers of various base sequences, such as poly(dG–dC), poly(dG–dm⁵C), poly(dG–dbr⁵C), and poly(dG–

dT)·poly(dA–dC). Some monoclonal antibodies reacted only with specific sequences in Z-DNA. Such antibodies were considered to recognize the surface of Z-DNA that replaces the major groove of B-DNA (90, 91), because portions of the purine and pyrimidine bases are accessible on this Z-DNA surface. Other antibodies bind to Z-DNAs having very different base sequences. These antibodies were considered to bind to the deoxyribose-phosphate backbone (90), which would not vary greatly with base-sequence changes in Z-DNA.

These views of antibody binding to Z-DNA have been tested more directly with chemical protection experiments (55) and NMR spectroscopy (54). Both techniques were applied to analyses of two monoclonal mouse IgG antibodies, Z22 and Z44, which recognize different sites on Z-DNA. Antibody Z22 reacts with Z-DNA of various sequences, including (dC–dG) and (dT–dG)·(dA–dC), whereas Z44 reacts only with (dG–dC) sequences.

B. Chemical Protection Studies

Chemical protection studies were performed with plasmids containing the 22- or 32-bp inserts $(dG–dC)_{11}$ or $(dG–dC)_{16}$ (55). In supercoiled plasmid DNA, the $(dG–dC)_n$ inserts are in the Z-DNA conformation, and the guanines in these segments are susceptible to modification by diethyl pyrocarbonate (92). Antibodies Z22 and Z44 both protected certain guanine residues in the Z-DNA form of the insert from modification by diethyl pyrocarbonate (55). In the presence of antibody Z22, the shielded guanines were in two regions, separated by 12 bp that were not protected. Each protected site involved two guanines on each DNA strand, defining a recognition site in a 6-bp segment of DNA. A guanine at the outer edge of this occluded segment became a newly hypersensitive site.

Within the $(dG–dC)_{11}$ insert, the centers of the protected segments were separated by 12 bp and were on the same face of the DNA helix. This suggested that two Fab sites of one antibody were bound to epitopes centered approximately 40 Å apart. The angle between Fab arms limits the proximity of two binding sites of one antibody molecule, and this limit was previously estimated to be approximately 100 Å (49, 93). To achieve binding at 40-Å intervals, the Fab arms would have to be closely packed and nearly parallel (55) (Fig. 2). An inward bend at the junction between the Fv and Fd domains of the Fab may allow such approximation. Alternatively, a curve in the DNA may allow it.

In a longer insert of 32-bp $(dG–dC)_{16}$, the two protected regions were separated by 22 bp; again, both regions were on the same face of the helix. A somewhat different pattern of chemical protection occurred on binding of antibody Z44 to the (dG–dC) inserts. More extensive regions of protection were observed and there was significant blocking of reactivity with diethyl

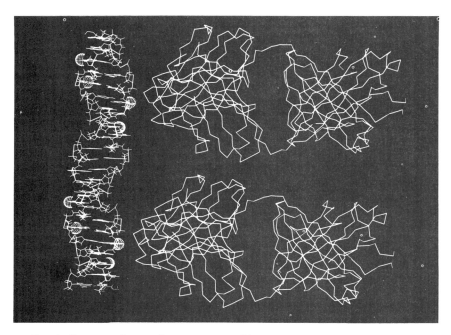

FIG. 2. Computer drawing for a comparison of dimensions found with a 22-bp Z-helix and two antibody Fab domains. The antibody domains, drawn for size comparison only, are those of the IgG$_1$ Ko1 protein Fab fragment (the three-dimensional structure of anti-Z-DNA antibody is not known). The van der Waals radii of sites on the Z-DNA helix that were protected from chemical modification by diethyl pyrocarbonate are shown on the Z-DNA helix by dotted spheres. [Reprinted with permission from the *Journal of Molecular Biology* (55).]

pyrocarbonate between the major regions of protection. This result was consistent with the previous suggestion that Z44 interacts with bases along the Z-DNA surface that replaces the major groove of B-DNA. Because the degree of supercoiling was varied systematically to convert the inserted sequences to the Z-DNA conformation, these experiments also measured the ability of antibody to stabilize the Z-DNA conformation. This stabilization was evident from the observation that the presence of antibody reduced the amount of supercoiling required for the transition of B-DNA to Z-DNA.

C. NMR Spectroscopic Analysis

NMR spectroscopy, which has been applied to analysis of several antigen–antibody reactions (94–96), confirmed that antibody Z44 interacts with portions of the bases on the Z-DNA surface that replaces the major groove (54). In the presence of the Fab fragment of antibody Z44 or Z22, peaks of the proton NMR spectrum of the hexanucleotide $(dG-dC)_3$ in 2.5-M NaCl were broadened, indicating that the oligonucleotide was bound by antibody. The Fab of unrelated mouse IgG did not cause broadening of the peaks. NOE experiments confirmed that the DNA bound by Z44 was in the Z-DNA configuration.

A saturation transfer experiment was performed to measure the transfer of energy from the protein to protons of the oligonucleotide that are in very close proximity to the protein (the transfer is related inversely to the sixth power of the distance between nuclei). When the protein was saturated by irradiation at a frequency corresponding to resonances of protons of aliphatic side-chains (0.5 ppm), there was significant transfer to the C5 proton of cytosine and less rapid transfer to the C8 proton of guanine, the C1′ proton of deoxyribose, and the C6 proton of cytosine (Fig. 3). In control experiments, irradiation of a mixture of irrelevant Fab and $(dG-dC)_3$ did not lead to a transfer of energy. The frequency of the radiation used to saturate the

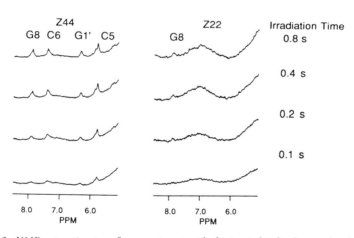

FIG. 3. NMR saturation transfer experiment with deuterated Fab of monoclonal anti-Z-DNA antibodies Z44 and Z22 and $d(C-G)_3$ in 2.5-M NaCl. The Fab of both Z22 and Z44 were prepared from hybridoma cells cultured with deuterated Phe, Trp, and Tyr in the medium. Irradiation of the protein resonances at 0.5 ppm resulted in saturation of the protein resonances. In the absence of protein or in the presence of nonspecific mouse Fab, irradiation at 0.5 ppm did not cause transfer to oligonucleotide proton resonances. In the presence of Z44 Fab, irradiation of the protein yielded transfer to the C5, C6, G8, and G1′ protons of the oligonucleotide bases. The most rapid transfer was to C5 proton, identifying it as a site of close interaction between protein and oligonucleotide. The C5 proton occurs on the Z-DNA surface that replaces the B-DNA major groove. In the presence of Z22, only limited transfer occurred, primarily to the G8 proton. Antibody Z22 does not interact closely with a large part of the Z-DNA surface that is recognized by antibody Z44. [Reprinted with permission from the *Journal of Biological Chemistry* (54).]

protein was chosen so as not to affect the oligonucleotide spectrum in the absence of antibody. This experiment measured directly the interaction of antibody Z44 with a specific portion of the Z-DNA surface, particularly with the C5 region of cytosine.

Monoclonal antibody Z22, which differs from Z44, being insensitive to base-sequence variations in Z-DNA, did not show the close approximation to cytosine and guanine, as there was little or no energy transfer from the saturated Z22 Fab to the base protons. Only a small peak in the guanine C8 proton was evident. This result is consistent with the previous conclusion that Z22 interacts mainly with the backbone, at least in part away from the base-containing surface.

Interaction of antibody with the tetramer $(dC-dG)_2$ was also examined by NMR spectroscopy (54). This oligonucleotide by itself has no distinct conformation in solution, either in 0.15- or 2.5-M NaCl; there were no NOEs from the base protons to the deoxyribose protons. In the presence of the Z22 Fab fragment, NOEs characteristic of *syn*-guanine conformation (from the guanine C8 proton to the deoxyribose C1′ and C2′ protons) were observed. This indicated that the antibody stabilized a conformational element characteristic of Z-DNA, whether the $(dC-dG)_2$ was in a duplex or single-stranded form.

D. Recognition of Z-RNA

The polyribonucleotide poly(rG–rC) can be converted to a left-handed Z-RNA structure at very high ionic strength, and can be stabilized in this form by bromination (97, 98). Immunochemical analysis indicates that Z-RNA shares some structural features with Z-DNA, as both the DNA and RNA forms react with certain antibodies to Z-DNA (99, 100), and some antibodies induced by immunization with Z-RNA cross-react with Z-DNA. On the other hand, there are distinct structural features as well, because some anti-Z-RNA antibodies react with Z-RNA but not with Z-DNA.

The reaction of the selective anti-Z-RNA antibodies with Z-RNA is sensitive to ionic strength (100). The antibodies react well with brominated poly(rG–rC) in 40-mM Tris buffer without added salt, but the reaction is decreased progressively by the addition of NaCl in the concentration range of 0.1 to 100 mM, or sodium phosphate in the range of 1 μM to 1 mM. Molecular modeling and energy minimization with counterions at varying proximity to the polynucleotide chain suggested that, at the very low ionic strength, the deep minor groove is relatively open, as in Z-DNA, and the 2′-OH groups would be accessible to antibody (thus, distinguishable from Z-DNA). At higher ionic strength, i.e., with counterions close to the chain, the groove would be closed, reducing access of antibody specific for Z-RNA to its antigenic recognition site.

Antibodies that react selectively with Z-RNA reacted with antigen in the cytoplasm of fixed protozoan cells, as detected by immunofluorescence (99), whereas autoantibodies to B-DNA, as expected, reacted with nuclear antigen. This finding suggested that cytoplasmic RNA may contain regions with a left-handed helical structure characteristic of Z-RNA. Immunofluorescent reactivity with antibody to Z-RNA was also observed in both the nucleoli and the cytoplasm of mammalian cells fixed with ethanol/acetone (100). The staining was prevented by pre-treatment of the fixed cells with RNase. Microinjection of monoclonal anti-Z-RNA antibody into mammalian cells led to inhibition of nucleolar RNA synthesis and inhibition of cell growth (100), suggesting that Z-RNA formation occurs physiologically in living cells, even without the removal of protein that may accompany fixation. The validity of the conclusion depends on the ability of the antibody to react *in vivo* only with Z-RNA, as it does with polynucleotides tested *in vitro*, and its lack of recognition of any other structure that may form within cellular RNA.

E. Cloning and Sequencing the Variable-Region cDNA of Antibodies to Z-DNA

Attempts to crystallize the Fab fragment of antibody Z22 have not succeeded (unpublished). A different approach, involving molecular genetic analysis, may help to define the Z22 and Z44 antibody sites that interact with nucleic acids. The cDNAs for the variable regions of the heavy and light chains have been cloned and sequenced. The two antibodies use members of the same small V_H gene family, V_H10, for the major portion of their heavy-chain variable regions; they differ from each other in 16 of the 300 bases in this segment. The two cDNAs differ much more extensively in their 5′ untranslated regions, indicating that Z22 and Z44 arise from different germline genes. Both the Z22 and Z44 V_H segments also differ by only 16 bases from two autoantibodies to DNA, one (DNA-4) from an MRL–*lpr* lupus mouse (5) and one (BV04-01) from an NZB/NZW lupus mouse (12). The 5′ untranslated region of the Z22 heavy-chain mRNA is very similar to that of the MRL–*lpr* autoantibody DNA-4. The V_H segment of autoantibody BV04-01 differs from a BALB/c germ-line gene, V_H10-I, by only three bases, and the V_H sequence of Z22 differs from the same V_H10-I germ-line gene by 12 bases. The spontaneously arising autoantibody to denatured DNA and the experimentally induced antibody to Z-DNA may arise from a single original germ-line gene, with more mutations associated with selectivity for the Z-DNA antigen. As noted above, a crystal structure of the NZB/NZW autoantibody BV04-01 is under study (16); such a structure could facilitate modeling and modification of the anti-Z-DNA antibodies.

Antibodies Z22 and Z44 use the same J_H gene segment and members of the same V_κ gene family; Z22 is very similar to $V_\kappa 10b$ and Z44 is closer in sequence to $V_K 10a$. Although the two antibodies to Z-DNA arise from different germ-line genes, they share extensive regions of similar structure, suggesting a convergent selection of these features for reactivity with DNA. On the other hand, the two antibodies differ in other regions. Z22 and Z44 use different J_K genes. They differ most strikingly from each other and from the autoantibodies in the diversity segment in the third CDR (CDR3) of the heavy chain and the CDR3 and CDR2 of the light chain. These regions may be important in determining the different specificities of the two antibodies. The heavy- and light-chain cDNAs of Z22 have been cloned into an expression vector (M. M. Brigido and B. D. Stollar, unpublished) in a plasmid construct designed to yield Fv fragments in the periplasmic space (102). With the ability to express wild-type and mutated versions of the cDNAs, it will be possible to test the roles of specific amino acids in Z-DNA binding.

F. Immunological Tests for the Presence of Z-DNA *in Vivo*

A major motivation for preparation of antibodies to Z-DNA remains the hope that they can address the question of whether Z-DNA occurs in natural nucleic acids within cells. This question is addressed by other techniques as well, and evidence from genetic experiments and *in vivo* chemical reactivity indicate that Z-DNA exists in living *E. coli* (103, 104).

Early immunohistochemical experiments identified Z-DNA in fixed polytene chromosomes of insects and in fixed animal and plant cell nuclei (reviewed in 21a). Two questions qualified the interpretation of the early findings: To what extent was Z-DNA formed during the process of fixation? To what extent was the antibody driving the formation of Z-DNA? The process of fixation may have acted by removal of chromatin protein, allowing torsional strain to drive Z-DNA formation (105–107). With minimal protein removal, some Z-DNA was still detected, and was present primarily in certain regions of decondensed chromatin in the polytene chromosomes (108, 109).

Z-DNA was subsequently detected in unfixed nuclei of *Drosophila* cells (110) and in polytene chromosomes that retained transcriptional activity through a procedure that applied pre-fixation with dilute formaldehyde before chromosomes were squashed in acetic acid (111). Z-DNA occurred primarily in interbands and other decondensed chromatin regions of the formaldehyde-fixed chromosomes, as in previous experiments with chromosomes fixed in acid only. A detailed study, involving both immunofluorescence and immunoelectron microscopy, identified Z-DNA in limited regions in unfixed or OsO_4-fixed nuclei of the dinoflagellate *Prorocentrum micans* (112). In this organism, the nucleus, bounded by a nuclear envelope, contains approximately 100 condensed chromosomes consisting of nucleofilaments of highly twisted DNA that is not associated with histones. Clusters of antibodies to Z-

DNA reacted primarily at the periphery of the chromosomes, near the segregation fork of dividing chromosomes, and in unwound DNA of the nucleolar organizer region. Antibodies to B-DNA reacted with many more sites on chromosomal nucleofilaments, extrachromosomal loops, and the unwound DNA of the nucleolus organizer region.

More closely related to the question of whether Z-DNA exists *in vivo*, it was detected immunochemically in metabolically active nuclei of permeabilized mammalian cells (*113*). Mouse myeloma cells were embedded singly in agarose–paraffin microbeads, and their membranes were lysed with Triton X-100. Nuclei retained their morphology and their ability to synthesize DNA and RNA, but became accessible to antibody. Biotinylated anti-Z-DNA antibody Z22 bound to these nuclei and was detected with ^{125}I-labeled streptavidin, whereas normal IgG did not bind. On exposure of nuclei to increasing concentrations of the anti-Z-DNA antibody, the amount of bound Z22 reached a plateau on addition of between 0.1 and 1 μg of antibody to 2.5 × 10^6 cells in 500 μl. The amount bound remained constant over a 100-fold range of antibody concentration, up to addition of approximately 100 μg to the 500-μl microbead suspension. At higher IgG concentrations, there was a large increase in antibody binding. It was concluded that the binding at low antibody concentration represented detection of preexisting Z-DNA, whereas the increased binding that occurred at high antibody concentration reflected the ability of the antibody to drive Z-DNA formation. The antibody binding was dependent on torsional strain in nuclear DNA, as it was prevented by pre-treatment of the nuclei with nicking concentrations of DNase I. This conclusion was also supported by the finding that the topoisomerase inhibitor camptothecin stabilized the antibody-binding structures in the nuclei.

G. The Effects of Antibody on the Equilibrium between B-DNA and Z-DNA

Anti-Z-DNA antibodies can assay the transition between B-DNA and Z-DNA structure, both in solution (*114–118*) and on a solid phase (*119*). Antibodies can also measure the presence of both B-DNA and Z-DNA conformations in a duplex oligonucleotide such as d[TCC(br^{5}CG)$_6$AGAGGA]·d-[TCCTCT(br^{5}CG)$_6$] (L. P. Kadalayil and B. D. Stollar, unpublished).

The use of anti-Z-DNA antibodies for such studies requires consideration of how the antibodies themselves may affect the transitions. This ability of antibody to shift the B-DNA/Z-DNA equilibrium has been studied in some detail (*115–118*). The shift depends on both the concentration and affinity of the antibody. The shift is demonstrated by the ability of antibody to lower the ionic strength required for the B-DNA/Z-DNA transition of poly(dG–dC) (*115, 117, 118*), to mediate Z-DNA formation in poly(dG–dC) at very low ionic strength (*118*), and to reduce the amount of supercoiling required for Z-DNA formation in closed circular DNA containing appropriate sequences (*55, 116, 118*). With sufficiently high concentrations of a high-affinity antibody, even linear poly(dG–dC) can be converted to Z-DNA at physiological ionic strength (*117*). The mechanism is considered to involve stabilization by antibody of Z-DNA conformation that is present in low concentration in equilibrium with the major B-DNA conformation under physiological ionic strength conditions (*115, 118*).

This ability of antibody to affect the B-DNA/Z-DNA equilibrium must be considered when antibody is to be used for the detection of pre-existing Z-DNA. When used as a reporter, the antibody should be used at a lower concentration than that required for significant stabilization of Z-DNA. This principle applies to the application of any antibody that can influence a structural transition in the target molecule.

H. Immunological Identification of Z-DNA Sites in DNA

The binding of antibodies to Z-DNA inserts in form V DNA (*120*), supercoiled plasmids (*114*) and supercoiled bacterial DNA (*120a*) (Fig. 4) can be visualized by electron microscopy and several of the binding sites can be mapped in relation to known restriction enzyme cutting sites (*121–123*).

In a recent study, looped structures, varying from 300 to 1000 bases in length, were visible in most of the plasmids in which antibody was bound to Z-DNA sites (*123*). Addition of a chemical cross-linking reagent without antibody yielded similar loops. This finding suggested that Z-DNA formation may facilitate the approximation of different portions of a long DNA molecule, thereby facilitating bivalent binding by protein or chemical cross-linking. The loops persisted when the antibody–plasmid complexes were cleaved with a restriction enzyme, and the origins of the loops were mapped in relation to the restriction site. Although a single plasmid had only one to five loops, the scoring of a large number of plasmids revealed 18 different sites of Z-DNA formation in addition to the two (dG–dC)$_n$ inserts. Certain pairs of Z-DNA-containing sites were cross-linked preferentially by antibody, and many of the sites occurred at the beginning or end of transcriptional units near sites that regulate transcription or replication (*123*).

A different approach assayed Z-DNA sites by identifying the restriction fragments to which anti-Z-DNA antibody became bound and was cross-linked by glutaraldehyde (*52, 124*). A prominent site in supercoiled SV40 DNA was found within a segment spanning positions 40 to 474, a nucleosome-free region in SV40 minichromosomes that contains promoter and enhancer sequences.

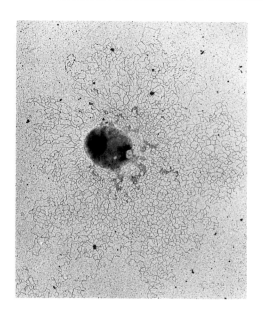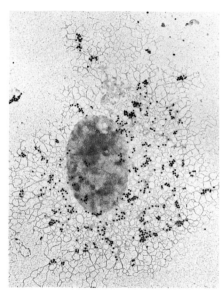

FIG. 4. Identification of Z-DNA in the DNA extruded from bacteria. Normal rabbit serum (left) or rabbit anti-Z-DNA serum (right), diluted 1:250, was incubated with the preparation, and bound antibody was detected with gold-labeled protein A. [Courtesy of W. Earnshaw. Reprinted with permission from Springer-Verlag Press (120a).]

The analysis of Z-DNA binding sites in natural DNA has been extended to nuclear DNA of *Drosophila hydei* (125), following a procedure applied previously to *E. coli* (126). A library of *Drosophila* DNA was prepared by cloning *Sau*3A fragments into a pUC8 vector (125). Antibody to Z-DNA was used to select supercoiled Z-DNA-containing plasmids from this library. Antibody–plasmid complexes were trapped on membrane filters, from which the plasmids were recovered. One plasmid, with a 272-base insert, was studied in detail. It contained a $(dG-dC)_3$ cluster capable of Z-DNA formation as well as other regions of alternating purine–pyrimidine sequence. By *in situ* hybridization with labeled plasmid DNA, the insert of the Z-DNA-containing plasmid was found to hybridize to a single locus of *Drosophila* polytene chromosomes. The locus, 4-75C1-2, is in a region that is developmentally regulated and can be induced by ecdysone to form a transcriptionally active puff. This region of the chromosome becomes strongly reactive with antibody to Z-DNA during developmental or chemically induced gene activation. The approach used in these experiments can help to focus the analysis of the very large amount of information present in a polytene chromosome stained by immunofluorescence with anti-Z-DNA antibody.

V. Variants of Double-stranded DNA: Poly(dA)·poly(dT) and "Bent" DNA

Antibodies have been induced by immunization of rabbits with MBSA complexes of the synthetic (B′) duplex poly(dA)·poly(dT) (127), which differs somewhat from B-DNA in structure (128), and with MBSA complexes of a plasmid fragment containing an insert of *Leishmania* kinetoplast DNA (127). The kinetoplast insert contains periodic poly(dA) tracts, which can cause the DNA to adopt a bent conformation (129). The synthetic poly(dA)·poly(dT) may also have a curved conformation. Antibodies induced by both antigens reacted with poly(dA)·poly(dT) and poly(dA)·poly(dU) but not with poly(dA–dT)·poly(dA–dT), which has a B-DNA structure. The antibodies to poly(dA)·poly(dT) reacted with both kinetoplast and nuclear DNA of the trypanosome *Crithidia* sp. These antibodies may be reagents for detecting the curved DNA structure.

VI. Triplex DNA

A. Specificity of Antibodies to Triplexes

Triple-helix formation has been demonstrated in certain synthetic polynucleotides. It occurs when poly(R) and poly(Y) strands are annealed under appropriate conditions (130–132). It may also occur within one molecule containing such tracts if two complementary duplex regions combine to form a triplex and one free single strand (133); this model can account for the S1-nuclease sensitivity of sequences such as $(G–A)·(T–C)$ within supercoiled plasmids (134). Poly(R)·poly(Y) sequences also occur frequently in the eukaryotic genome. It has been suggested that triple-helix formation *in vivo* could be involved in chromatin condensation or, in view of the location of poly(R)·poly(Y) tracts in 5′-flanking regions of a number of genes, could be involved in the regulation of gene transcription. There has been interest, therefore, in the preparation of immunological reagents specific for triplex structure.

Early experiments with the triple-helical poly*ribo*nucleotides indicated that they are strongly immunogenic in complexes with MBSA (135). $(U)_n·(A)_n·(U)_n$, $(U)_n·(A)_n·(I)_n$, and $(I)_n·(A)_n·(I)_n$ are distinguishable from each other and from double-helical or single-stranded polynucleotides (136). Structures with poly(rA) annealed to any two poly(Y) strands—poly(U), poly(dU), or poly(dT)—are serologically identical. They are, however, totally distinct from analogous triplex structures built on poly(dA) instead of poly(rA) (137). Reciprocally, antibodies induced by $(U)_n \cdot (dA)_n \cdot (U)_n$ react equally with the immunogen and $(U)_n \cdot (dA)_n \cdot (dT)_n$ or $(dT)_n \cdot (dA)_n \cdot (dT)_n$, but not with triple helices of poly(rA) and the same poly(Y)s. These findings indicate that serological reagents can be used to distinguish a variety of triple-helical polynucleotides from each other and from double-helical structures, but that certain triple helices can be recognized as a class of similar structures even if their base compositions differ.

A monoclonal antibody to triplex DNA (JEL-318) was obtained from a mouse immunized with $(dT-dm^5C)_n \cdot (dG-dA)_n \cdot (dm^5C^+ - dT)_n$, a three-stranded structure formed most readily at low pH but stable at neutral pH (138). The antibody did not bind to structures with the same poly(Y)s and poly(dG–dm⁶A), a poly(R) strand that cannot participate in triplex formation. The antibody also failed to react with native DNA or other duplex synthetic polynucleotides. On the other hand, it did react with several complexes of varying base composition that have the potential for triplex formation, including $(dT)_n \cdot (dA)_n \cdot (U)_n$ and $(dT)_n \cdot (dA)_n \cdot (dT)_n$. The Fab fragment of this monoclonal antibody has been crystallized (139).

B. Reagent Applications of Antibodies to Triple Helices

The monoclonal antibody JEL-318 detected triplex structures in super-coiled plasmids with $(dT-dC) \cdot (dG-dA)$ inserts alone or when an exogenous third strand of $(dT-dm^5C)$ was incubated with the plasmid at low pH (140). The formation of a triple-stranded structure requires low pH because the methylcytosine of the third strand must be protonated in order to form a Hoogstein base-pair with the N7 of guanine. Once formed, the triplex can persist at neutral pH for several hours. An intramolecular triplex also occurred in a plasmid with an insert of $d(TCC)_{15} \cdot d(GGA)_{15}$. The presence of a triplex was identified by the ability of antibody to retard the electrophoretic migration of the plasmid in agarose gel, and by an immunoblotting procedure. Immunoblotting also detected reactive species in total cell extracts of eukaryotic cells, but not of bacteria.

Antibody JEL-318 was also used to test for the presence of triple-helical structures in eukaryotic nuclei and chromosomes (138, 140a). Immunofluorescent staining of acid-fixed mouse lymphocytes showed variable patterns of nuclear staining, with a uniform speckled appearance in some nuclei and staining of heterochromatin clumps in others. Fixed human cells showed only the uniform speckled staining. Fixed mouse chromosomes were stained most intensely at the centromere heterochromatin and the G-bands of the chromosomal arms. Human chromosomes showed mainly the G-band correlation. Unfixed chromosomes were highly condensed and did not yield immunofluorescent staining. This raised the question of whether the staining of fixed cells was due to the formation of triplex during acid fixation, a condition that would favor its formation. Decondensation of the chromosomes in neutral EDTA-containing buffer did lead to staining, as did acetone fixation of nuclei without acid, so that low pH is not required for the detection of a triplex in cellular or chromosomal DNA. Whether decondensation simply made the triplex accessible to antibody or involved changes that favored triplex formation could not be addressed.

VII. Antibodies to RNA·DNA

A. Specific Recognition of RNA·DNA by Antibodies

Antibodies identify unique structure in helical nucleic acids in which one strand is RNA and one is DNA. Poly(rA)·poly(dT) is a synthetic polynucleotide model for this structure. Physical studies indicate that it has some features of a B-helix (*141*) and some features of an A-helix (*142*). Certain A-like features are also recognized immunologically, in that some of the antibodies induced by poly(I)·poly(C) cross-react with the RNA·DNA (*143*). Poly(rA)·poly(dT) (*144*) and RNA·DNA of mixed base composition (*145*), complexed to MBSA, are potent nucleic-acid immunogens, yielding more than 1 mg/ml of antibody in serum. The A-helical features induce some antibody that cross-reacts with double-stranded RNA (*144, 145*), but a significant fraction of the antibodies recognize the unique features of hybrid structure. The hybrid-specific antibodies do not cross-react with single- or double-stranded DNA or RNA alone, but do react with RNA·DNA helices of varying base composition, including poly(rI)·poly(dC). Monoclonal anti-hybrid antibodies that have low cross-reactivity with double-stranded RNA have been induced by an RNA·DNA of mixed base composition (*146*).

Antibodies to poly(A)·poly(dT) have been applied to assay the unique hybrid structure among mixed conformations in a single oligonucleotide (*147*). The model oligonucleotide for this study had a central core of 12 bp of alternating dG–dC sequence, flanked by $(rA)_{12}·(dT)_{12}$ on either side of the core. The 36-bp duplex contained both B-DNA and RNA·DNA structures at physiological ionic strength; and the core had a Z-DNA structure at high ionic strength. The model, therefore, presents two kinds of junctions between varying helical nucleic-acid conformations.

B. Use of Antibodies to RNA·DNA in Gene-probe Assays

Antibodies to RNA·DNA have served as general reagents for gene-probe assays. Antibody immobilized on a solid phase can capture hybrids formed by a DNA oligonucleotide probe and complementary sequences unique to

Campylobacter rRNA (*148*), providing a basis for a diagnostic assay for detection of this organism. Assays with the monoclonal anti-hybrid antibodies have been developed more extensively for the measurement of either RNA (*149*) or DNA (*150*) with unique base sequences. A recently reported specific application of anti-hybrid antibody in a gene-probe assay identified hybrids between PCR-amplified HIV-1 DNA and a corresponding RNA probe. The combination of PCR and enzyme-linked immunoassay allowed the detection of 10 copies of HIV DNA; the assay identified HIV in peripheral blood mononuclear cells from 32 of 33 seropositive patients (*151*).

VIII. Branched-chain Ribonucleic Acid

Branched RNA structures are formed during the splicing of mRNA (*153*). Identification of the branched structure as an intermediate in the process requires a specific substrate and electrophoretic assay. Antibody to the branched structure was sought as a general means to identify and purify the branched-structure intermediates (*153*). The hapten used for immunization of rabbits was a chemically synthesized tetranucleotide (G–A[G]–C), i.e., G3′p5′A[2′p5′G]3′p5′C. The tetranucleotide was oxidized with periodate and conjugated to hemocyanin for preparation of the immunogen. The immune serum formed specific complexes with radiolabeled G–A[G]–C. The complexes were captured by protein A–Sepharose. Binding of the labeled tetranucleotides was inhibited by 10-nM unlabeled tetranucleotide, or a 1000-fold higher concentration of A2′p5′G, and only weakly by a high concentration of other mono- and dinucleotides. Affinity-purified antibodies to the tetranucleotide recognized both linear and circular native branched structures formed during *in vitro* mRNA splicing with a HeLa-cell nuclear extract (*153*).

IX. Cruciform DNA

a. Epitopes for Antibodies to Cruciform DNA

The cruciform junction is an interesting conformational variant of DNA that has been the subject of much investigation *in vitro* and speculation over its possible existence *in vivo* (*154*). A cruciform junction can form when inverted repeat sequences occur in DNA, because there is a possibility for intra-strand as well as inter-strand base-pairing. Both the linear duplex and cruciform-containing structures exist in an equilibrium mixture; formation of the cruciform is favored by the torsional strain of supercoiling (*155*). With structures first studied in detail, the rates of cruciform formation were unfavorable for its formation within cells (*156*). The rates, however, are strongly affected by the base sequences of neighboring regions so that, with appropriate flanking sequences, a cruciform structure might be formed *in vivo* (*154, 157*). Therefore, there has been interest in developing antibodies specific for the cruciform structure, as they could be reagents to test for the presence of such junctions in cellular DNA.

A stable cruciform junction is required for induction of antibodies. Two approaches to prepare such a stable structure have been used. One is the synthesis of four oligonucleotides with sequences predetermined so that they can interact only in a way that forms a four-way junction. Such sequences have been prepared and their assembly into the junction structure has been characterized (*158, 159*). In my laboratory, we did not detect cruciform-specific antibodies in sera of rabbits or mice immunized with these preparations.

Another group has been successful in using a different stabilized junction as an immunogen (*160*). It was a heteroduplex DNA, prepared by annealing one strand of the origin-of-replication region of wild-type SV40 (which contains an inverted repeat sequence) with a second strand mostly complementary to the first, except for replacement of the inverted repeat with one of unrelated sequence. In this structure, the inverted repeats could not form a linear duplex; each strand formed a stem–loop opposite the other strand, giving rise to the four-way junction. Two monoclonal antibodies were prepared, one of IgG1 and one of IgM isotype. The antibodies specifically retarded the electrophoretic migration of the junction-containing DNA. They did not react with linear duplex DNA, single-stranded DNA, a single-stranded stem–loop (hairpin), or with tRNA.

The site of binding was mapped with nuclease-protection experiments (*161*). Neither antibody protected against cleavage at the ends of the loops by mung-bean nuclease; nor did prior cleavage by mung-bean nuclease prevent the binding of antibody. On the other hand, the antibodies did protect against specific cleavage of the elbows at the base of the cruciform structure by T7 endonuclease. With the original structure used for immunization, protection was at two of the elbows on diagonally opposite corners of the base of the four-way junction. These antibodies also protected a cruciform structure of completely different sequence, but built on the same principle (in this case, protecting all four corners at the base of the junction). Therefore, the antibodies recognized the conformation at the origin of the junction, rather than a specific purine or pyrimidine sequence.

B. Reagent Applications of Antibodies to Cruciforms

The conformation-dependent specificity of these antibodies allowed their application to studies of cellular DNA. In view of the occurrence of inverted repeat sequences in DNA enriched for origins of replication, the effect of the antibodies on DNA replication was tested (*162*). Synchronized permeabilized monkey CV-1 cells were exposed to monoclonal anti-cruciform (or control antibody of the same isotype) during a period of release from a block into the S phase of the cell cycle. Both antibodies stimulated a 3- to 4-fold increase in the incorporation of labeled dCTP into acid-insoluble product 400 to 1000 bp in length. About one-half of the increase was blocked by the presence of a low concentration of aphidicolin, indicating that it was due to action of α- and/or δ-DNA polymerase; the rest may have been due to primase activity. When the products were hybridized with specific probes, it was seen that there was a comparable 3- to 5-fold increase in the synthesis of gene segments present in few copies near origins of replication, and an even higher increase in synthesis of c-*myc* DNA, but no increase in synthesis of *fos* or highly repetitive DNA sequences. It was concluded that the antibodies may have stabilized a cruciform conformation, allowing continuous initiation of replication at sites near, but not within, a sterically hindered range of the antibody binding sites.

X. Antibodies to Modified Nucleosides and Nucleotides: Bromodeoxyuridine

Antibodies to 5-methylcytosine and 7-methylguanosine or 7-methylguanosine 5'-phosphate have been discussed in previous reviews (*19, 21a*). In recent years, a wide application of antibodies to bromodeoxyuridine has developed for the measurement of newly replicated DNA, and antibodies to biotinylated nucleotides (*163*) and digoxigenin-modified nucleotides (*164*) have been applied to development of nonradioactive gene-probe technology. The anti-bromodeoxyuridine antibodies can be considered as anti-nucleic-acid antibodies, whereas the antibodies to biotin and digoxigenin are prepared independently of the nucleic acids.

The generally applicable procedure of preparing nucleoside–protein conjugates for immunization (oxidation of the nucleoside with periodate, formation of Schiff bases by the oxidized nucleoside with amino groups of protein, and reduction of the Schiff base) was used for induction of antibodies to 5-bromodeoxyuridine (*165*). Both polyclonal and monoclonal anti-BrdU antibodies cross-react with other halogenated nucleosides (5-IdU and 5-FdU), but do not react with unmodified uridine or cytidine or purine nucleosides (*166*).

Monoclonal antibodies to BrdU are among the few anti-nucleic-acid antibodies available from several commercial sources. Because 5BrdU can be incorporated into replicating DNA, anti-BrdU antibodies have become valuable reagents for identifying and quantifying replicated DNA. The antibodies have been applied both in immunoassay of soluble DNA in cells extracts and in histochemical analyses. In both cases, assays can be performed without radioactivity.

With quantitative immunohistochemistry, anti-BrdU antibodies have been used to measure *in situ* the fraction of cells undergoing replication, the length of the cell cycle, and the length of the S phase (*167*). The sensitivity was similar to that of autoradiography after incorporation of ^{3}H-labeled nucleotides. A recent application allowed a combined assay of overall BrdU incorporation and cell counting on one set of cells (*168*) in culture. Schwann cells were grown in culture in 96-well microtiter plates. A solid-phase enzyme-linked immunoassay was used to quantify BrdU-labeled cells in fixed monolayers on these plates, and the same cells served as a substrate for histochemical staining, allowing enumeration of the stained cells to complement the data on the overall level of BrdU incorporation (Fig. 5).

XI. Antibodies to Alkylated Nucleic Acids

The preparation and application of antibodies to carcinogen–DNA adducts have been reviewed in this series (*20*) and elsewhere (*169*). This has been an active area of research in recent years, with increasing emphasis on the use of monoclonal antibodies and specific application to measuring adducts in cells or cell products.

Chemical modifications in DNA greatly enhance its immunogenicity (*18*, *169*, *170*). Because of the relatively low immunogenicity of DNA itself, the formation of antibodies to the modified features usually predominates overwhelmingly in the response to altered DNA. Therefore, it has been relatively easy to produce antibodies specific for given carcinogen–DNA adducts (*171*), or to products of UV irradiation (*172*) or photooxidation (*173*). Although the background of reactivity with unaltered DNA is usually very low, it is not zero. Injection of adjuvant alone can, in fact, expand populations of B cells that produce autoantibodies to denatured and native DNA (*26–28*). This may amount to quantities of several micrograms per milliliter, whereas antibodies to modified DNA may amount to 1–2 mg/ml. In the search for monoclonal antibodies, one may find either highly specific antibodies to the modified DNA, or cross-reactive representatives of the autoantibody population. The aim in immunochemical studies of chemically modified DNA has been to prepare antibodies of high affinity and selectivity, so that small amounts of modified structure can be identified *in situ* or in DNA extracted from cells of subjects exposed to the modifying agents.

A. *cis*-Diamminedichloroplatinum(II) (Cisplatin) DNA

Two kinds of immunogens have been used for preparation of both polyclonal and monoclonal antibodies to DNA alkylated with cisplatin. One was macromolecular DNA modified *in vitro* with cisplatin and then mixed with MBSA. This cisplatin-DNA–MBSA complex yielded antibodies that reacted strongly with the modified DNA, but not with untreated DNA (*174–176*).

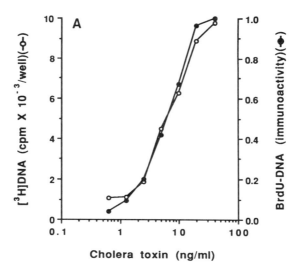

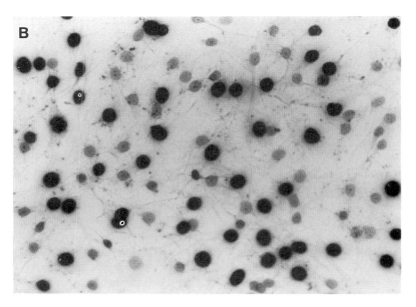

FIG. 5. (A) Comparison of immunoassay with anti-BrU antibody and radioactive thymidine uptake for measurement of DNA synthesis in Schwann cells treated with cholera toxin as a mitogen. Microcultures were treated for 16 hr with the indicated concentrations of cholera toxin in the presence of either 5BrdU (10 μM) or [^{3}H]thymidine (80 nM). (B) Immunocytochemical staining of BrdU-labeled nuclei of the same cell used in the immunoassay in (A). The BrdU-containing DNA was stained by addition of the chromogen diaminobenzidine (darkly stained nuclei). The nuclei were counterstained with toluidine blue to identify BrdU-negative DNA (lightly stained nuclei).

The antibodies reacted with cisplatin-modified poly(dG)·poly(dC) much more strongly than with cisplatin-poly(dG–dC)·poly(dG–dC), suggesting that they identify the major sites of adduct formation, which involve cisplatin linking of adjacent guanines (177). Examination of the specificity of monoclonal antibodies to cisplatin-modified DNA indicated that the determinant does not involve simply the substituted platinum, because these antibodies reacted equally well with several analogs having varying substituents, including bulky groups, on the amines (178). Furthermore, whereas cisplatin-modified poly(dG)·poly(dC) was bound by the monoclonal antibodies, the dinucleoside phosphate dG–dG with guanines cross-linked by cisplatin was not. There is some unwinding of the DNA helix in the area of adduct formation, reflected in the increasing accessibility of adenine, cytosine, and thymine to corresponding anti-nucleoside antibodies (83). The anti-cisplatin-DNA antibodies do not react with unmodified denatured DNA, however, or with single-stranded cisplatin-modified poly(dG), so the unwinding alone does not account for the antibody binding. Rather, the monoclonal antibodies to cisplatin-modified DNA appear to recognize the distorted helical structure around the site of adduct formation. Different antibodies were induced by immunization with transplatin-modified DNA, which also causes local denaturation near the adduct formation (178). Antibodies to transplatin-modified DNA did cross-react with denatured DNA, although they reacted more strongly with the alkylated DNA.

A second kind of immunogen has been formed by alkylation of various nucleoside–nucleotide mixtures or dinucleotides, which were then used as classical haptens conjugated to protein carriers (179). For one hapten, cisplatin was added to a mixture of deoxyguanosine and dGMP in order to cross-link the guanine bases and thereby to mimic the most abundant product of DNA alkylation, [cisplatin(NH$_3$)$_2$]d(pG–pG). These anti-cisplatin-dGG antibodies reacted with native DNA modified by cisplatin, but only when the ratio of platinum to nucleotide in the DNA was larger than 0.08; maximal activity occurred when the ratio was 0.18. The appearance of DNA reactivity at these ratios reflected the local denaturation caused by alkylation, an effect confirmed by spectroscopic measurements. In fact, the antibodies reacted with *denatured* cisplatin-modified DNA even at a low platinum/nucleotide ratio. They also reacted with digested fragments of cisplatin-modified DNA. The anti-cisplatin-dGG antibodies had a much lower affinity for modified mononucleotide or cisplatin-d(pA–pG) than for the cisplatin-d(pG–pG). Additional antibodies were induced by cisplatin-dGMP and cisplatin-d(A–G), so that reagents could be made available for both the major and minor adducts formed on treatment of DNA with cisplatin.

Antibodies to cisplatin-modified DNA and to cisplatin-modified nucleotides have been applied to quantification of the alkylated DNA in cell lines in culture (180, 181), in peripheral blood cells of patients treated with cisplatin (182, 193), and in tumor cells and spleen, liver, kidney, and blood cells of lymphocytoma-bearing rats (184, 185). Quantitative measurement of immunohistochemical staining with anti-cisplatin-DNA antibodies has been applied to measurement of the formation and repair of adducts in several tissues after injection of cisplatin into rats (186), and to correlation of adduct formation with sensitivity to killing by cisplatin (187). The two kinds of antibodies, anti-cisplatin-DNA and anti-cisplatin-d(G–G) give similar values for adduct formation when the extent of alkylation of DNA is high. However, at low substitution, the anti-dinucleotide antibodies measure a 14- to 300-fold higher number of adducts than do the anti-cisplatin-DNA antibodies. Under these conditions, the platinum levels measured by the anti-cisplatin-dinucleotide antibodies are similar to the values measured by atomic absorption spectroscopy (188).

B. Melphalan

Melphalan is a phenylalanine mustard used as a cancer chemotherapeutic agent. It alkylates guanine, particularly at N7 (189). As it is bifunctional, melphalan forms guanine–guanine cross-links within the nucleic acid. Native DNA alkylated with melphalan has been used to immunize rats, from which rat/rat hybridomas have been prepared (190). An IgG2b monoclonal antibody was characterized as being specific for this alkylated DNA, but unreactive with untreated DNA. It bound to melphalan–native DNA adducts, but even more strongly to melphalan–denatured DNA or melphalan–RNA. The reactive adducts were labile to heat or alkali. The antibody could detect about 30 fmol of adduct per assay in moderately substituted denatured DNA.

In studies of the reactive determinant, isolated guanylic acid and guanine were alkylated with melphalan (191). Products included nucleotide or base dimers cross-linked through their N7 atoms. The cross-linked nucleotide was bound with much higher affinity than the cross-linked base, indicating that the epitope extended to the sugar and phosphate portions. An unexpected immunoreactive product was a nucleotide cross-linked between the N7 of one GMP and the phosphate of another. These alkylated bases, mononucleotides, and dimers had as high an affinity as melphalan-*native* DNA in competition for the monoclonal antibody binding, but they had a lower affinity than the adducts in melphalan-*denatured* DNA.

C. N-2-Acetylaminofluorene

DNA alkylated by N-2-acetylaminofluorene was one of the first carcinogen-modified DNA structures to be studied immunochemically, and has been the subject of many investigations (169, 171). After N-2-acetylaminofluorene is fed to animals, alkylated DNA containing adducts at the C8 position of guanine can be detected immunologically. The major product is the deacetylated N-(8-deoxyguanosinyl)-aminofluorene, and antibodies to the alkylated DNA react with this adduct with a 100-fold higher affinity than with the acetylated aminofluorene derivative of guanine. Recent applications include the histochemical localization of DNA adducts in rat liver (192) and their quantification by microfluorimetry (193).

A combination of antibodies to the aminofluorene–guanine adduct and to BrU allows measurement of adduct formation in relation to replication in metaphase chromosomes of cultured cells (194). These experiments revealed that regions active in DNA synthesis are most susceptible to carcinogen-induced damage, and that the sites of damage are different in early and late stages of the S phase. The localization of *in vivo* DNA modification by carcinogen, therefore, depends on the cell cycle stage at the time of exposure.

D. Other DNA-modifying Reagents

Polyclonal and monoclonal antibodies to O^6-ethyldeoxyguanosine have been prepared and used to quantify the appearance and removal of the alkylated base in DNA modified by ethylnitrosourea (195–197). A detailed thermodynamic analysis of three monoclonal antibodies to O^6-ethyl-2'-deoxyguanosine under varying conditions of pH, ionic strength, solvent polarity, and temperature indicated that van der Waals forces were predominant determinants of specific interactions of antibody with the alkylated base (198). A monoclonal antibody was used to develop a specific assay for the "repair" enzyme activity that removes O^6-alkylguanine residues (199). Several kinds of carcinogen–DNA adducts can be measured immunohistochemically in tissues (200–202) as well as in extracted DNA. Specific antibodies have also been prepared with DNA modified by carbodiimide (203), biphenyls (204), and polycyclic aromatic hydrocarbons (205).

Alkylation of DNA with dimethylnitrosamine forms 7-methylguanosine, which can be detected with a specific antibody (206). Earlier studies noted the lability of the imidazole ring, especially at alkaline pH, in 7-methylguanosine; most antibodies induced by nucleoside–protein conjugates made with 7-methylguanosine by standard procedures were directed against the ring-opened form (207). The more recent study took advantage of the lability of the imidazole ring, applying high-affinity antibodies deliberately prepared against the ring-opened form of 7-methylguanosine. These antibodies were used to detect the methylated base in DNA from peripheral blood cells; treatment of the digested DNA with alkali converted the methylated base to the ring-opened form, which was then detected with an immunoassay.

XII. Summary and Future Prospects

In the 1960s and early 1970s, several workers established that nucleic acids can induce and react with specific antibodies, overturning previous views that nucleic acids were nonantigenic. As more types of antibodies to nucleic acids have become available, both from autoimmune subjects and from experimentally immunized animals, they have been used increasingly as biochemical reagents. They have also been a focus for investigation of the nature of autoimmune responses.

In the last 10 years, there has been much progress in the structural analysis of how antibodies recognize a variety of nucleic-acid epitopes in single bases, nucleosides and nucleotides, short oligonucleotides, single-stranded DNA, RNA, certain double- and triple-helical polynucleotides, and variants such as cruciform structures. The definition of specificity (and, in some cases, of cross-reactivity) for nucleic-acid epitopes has been greatly facilitated by the preparation of hybridomas that produce monoclonal antibodies. In recent years, hybridomas have also allowed analysis of the genes that encode the variable regions of antibodies to nucleic acids. The heavy- and light-chain variable-region cDNAs of many autoantibodies to DNA and a few experimentally induced antibodies have been cloned and sequenced. Very diverse amino-acid sequences make up the CDR loops of the many antibodies for which the primary structure is known. This information, along with the development of plasmid vectors that allow expression of immunoglobulin genes and production of recombinant antibody fragments, opens the door to a future in which a rich variety of specific nucleic-acid-binding reagents may be designed and synthesized. In the course of such research, much will be learned about the many ways in which proteins can interact specifically with nucleic acids.

ACKNOWLEDGMENTS

Research in my laboratory has been supported by grants from the NSF and NIH. Current support is provided by Grants GM32375, AI19794, and AR38820 from the NIH.

REFERENCES

1. S. C. Harrison and A. K. Aggarwal, *ARB* **59**, 933 (1990).
2. R. Schleif, *Science* **241**, 1182 (1988).
3. D. R. Davies, E. A. Padlan and S. Sheriff, *ARB* **59**, 439 (1990).
4. W. Trepicchio, Jr., A. Maruya and K. J. Barrett, *J. Immunol.* **139**, 3139 (1987).
5. R. Kofler, D. J. Noonan, R. Strohal, R. S. Balderas, N. P. H. Moller, F. J. Dixon and A. N. Theofilopoulos, *Eur. J. Immunol.* **17**, 91 (1987).
6. D. Eilat, *Mol. Immunol.* **27**, 203 (1990).
7. H. DerSimonian, K. P. W. J. McAdam, C. Mackworth-Young and B. D. Stollar, *J. Immunol.* **142**, 4027 (1989).
8. K. A. Siminovitch, V. Misener, P. C. Kwong, Q.-L. Song and P. P. Chen, *J. Clin. Invest.* **84**, 1675 (1989).

9. A. Davidson, A. Smith, J. Katz, J.-L. Preud'homme, A. Solomon and B. Diamond, *J. Immunol.* **143**, 174 (1989).

10. M. Shlomchik, M. Mascelli, H. Shan, M. Z. Radic, D. Pisetsky, M. Rothstein and M. Weigert, *J. Exp. Med.* **171**, 265 (1990).

11. T. N. Marion, D. M. Tillman and N.-T. Joun, *J. Immunol.* **145**, 2322 (1990).

12. R. G. Smith and E. W. Voss, Jr., *Mol. Immunol.* **27**, 463 (1990).

13. B. P. Tsao, F. M. Ebling, C. Roman, N. Panosian-Sahakian, K. Calame and B. H. Hahn, *J. Clin. Invest.* **85**, 530 (1990).

14. M. M. Brigido and B. D. Stollar, *J. Immunol.* **146**, 2005 (1991).

15. M. Cygler, A. Boodhoo, J. S. Lee and W. F. Anderson, *JBC* **262**, 643 (1987).

16. A. B. Edmundson, J. N. Herron, K. R. Ely, X.-M. He, D. L. Harris and E. W. Voss, Jr., *Philos. Trans. R. Soc. London B* **323**, 495 (1989).

17. B. D. Stollar, *in* "The Antigens" (M. Sela, ed.), pp. 1–89. Academic Press, New York, 1973).

18. B. D. Stollar, *CRC Crit. Rev. Biochem.* **3**, 45 (1975).

19. T. W. Munns and M. K. Liszewski, *This Series* **24**, 109 (1980).

20. P. T. Strickland and J. M. Boyle, *This Series* **31**, 1 (1984).

21. E. W. Voss, Jr., "Anti-DNA Antibodies in SLE." CRC Press, Boca Raton, Florida, 1987.

21a. B. D. Stollar, *CRC Crit. Rev. Biochem.* **20**, 1 (1986).

22. W. F. Anderson, M. Cygler, R. P. Braun and J. S. Lee, *Bioessays* **8**, 69 (1988).

23. B. D. Stollar, *Int. Rev. Immunol.* **5**, 1 (1989).

24. B. D. Stollar, *in* "Methods in Enzymology" (H. Van Vunakis and J. J. Langone, eds.), Vol. 70, p. 70. Academic Press, New York, 1980.

25. C. M. Huang, H. J. S. Huang, M. Glembourtt, C. P. Liu and S. N. Cohen, *in* "Rapid Detection and Identification of Infectious Agents" (D. T. Kingsbury and S. Falkow, eds.), pp. 257–279. Academic Press, Orlando, Florida, 1985.

26. G. J. Fournié, P. H. Lambert and P. A. Miescher, *J. Exp. Med.* **140**, 1189 (1974).

27. R. Dziarski, *J. Immunol.* **128**, 1026 (1982).

28. M. P. Madaio, S. Hodder, R. S. Schwartz and B. D. Stollar, *J. Immunol.* **132**, 872 (1984).

29. U. Scheer, K. Messner, R. Hazan, I. Raska, P. Hansmann, H. Falk, E. Spiess and W. W. Franke, *Eur. J. Cell Biol.* **43**, 358 (1987).

30. A. Jacob and T. M. Jacob, *NARes* **10**, 6273 (1982).

31. Y. N. Vaishnav and A. Antony, *J. Immunol. Methods* **118**, 25 (1989).

32. G. S. Gilkeson, J. P. Grudier, D. G. Karounos and D. S. Pisetsky, *J. Immunol.* **142**, 1482 (1989).

33. T. Flagstad, K. Fredriksen, B. Dahl, T. Traavik and O. P. Rekvig, *PNAS* **85**, 8171 (1988).

34. K. Fredriksen, T. Traavik and O. P. Rekvig. *Scand. J. Immunol.* **32**, 197 (1990).

35. R. P. Braun and J. S. Lee, *J. Immunol.* **141**, 2084 (1988).

36. I. Sekigawa, Y. Ishida, S. Hirose, H. Sato and T. Shirai, *J. Immunol.* **136**, 1247 (1986).

37. S. Shivakumar, G. C. Tsokos and S. K. Datta, *J. Immunol.* **143**, 103 (1989).

38. G. S. Gilkeson, A. J. Pritchard and D. S. Pisetsky, *Eur. J. Immunol.* **20**, 1789 (1990).

39. E. Engvall, *Lancet* **2**, 1410 (1976).

40. F. Fish and M. Ziff. *Arthritis Rheum.* **24**, 534 (1981).

41. R. B. Eaton, G. Schneider and P. H. Schur, *Arthritis Rheum.* **26**, 52 (1983).

42. R. L. Rubin, F. G. Joslin and E. M. Tan, *J. Immunol. Methods* **6**, 359 (1983).

43. S. Aotsuka, M. Okawa-Takatsuji, M. Kinoshita and R. Yokohari, *Clin. Exp. Immunol.* **73**, 436 (1988).

44. W. Emlen, P. Jarusiripipat and G. Burdick, *J. Immunol. Methods* **132**, 91 (1990).

45. M. Zouali and B. D. Stollar, *J. Immunol. Methods* **78**, 1173 (1986).

46. J. F. Rabek, *in* "Polymers and Biomolecules" (A. A. Frimer, ed.), p. 16. CRC Press, Boca Raton, Florida, 1985.

47. A. Möller, J. E. Gabriels, E. M. Lafer, A. Nordheim, A. Rich and B. D. Stollar, *JBC* **257**, 12081 (1982).
48. L. A. Aarden, F. Lakmaker and T. E. W. Feltkamp, *J. Immunol. Methods* **10**, 39 (1976).
49. M. Papalian, E. Lafer, R. Wong and B. D. Stollar, *J. Clin. Invest.* **65**, 469 (1980).
50. R. M. Lewis, B. D. Stollar and E. B. Goldberg, *J. Immunol. Methods* **3**, 365 (1973).
51. A. Nordheim, R. E. Herrera and A. Rich. *NARes* **15**, 1661 (1987).
52. A. Nordheim and K. Meese, *NARes* **16**, 21 (1988).
53. L. A. Aarden, E. R. deGroot and T. E. W. Feltkamp, *Ann. N.Y. Acad. Sci.* **254**, 505 (1975).
54. D. Sanford and B. D. Stollar, *JBC* **265**, 18608 (1990).
55. L. Runkel and A. Nordheim, *JMB* **189**, 487 (1986).
56. B. H. Hahn and F. M. Ebling, *J. Immunol.* **132**, 187 (1984).
57. B. D. Stollar, G. Zon and R. W. Pastor, *PNAS* **83**, 4469 (1986).
58. F. Tron, D. Charron, J.-F. Bach and N. Talal, *J. Immunol.* **125**, 2805 (1980).
59. R. P. Braun and J. S. Lee, *NARes* **14**, 5049 (1986).
60. R. Ali, H. Dersimonian and B. D. Stollar, *Mol. Immunol.* **22**, 1415 (1985).
61. R. P. Braun and J. S. Lee, *J. Immunol.* **139**, 175 (1987).
62. J. D. McGhee, *Biopolymers* **15**, 1345 (1976).
63. A. D. Frankel, G. K. Ackers and H. O. Smith, *Bchem* **24**, 3049 (1985).
64. E. M. Lafer, J. Rauch, C. Andrzejewski, Jr., D. Mudd, B. Furie, B. Furie, R. S. Schwartz and B. D. Stollar, *J. Exp. Med.* **153**, 897 (1981).
65. T. Kubota, T. Akatsuka and Y. Kanai, *Immunol. Lett.* **14**, 53 (1986).
66. Y. J. Jang and B. D. Stollar, *J. Immunol.* **145**, 3353 (1990).
67. E. Livneh, Noy, S. Tel-Or, J. Sperling and D. Elad, *Bchem* **21**, 3698 (1982).
68. M. D. Shetlar, *Photochem. Photobiol. Rev.* **5**, 105 (1976).
69. M. D. Shetlar, J. Christensen and K. Hom, *Photochem. Photobiol.* **39**, 125 (1984).
70. R. Mezanotte, D. Peretti, M. G. Ennas, R. Vanni and A. T. Sumner, *Cytogenet. Cell Genet.* **50**, 54 (1989).
71. M. Martin, S. M. Diaz de la Espina and F. J. Medina, *Chromosoma* **98**, 368 (1989).
72. D. Stollar, L. Levine, H. I. Lehrer and H. Van Vunakis, *PNAS* **48**, 874 (1962).
73. T. W. Munns and S. K. Freeman, *Bchem* **28**, 10048 (1989).
74. B. D. Stollar, B.-S. Huang and M. Blumenstein, *in* "Fouth Conversation in Biomolecular Sterodynamics" (R. H. Sarma, ed.), pp. 69–84. Adenine, Guildersland, New York, 1985.
75. T. W. Munns, M. K. Liszewski and B. H. Hahn, *Bchem* **23**, 2958 (1984).
76. R. H. Weisbart, R. A. Garrett, M. R. Liebling, E. V. Barnett, H. E. Paulus and D. H. Katz, *Clin. Immunol. Immunopathol.* **27**, 403 (1983).
77. M. Zouali and B. D. Stollar, *J. Clin. Invest,* **78**, 1173 (1986).
78. J. S. Lee, J. R. Lewis, A. R. Morgan, T. R. Mosmann and B. Singh, *NARes* **9**, 1707 (1981).
79. C. Andrzejewski, J. Rauch, E. Lafer, B. D. Stollar and R. S. Schwartz, *J. Immunol.* **126**, 226 (1981).
80. Y. Shoenfeld, J. Rauch, H. Massicotte, S. K. Datta, J. André-Schwartz, B. D. Stollar and R. S. Schwartz, *N. Engl. J. Med.* **308**, 414 (1983).
81. J. S. Lee, D. F. Dombroski and T. R. Mosmann, *Bchem* **21**, 4940 (1982).
82. R. R. P. Kardost, P. A. Billing and E. W. Voss, Jr., *Mol. Immunol.* **19**, 963 (1982).
83. W. I. Sundquist, S. J. Lippard and B. D. Stollar, *Bchem* **25**, 1520 (1986).
84. G. P. van der Schans, A. A. W. M. van Loon, R. H. Groenendijk and R. A. Baan, *Int. J. Radiat. Biol.* **55**, 747 (1989).
85. A. Rich, A. Nordheim and A. H. J. Wang, *ARB* **53**, 791 (1984).
86. T. M. Jovin, D. A. Soumpasis and L. P. McIntosh, *Annu. Rev. Phys. Chem.* **38**, 521 (1987).
87. A. Nordheim, *Nucleic Acids Mol. Biol.* **1**, 112 (1987).
88. E. M. Lafer, R. P. C. Valle, A. Möller, A. Nordheim, P. S. Schur, A. Rich and B. D. Stollar, *J. Clin. Invest.* **71**, 314 (1983).

89. H. R. Bergen III, M. J. Losman, T. O'Connor, W. Zacharias, J. E. Larson, M. A. Accavitti, R. D. Wells and W. J. Koopman, *J. Immunol.* **139**, 743 (1987).
90. E. M. Lafer, A. Möller, R. P. C. Valle, A. Nordheim, A. Rich and B. D. Stollar, *CSHSQB* **47**, 155 (1983).
91. D. A. Zarling, D. J. Arndt-Jovin, M. Robert-Nicoud, L. P. McIntosh, R. Thomae and T. M. Jovin, *JMB* **176**, 369 (1984).
92. B. H. Johnston and A. Rich, *Cell* **42**, 713 (1985).
93. R. E. Cathou, *in* "Comprehensive Immunology" (G. W. Litman and R. A. Good, eds.), p. 37. Plenum, New York, 1978.
94. J. Anglister, T. Frey and H. M. McConnell, *Bchem* **23**, 1138 (1984).
95. J. Anglister, T. Frey and H. M. McConnell, *Nature* **315**, 65 (1985).
96. W. Ito, M. Nishimura, N. Sakato, H. Fujio and Y. Arata, *J. Biochem.* **102**, 643 (1987).
97. C. C. Hardin, D. A. Zarling, J. D. Puglisi, M. O. Trulson, P. W. David and I. Tinoco, Jr., *Bchem* **26**, 5191 (1987).
98. C. C. Hardin, D. A. Zarling, S. K. Wolk, W. S. Ross and I. Tinoco, Jr., *Bchem* **27**, 4169 (1988).
99. D. A. Zarling, C. S. Calhoun, C. C. Hardin and A. H. Zarling, *PNAS* **84**, 6117 (1987).
100. D. A. Zarling, C. J. Calhoun, B. G. Feuerstein and E. P. Sena, *JMB* **211**, 147 (1990).
102. A. Skerra and A. Pluckthun, *Science* **240**, 1038 (1988).
103. A. Jaworsky, W.-T. Hsieh, J. A. Blaho, J. E. Larson and R. D. Wells, *Science* **238**, 773 (1987).
104. A. Rahmouni and R. D. Wells, *Science* **246**, 358 (1989).
105. R. J. Hill, F. Watt and B. D. Stollar, *Exp. Cell Res.* **153**, 469 (1984).
106. L. J. Peck, A. Nordheim, A. Rich and J. C. Wang, *PNAS* **79**, 4560 (1982).
107. D. J. Arndt-Jovin, M. Robert-Nicoud, Zarling, C. Greider, E. Weimer and T. M. Jovin, *PNAS* **80**, 4344 (1983).
108. A. Nordheim, M. L. Pardue, E. M. Lafer, A. Möller, B. D. Stollar and A. Rich, *Nature* **294**, 417 (1981).
109. A. Nordheim, M. L. Pardue, L. M. Weiner, K. Lowenhaupt, P. Scholten, A. Möller, A. Rich and B. D. Stollar, *JBC* **261**, 468 (1986).
110. F. Lancillotti, M. C. Lopez, C. Alonso and B. D. Stollar, *J. Cell Biol.* **100**, 1759 (1985).
111. F. Lancillotti, M. C. Lopez, P. Arias and C. Alonso, *PNAS* **84**, 1560 (1987).
112. M.-O. Soyer-Gobillard, M.-L. Geraud, D. Coulaud, M. Barray, B. Theveny, B. Revet and E. Delain, *J. Cell Biol.* **111**, 293 (1990).
113. B. Wittig, T. Dorbic and A. Rich, *J. Cell Biol.* **108**, 755 (1989).
114. A. Nordheim, E. M. Lafer, L. J. Peck, J. C. Wang, B. D. Stollar and A. Rich, *Cell* **31**, 309 (1982).
115. T. M. Jovin, L. McIntosh, D. J. Arndt-Jovin, D. A. Zarling, M. Robert-Nicoud, J. H. Van de Sande, K. F. Jorgenson and F. Eckstein, *J. Biomol. Struct. Dyn.* **1**, 21 (1983).
116. F. Azorin, A. Nordheim and A. Rich, *EMBO J.* **2**, 649 (1983).
117. E. M. Lafer, R. Sousa and A. Rich, *EMBO J.* **4**, 3655 (1985).
118. E. M. Lafer, R. Sousa, A. Rich and B. D. Stollar, *JBC* **261**, 6438 (1986).
119. T. J. Thomas, M. J. Baarsch and R. P. Messner, *Anal. Biochem.* **168**, 358 (1988).
120. M. C. Lang, B. Malfoy, A. M. Freud, M. Daune and M. Leng, *EMBO J.* **1**, 1149 (1982).
120a. B. D. Stollar, *in* "Unusual DNA Structures" (R. D. Wells and S. C. Harvey, eds.), pp. 253–265. Springer-Verlag, New York, 1988.
121. F. D. Miller, K. F. Jorgenson, R. J. Winkfein, J. H. Van de Sande, D. A. Zarling, J. Stockton and J. B. Rattner, *J. Biomol. Struct. Syn.* **1**, 611 (1983).
122. B. Revet, D. A. Zarling, T. M. Jovin and E. Delain, *EMBO J.* **3**, 3353 (1984).
123. H. Castleman, L. H. Hanau, W. Zacharias and B. F. Erlanger, *NARes* **16**, 3977 (1988).
124. A. Nordheim and A. Rich, *Nature* **303**, 674 (1983).

125. A. Jiminez-Ruiz, J. M. Requena, F. Lancillotti, G. Morales, M. C. Lopez and C. Alonso, *NARes* **17**, 4579 (1989).
126. R. Thomae, S. Beck and F. M. Pohl, *PNAS* **80**, 5550 (1983).
127. S. Diekmann and D. A. Zarling, *NARes* **15**, 6063 (1987).
128. S. Arnott, R. Chandrasekaran, I. H. Hall and L. C. Puigjaner, *NARes* **11**, 3131 (1983).
129. D. M. Crothers, T. E. Haran and J. G. Nadeau, *JBC* **265**, 7093 (1990).
130. M. Riley, B. Maling and M. Chamberlin, *JMB* **20**, 359 (1966).
131. J. S. Lee, D. A. Johnson and A. R. Morgan, *NARes* **6**, 3073 (1979).
132. S. Arnott, D. W. L. Hukins, S. D. Dover, W. Fuller and A. R. Hodgson, *JMB* **81**, 107 (1983).
133. V. I. Lyamichev, S. M. Mirkin and M. D. J. Frank-Kamanetskii, *Biomol. Struct. Dyn.* **3**, 327 (1985).
134. D. E. Pulleyblank, D. B. Haniford and A. R. Morgan, *Cell* **42**, 271 (1985).
135. F. Lacour, E. Nahon-Merlin and M. Michelson, *Curr. Top. Microbiol. Immunol.* **62**, 1 (1973).
136. L. C. Rainen and B. D. Stollar, *Bchem* **16**, 2003 (1977).
137. B. D. Stollar and V. Raso, *Nature* **250**, 231 (1974).
138. J. S. Lee, G. D. Burkholder, L. J. P. Latimer, B. L. Haug and R. P. Braun, *NARes* **15**, 1047 (1987).
139. A. Boodhoo, C. D. Mol, J. S. Lee and W. F. Anderson, *JBC* **263**, 18578 (1988).
140. J. S. Lee, L. J. P. Latimer, B. L. Haug, D. E. Pulleyblank, D. M. Skinner and G. D. Burkholder, *Gene* **82**, 191 (1989).
140a. G. D. Burkholder, L. J. P. Latimer and J. S. Lee, *Chromosoma* **97**, 185 (1988).
141. S. B. Zimmerman and B. H. Pheiffer, *PNAS* **78**, 78 (1981).
142. A. H.-J. Wang, S. Fujii, J. H. van Boom, G. A. van der Marel, S. A. A. van Boeckel and A. Rich, *Nature* **299**, 601 (1982).
143. B. D. Stollar, *Science* **169**, 609 (1970).
144. Y. Kitagawa and B. D. Stollar, *Mol. Immunol.* **19**, 413 (1982).
145. H. Nakazato, *Bchem* **19**, 2835 (1980).
146. S. J. Boguslawski, D. E. Smith, M. A. Michalak, K. E. Mickelson, C. O. Yehle, W. L. Patterson and R. J. Carrico, *J. Immunol. Methods* **89**, 123 (1986).
147. D. G. Sanford, K. J. Kotkow and B. D. Stollar, *NARes* **16**, 10643 (1988).
148. B. D. Stollar and A. Raschtchian, *Anal. Biochem.* **161**, 387 (1987).
149. F. Coutlee, R. H. Yolken and R. P. Viscidi, *Anal. Biochem.* **181**, 153 (1989).
150. F. Coutlee, L. Bobo, K. Mayur, R. H. Yolken and R. P. Viscidi, *Anal. Biochem.* **181**, 96 (1989).
151. F. Coutlee, B. Yang, L. Bobo, K. Mayur, R. Yolken and R. Viscidi, *AIDS Res. Hum. Retroviruses* **6**, 775 (1990).
152. R. A. Padgett, P. J. Grabowski, M. M. Konarska, S. Seiler and P. A. Sharp, *ARB* **55**, 1119 (1986).
153. J. D. Reilly, S. K. Freeman, R. F. Melhem, R. Kierzek, M. H. Caruther, M. Edmonds and T. W. Munns, *Anal. Biochem.* **185**, 125 (1990).
154. R. D. Wells, *JBC* **263**, 1095 (1988).
155. M. Gellert, K. Mizuuchi, M. H. O'Dea, H. Ohmori and J. Tomizawa, *CSHSQB* **43**, 35 (1978).
156. M. Gellert, M. H. O'Dea and K. Mizuuchi, *PNAS* **80**, 5545 (1983).
157. D. M. J. Lilley, *CSHSQB* **47**, 101 (1983).
158. N. C. Seeman and N. R. Kallenback, *Biophys. J.* **44**, 201 (1983).
159. N. C. Seeman, M. F. Maestre, R. I. Ma and N. R. Kallenbach, *Prog. Clin. Biol. Res.* **172A**, 99 (1985).
160. L. Frappier, G. B. Price, R. G. Martin and M. Zannis-Hadjopoulos, *JMB* **193**, 751 (1987).

161. L. Frappier, G. B. Price, R. G. Martin and M. Zannis-Hadjopoulos, *JBC* **264**, 334 (1989).
162. M. Zannis-Hadjopoulos, L. Frappier, M. Khoury and G. B. Price, *EMBO J.* **7**, 1837 (1988).
163. P. R. Langer-Safer, M. Levine and D. Ward, *PNAS* **79**, 4381 (1982).
164. G. Gentilomi, M. Musiani, M. Zerbini, G. Gallinella, D. Gibellini and M. La Placa, *J. Immunol. Methods* **125**, 177 (1989).
165. H. Gratzner, *Science* **218**, 474 (1982).
166. M. R. Miller, C. Heyneman, S. Walker and R. G. Ulrich, *J. Immunol.* **136**, 1791 (1986).
167. M. W. Miller and R. S. Nowakowski, *Brain Res.* **457**, 44 (1988).
168. D. Muir, S. Varon and M. Manthorpe, *Anal. Biochem.* **185**, 377 (1990).
169. M. C. Poirier, *J. Natl. Cancer Inst.* **67**, 515 (1981).
170. R. Gruenewald and B. D. Stollar, *J. Immunol.* **111**, 106 (1973).
171. M. Leng, E. Sage, R. P. P. Fuchs and M. P. Saune, *FEBS Lett.* **92**, 207 (1978).
172. E. Seaman, H. Van Vunakis and L. Levine, *JBC* **247**, 5709 (1972).
173. E. Seaman, L. Levine and H. Van Vunakis, *Bchem* **5**, 1216 (1966).
174. B. Malfoy, B. Hartmann, J. P. Macquet and M. Leng, *Cancer Res.* **41**, 4127 (1981).
175. M. C. Poirier, S. J. Lippard, L. A. Zwelling, H. M. Ushay, D. Kerrigan, C. C. Thill, R. M. Santella, D. Grunberger and S. H. Yuspa, *PNAS* **79**, 6443 (1982).
176. S. J. Lippard, H. M. Ushay, C. M. Merkel and M. C. Poirier, *Bchem* **22**, 5165 (1983).
177. A. L. Pinto and S. J. Lippard, *BBA* **780**, 167 (1984).
178. W. I. Sundquist, S. J. Lippard and B. D. Stollar, *PNAS* **84**, 8225 (1987).
179. A. M. J. Fichtinger-Schepman, R. A. Baan, A. Luiten-Schuite, M. van Dijk and P. H. M. Lohman, *Chem.–Biol. Interact.* **55**, 275 (1985).
180. A. C. M. Plooy, A. M. J. Fichtinger-Schepman, H. H. Schutte, M. van Dijk and P. H. M. Lohman, *Carcinogenesis* **6**, 561 (1985).
181. P. Bedford, A. M. J. Fichtinger-Schepman, S. A. Shellard, M. C. Walker, J. R. W. Masters and B. T. Hill, *Cancer Res.* **48**, 3019 (1988).
182. E. Reed, R. F. Ozols, R. Tarone, S. H. Yuspa and M. C. Poirier, *PNAS* **84**, 5024 (1987).
183. A. M. J. Fichtinger-Schepman, A. T. van Oosterom, P. H. M. Lohman and F. Berends, *Cancer Res.* **47**, 3000 (1987).
184. E. Reed, C. L. Litterst, C. C. Thill, S. H. Yuspa and M. C. Poirier, *Cancer Res.* **47**, 718 (1987).
185. A. M. J. Fichtinger-Schepman, C. P. J. Vendrik, W. C. M. van Dijk-Knijnenburg, W. H. de Jong, A. C. E. van der Minnen, A. M. E. Claessen, S. D. van der Velde-Visser, G. de Groot, K. L. Wubs, P. A. Steerenberg, J. H. Schornagel and F. Berends, *Cancer Res.* **49**, 2862 (1989).
186. P. M. A. B. Terheggen, R. G. van der Hoop, B. G. J. Floot and W. H. Gispen, *Toxicol. Appl. Pharm.* **99**, 334 (1989).
187. P. M. A. B. Terheggen, J. Y. Emondt, B. G. J. Floot, P. I. Schrier, R. Dijkman, L. den Engelse and A. C. Begg, *Cancer Res.* **50**, 3556 (1990).
188. A. M. J. Fichtinger-Schepman, R. A. Baan and F. Berends, *Carcinogenesis* **10**, 2367 (1989).
189. K. W. Kohn, J. A. Hartley and W. B. Mattes, *NARes* **15**, 10531 (1987).
190. M. J. Tilby, J. M. Styles and C. E. J. Dean, *Cancer Res.* **47**, 1542 (1987).
191. M. J. Tilby, P. D. Lawley and P. B. Farmer, *Chem–Biol. Interact.* **73**, 183 (1990).
192. H. S. Huitfeldt, E. F. Spangler, J. Baron and M. C. Poirier, *Cancer Res.* **47**, 2098 (1987).
193. H. S. Huitfeldt, E. F. Spangler, J. M. Hunt and M. C. Poirier, *Carcinogenesis* **7**, 123 (1986).
194. O. A. Olivero, H. Huitfeldt and M. C. Poirier, *Mol. Carcinogenesis* **3**, 37 (1990).
195. R. Müller and M. F. Rajewski, *Cancer Res.* **40**, 887 (1980).

196. R. Müller and M. F. Rajewsky, *Cancer Res.* **43**, 2897 (1983).
197. A. A. Wani, R. E. Gibson-D'Ambrosio and S. M. D'Ambrosio, *Carcinogenesis* **5**, 1145 (1984).
198. S. C. Yuhasz, D. F. Senear, J. Adamkiewicz, M. F. Rajewski, P. O. P. Ts'o and L. Kan, *Bchem* **26**, 2334 (1987).
199. P. Nehls and M. R. Rajewski, *Carcinogenesis* **11**, 81 (1990).
200. K. Nakagawa, Y. Nakatsuru and T. Ishikawa, *J. Invest. Dermatol.* **92**, 275S (1989).
201. E. Scherer and J. Van Benthem, *J. Histochem. Cytochem.* **38**, 433 (1990).
202. T. Shirai, A. Nakamura, S. Fukushima, M. Tada, T. Morita and N. Ito, *Carcinogenesis* **11**, 653 (1990).
203. A. A. Wani, J. K. Sullivan and J. Lebowitz, *NARes* **17**, 9957 (1989).
204. M. Tada, H. Aoki, M. Kojima, T. Morita, T. Shirai, H. Yamada and N. Ito, *Carcinogenesis* **10**, 1397 (1989).
205. A. Weston, M. J. Newman, D. L. Mann and B. R. Brooks, *Carcinogenesis* **11**, 859 (1990).
206. P. Degan, R. Montesano and C. P. Wild, *Cancer Res.* **48**, 5065 (1988).
207. L. Rainen and B. D. Stollar, *NARes* **5**, 4877 (1978).

Oligodeoxynucleotides as Antisense Inhibitors of Gene Expression

MRIDUL K. GHOSH
AND JACK S. COHEN

Cancer Pharmacology Section
Pharmacology Department
Georgetown University Medical School
Washington, D.C. 20007

I. Oligonucleotides as Informational Drugs

Perforce, all drugs contain the information in their molecular structure that defines their selectivity. Generally, this information is in the form of a few chemical groups forming hydrogen bonds that provide the selectivity of binding of the small drug molecule to a protein active site. Inhibiting a particular enzyme may prevent the functioning of an essential metabolic pathway, leading to the desired pharmacological result. Selectivity is also manifested in the absence of strong secondary binding to other sites.

However, the rules governing this kind of drug selectivity have been very difficult to determine, since, due to the tertiary folding of the protein, the fit for each drug molecule may be quite distinct. Usually only by finding enzymes with similar functions can a structural–functional motif for the drug interaction become evident. The use of molecular modeling based on crystallographic and NMR results to improve drug design has led, in several cases, to improvements of binding, but rarely to improved drug efficacy.

We use the term "informational drug" to convey the concept that a drug molecule is synthesized to have specific information encoded in it. This is definitely not a result of a natural product happening to have evolved a particular protein affinity. Two sets of informational molecules are found in biological systems, namely, the nucleic acids and the proteins. The former are the basis of genetic function and contain the most selective informational

79

Progress in Nucleic Acid Research
and Molecular Biology, Vol. 42

interaction yet found in biological molecules, that has evolved over eons, namely, hydrogen-bonded (Watson–Crick) base-pairing. We can consider this interaction as the target of a new type of drug molecule, synthesized with a specific base sequence designed to interact with a target nucleic acid containing the complementary sequence.

In the earliest and most developed example of this approach, oligodeoxynucleotides and their analogs have been applied as antisense inhibitors of gene expression to bring about *translation arrest* (1, 2). In Table I are listed most of the applications of this approach so far reported, including antiviral

TABLE I

INHIBITION OF EXPRESSION BY ANTISENSE
OLIGODEOXYNUCLEOTIDES[a]

System	Oligo analog	Reference
Viruses		
Rous sarcoma	PO	3
VSV	PMe	4
	PO	5
	PO	6
HSV	PO	6a
	PMe	7
SV40	PMe	8, 9
Influenza	PO	10
Sendai virus	PO	11
TMV	PO	12
HIV	PO	13, 14
	PS	14–16
	PN	14
	PMe	17, 18
Mammalian genes[b]		
c-*myc*	PO	6, 19, 20–22
	PS	22
c-*fos*	PO	23
c-*myb*	PO	24
c-*mos*	PO, PS	25, 26
N-*ras*	PMe	27, 28
PCNA	PO	29
cAMP kinase	PO	30, 31
bcl-2	PO, PS	32, 33
*erb*B-2	PO	34

[a]VSV, Vesicular stomatitis virus; HSV, herpes simplex virus; SV40, simian virus 40; TMV, tobacco mosaic virus; HIV, human immunodeficiency virus; PO, normal phosphodiester; PMe, methylphosphonate; PS, phosphorothioate; PN, phosphoramidate; PCNA, proliferating cell nuclear antigen.

[b]Includes proto-oncogenes and other growth-related genes.

TABLE II
TYPES OF INFORMATIONAL DRUGS

Target	Molecule	Information
mRNA	Antisense oligodeoxynucleotide	W–C[a] base sequence
mRNA	Ribozyme	RNA base sequence
DNA	Oligodeoxynucleotide	triplex base sequence
Polymerase	Oligodeoxynucleotide	protein site
Transcription factor	Oligodeoxynucleotide	protein site
Protease	Peptide	protein site

[a]W–C, Watson–Crick.

applications (35). It should be emphasized that most of these studies were published within the past few years. The number is increasing rapidly and, accordingly, this review is not intended to be comprehensive. This approach developed partly from the use of antisense mRNA to inhibit the expression of the target (sense) mRNA (36). In certain cases, antisense mRNAs occur naturally as a regulatory mechanism (37, 37a). But *antisense oligodeoxynucleotides* are more practicable as a therapeutic approach.

Once this approach is recognized in principle, other examples can be seen to fit a pattern (Table II), such as the use of oligodeoxynucleotides to form a triple-strand helix with duplex DNA (see Section VII) but with a different base triplet code, in order to arrest transcription (the opening of duplex DNA is not considered facile enough to allow the access of an oligo to interact with one of the strands. The development of synthetic oligoribonucleotides as ribozymes (Section VII) is another example, in which the information for the selectivity is encoded in the portions of the oligomer flanking the catalytic site.

Another example is the use of oligodeoxynucleotides to bind to protein sites that recognize specific sequences of bases, thus inhibiting polymerase action or bringing about transcription arrest by sequestering specific transcription cofactors (131). Thus, a new area of pharmacology is developing that is differentiated by the purposeful inclusion of information in the form of nucleic-acid bases in a putative oligonucleotide drug molecule.

Among the first attempts to develop an **analog** of an oligodeoxynucleotide (Fig. 1) as an inhibitor of gene expression was the work of Miller *et al.* (9). Several years ago, Blake *et al.* published some influential papers (38, 39) that were important but limited. They were important because they showed clearly selective inhibition of β-globin expression by methylphosphonate oligodeoxynucleotide analogs in a cell-free system. But it is evident that sequences as small as tetramers can not be expected to hybridize effectively with target sequences as reported (39). The objective of using the methyl-

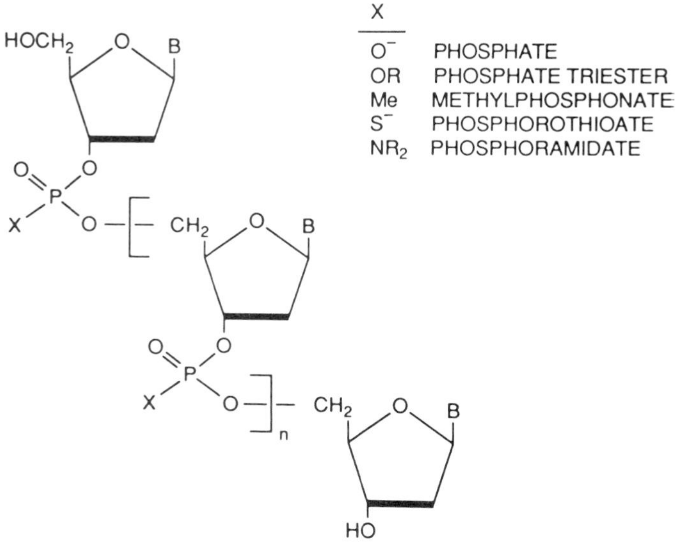

FIG 1. Structure of an oligodeoxynucleotide, where B represents the bases (A, T, G, and C), and X = O$^-$ for a natural phosphodiester, or a substituent as shown.

phosphonate analog was to make the oligonucleotide resistant to deoxy-ribonucleases, predominantly exonucleases, that are present both *in vivo* and *in vitro*. They also considered that the substitution of a methyl group for a charged oxygen, producing a neutral oligodeoxynucleotide analog, would give more efficient cellular uptake. This is considered in Section IV.

These results led us to synthesize appropriate oligos and analogs to test for antisense inhibition of HIV, in collaboration with Broder *et al.* at NCI (*40*). It became evident to us that although the natural and methylphosphonate oligos showed no reproducible activity against HIV in the cytopathic assay, the phosphorothioate analogs did (*15*).

While this work was in progress, a paper appeared that also claimed inhibition of HIV by several natural oligos targeted against several sites in the HIV genome (*13*). Zamecnik had pioneered in the use of natural phosphodiester oligos to inhibit Rous sarcoma virus (*3*). However, natural phosphodiester oligos are degraded by nucleases in the medium (*41*), which makes necessary higher concentrations to achieve a significant inhibitory effect (unless heat-treated or serum-free medium is used) (*13*). There is also toxicity arising from the presence of small oligos (as a result of endo-nucleases) and mononucleotides (from exonucleases) in relatively high con-centrations. Thus, we chose to test chemically modified oligos targeted against a highly conserved region in the *rev* gene, since the HIV genome is known to be highly variable (*42*).

II. Phosphorothioate Oligodeoxynucleotides

A. Physicochemical Properties

The phosphorothioate analogs of oligodeoxynucleotides ("S-oligos") are used to illustrate how any such analog should be tested for its physico-chemical properties before it can be considered a potentially useful analog for antisense inhibition. Since we found these S-oligos to be the most effective analogs for a variety of reasons (detailed below), we focus on these particular analogs.

The first important application of phosphorothioate analogs was to delineate the stereochemistry of the RNase mechanism (*43*). In subsequent work, it was shown that these analogs are potent inhibitors of nucleases (*44*). Subsequent studies improved the synthesis so that one could insert a sulfur atom at a specific phosphodiester site in a small oligodeoxynucleotide, using an automatic synthesizer with phosphoramidite precursors (*45*). This was done to permit assignment of specific resonances in the ^{31}P NMR spectra of oligos (*46*), although this approach was soon replaced by a much simpler two-dimensional heteronuclear NMR technique (*47*).

We tested the S-oligos partly because they are simpler to synthesize than the methylphosphonates. The S-oligos only require a sulfurization in place of the normal oxidation step as the last step in the cyclic synthesis (Fig. 2), while the methylphosphonates require a methylphosphonamidite precursor (Fig. 3). However, the method of synthesis of S-oligos was slow and cumbersome initially, since the solvent being used (pyridine) was inadequate, and this required heating the column for the sulfurization step to 60°C and waiting for several hours. Subsequently, we became aware of the use of carbon disulfide with triethylamine (*48*), which reduced the time of the sulfurization step to minutes at room temperature (*49*). The hydrogen phosphonate method that had been described (*50*) was also improved (*51*).

Phosphorothioates contain perhaps the most conservative substitution, and are among the earliest used of all modified analogs of naturally occurring phosphodiesters (*44*). They contain a sulfur atom in the phosphodiester group in place of one of the nonbridging oxygens, and thus they have the same charge as the parent compound. The results with regard to the antiviral activity of phosphorothioate polyribonucleotides (*52*), together with their resistance to snake venom phosphodiesterase (*53–55*), provided the impetus to introduce the phosphorothioate linkage into DNA. This type of modification is of great significance, because it offers stability to enzymatic attack as

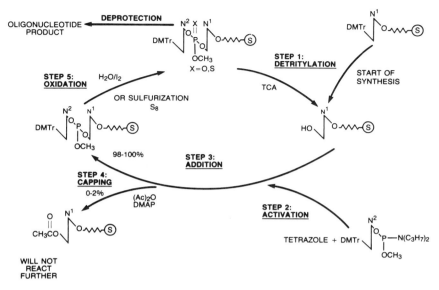

FIG 2. Stepwise synthesis of an oligodeoxynucleotide from phosphoramidite precursors (step 2). Note that the oxidation step (step 5) from P(III) to P(V) can be replaced with a sulfurization to make phosphorothioates.

well as maintaining the same charge and a similar geometry for minimal interference with the structure of duplex DNA. Since the physicochemical properties are one of the major determinants of the efficiency of antisense oligonucleotides, this section describes the changes in physicochemical properties due to the introduction of a sulfur atom into the molecule.

Replacement of a nonbridging oxygen atom by any other atom produces a chiral center at phosphorus, which leads to the formation of a pair of diastereomers. The absolute configuration of these diastereomers at phosphorus is designated according to convention as either Rp or Sp. The presence of such diastereomers creates a major problem for antisense applications in elucidating a structure–activity relationship. For example, the Sp isomers, but not the Rp isomers, of dinucleoside phosphorothioates are

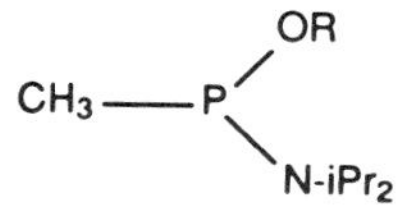

FIG 3. Structure of a methyphosphonamidite required to synthesize methylphosphonates (see Fig. 1) via the stepwise automated procedure shown in Fig. 2.

hydrolyzed selectively by various nucleases, including P1 and S1 (56, 57).

An oligonucleotide containing n phosphorothioate groups will have 2^n stereoisomers; theoretically, 50% of them should show resistance to nuclease attack. In other words, 50% of the resistant variety will act as inhibitors in the hydrolysis of the other 50% by nucleases. This assumption is only valid, however, when the stereoisomers are evenly distributed into all-Rp and all-Sp varieties. In actual practice, since the synthesis method used is non-stereospecific, the probability of such a distribution occurring is very low, and one would expect that only a few of the molecules will have the desired configuration for either maximum stability or maximum susceptibility. The chirality problem can be avoided if the second nonbridging phosphate oxygen is also replaced by another sulfur atom, forming a phosphorodithioate. However, these compounds are more difficult to synthesize (45, 58) and it is not clear that they are worth the extra effort.

Although the substitution by sulfur retains the property of high water solubility, the phosphorothioates are somewhat less water-soluble than the normal phosphodiester oligonucleotides. This difference could be explained by the length of the P—S bond and the radius of the sulfur atom. The phosphorothioate bond is longer than that of the normal phosphodiester (1.85 versus 1.61 Å) (59, 60), and the van der Waals radius of sulfur is 0.45 Å larger than that of oxygen.

One of the most striking features of the phosphorothioates is their stability toward nuclease attack (44, 61, 62); this has great potential, particularly when the use of oligonucleotides is very much restricted due to their susceptibilities to nucleases. Stein et al. (49) compared the susceptibilities of a series of normal oligonucleotides (all-PO) and their phosphorothioate derivatives (all-PS) toward three different nucleases: S1 (predominantly an endonuclease), P1 (endo- and exonuclease), and snake venom phosphodiesterase (SVP, a 3′,5′ exonuclease). The all-PS analogs were more stable than the all-PO derivatives toward the enzymes tested. This was very prominent with SVP, where the relative $t_{1/2}$ of the all-PS is about 10^{-2}–10^{-3} that of the all-PO. With other nucleases, the digestion also proceeded one-half to one-forty-fifth as fast as the all-PS analog. In our recent studies with 17-mer oligodeoxynucleotides (complementary to the coding region of rabbit β-globin mRNA) containing various ratios of PS and PO, we confirmed that the compound containing 100% PS is digested significantly slower than the all-PO by S1 nuclease (62a) (Fig. 4).

Resistance of phosphorothioates toward nuclease attack could be due to lack of binding of thio compounds to the enzyme, to lack of cleavage of the phosphorothioate bond, or to slow dissociation of the enzyme–oligo complex. Recent structural studies of DNase I show that several phosphate groups are

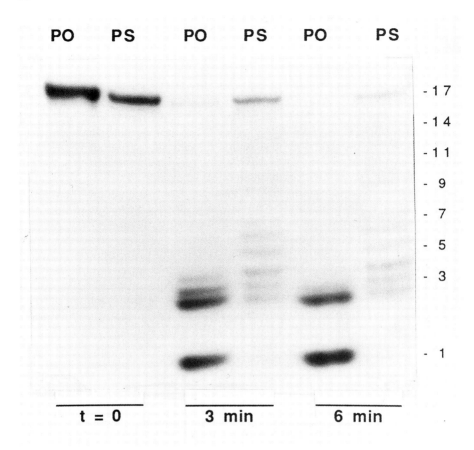

FIG 4. Gel electrophoresis of ^{32}P end-labeled anti-β-globin 17-mers (PO and PS) showing cleavage by S1-endonuclease. PO is the more rapidly cleaved.

bound on either side of the active site (63). The rapid cleavage of poly[d(AsT)] and poly[d(sTsTG)]·poly[d(CsAsA)] by DNase I (64) suggests that binding to the substrate is not restricted by the thio groups. However, there was no correlation between the resistance to digestion by pancreatic DNase I and the phosphorothioate content. It was assumed that the stability of some of the thio compounds might be due to the conformation changes of the enzyme following binding with phosphorothioate molecules, which make the unmodified phosphodiester bonds unrecognizable or unreactive.

   Phosphorothioate oligonucleotides are capable of forming duplexes following hybridization with their complementary strands of ribo- or deoxy-oligonucleotides, with the stability of the duplex decreasing in the sequence [RNA·RNA] > [RNA·DNA] > [DNA·DNA] (65). The hybridizing ability between the oligonucleotides is characterized by the melting temperature (T_m), the temperature needed to dissociate 50% of the duplex. Melting temperatures, in other words, depend on the relative stability of the duplex.

LaPlanche et al. (46) synthesized an octamer [d(GGsAATTCC)] containing one phosphorothioate linkage in the molecule and compared the T_m of "Sp–Sp" and "Rp–Rp" combinations of the self-complementary sequence with that of the parent duplex. They found the T_m of the Sp–Sp duplex (34.1 ± 1°C) to be almost identical to that of the parent duplex (33.9 ± 1°C), while the T_m for the Rp–Rp duplex (31.7°C) was about 2.4°C below that of the parent duplex. This suggests that introduction of chirality affects the stability of the duplex. A lower T_m, which indicates the destabilization of the self-complementary duplex, may arise from the orientation of the sulfur in the Rp–Rp duplex. The same T_m values between the parent and the Sp–Sp duplex, on the other hand, may suggest that, except for the chemistry of the internucleoside linkage, there is very little difference (if any) between Sp isomers and the normal oligonucleotides.

The better acceptance of Sp isomers by DNA polymerase I or T4 DNA polymerase in DNA synthesis (55, 66), and their susceptibilities to S1 and P1 nuclease (56, 57), also suggest the possibility of their identical nature. The phosphorothioate analogs of d(G·C)$_4$ and d(C·G)$_4$ containing Sp-phosphorothioate groups behaved like the parent compound (69). However, X-ray studies (70) demonstrate the conformationally equivalent nature of the phosphate and Rp-phosphorothioate linkage, when the Rp isomer is present 5′ to each cytidine residue of a hexamer containing repeating units of d(G·C). However, further enzymatic digestion studies with an analog containing 100% Rp and Sp isomers and comparing the results with that of the normal congener should resolve this question.

The influence of phosphorothioate on the B-to-Z transformation and its dependence on the chirality of the sulfur has been well documented. The phosphorothioate analog of poly[d(G·C)] transforms (B to Z) much more rapidly than does the parent compound when the Rp isomer of phosphorothioate is located 5′ to deoxycytidine (67, 68). No such transition was seen with the Rp phosphorothioate 5′ to guanosine. A similar influence of the Rp-phosphorothioate group on the transition is seen with the phosphorothioate analogs of d(G–C)$_4$ and d(C–G)$_4$ (69). On the other hand, the presence of sulfur has very little effect on the B–Z transition (70).

Determinations of the T_m's of a series of phosphorothioate homo-polymers of deoxycytidine and deoxythymidine with poly(rA) and poly (rI), respectively, showed that there is a decrease of T_m by about 15–20°C for the modified analogs relative to the normal congener of equal length (49). The melting curves generated for phosphorothioates fit the equation for a two-state transition model and ran parallel with that of the normal analog. The parallel nature of the curve indicated a similar slope (enthalpy of melting), suggesting that the introduction of chirality had no effect. Had the many streoisomers expected to be present exhibited different T_m's, a broadened slope, due to formation of many unstable duplexes, would have been seen. The depression of T_m values was much higher with A·T pairs than with the G·C pairs, as expected (49, 71).

Both chirality and the position of the phosphorothioate residue in a partially modified oligonucleotide affect the melting temperature. The T_m's were 15°C and 5°C less than those of the parent compounds, when the Rp isomer of phosphorothioate is located 5' to the thymidine or to adenine, respectively, in poly[d(A·T)] (72). In a different experiment with the same polymer, i.e., poly[d(A·T)], these values were determined to be 12°C and 2°C, respectively (73). With poly[d(G·C)], the T_m's varied from that of the parent compound with the change in the position of the Rp isomer of phosphorothioate (67). The presence of the Rp isomer 5' to cytidine gave rise to a larger decrease (8°C) than when it was 5' to guanosine (2°C). No such changes in T_m's were found, compared to the parent compound, with phosphorothioate groups of either configuration 5' to guanosine in d(G·C)$_4$ analogs, where the T_m decreases by 10°C and 5°C, respectively, for the Rp and Sp isomer 5' to cytidine (69).

In another study, a phosphorothioate group located 5' to a pyrimidine shows a larger decrease than when it is 5' to a purine (64). In our recent study (62a) with several oligonucleotides (17-mers, complementary to the coding region of β-rabbit globin mRNA) containing different ratios of PS and PO, we found that the T_m was reduced by 11°C for the all-PS relative to the all-PO, with the difference diminishing with increased PO content (Fig. 5). Our results also demonstrate that the phosphorothioate 5' to a purine residue shows a lesser decrease in T_m.

The results from our T_m experiments with complementary oligonucleotides do not agree with other findings (65), unless the molecule contains a substantial amount (55–100%) of phosphorothioate residue. The latter indicated that an RNA·DNA duplex is more stable than a DNA·DNA duplex. In contrast, we have found that the temperature needed for 50% dissociation of the RNA·oligodeoxynucleotides is more or less the same as that of the duplex formed between the two oligodeoxynucleotides (62a). However, the validity of this comparison may be questionable, particularly since it was the stability of high-molecular-weight duplexes that was described (65).

RNase H digests the RNA strand following complex formation with a complementary oligodeoxynucleotide; it is present in virtually all cell types (74–76). It is reported that it digests the RNA counterpart, poly(rA), much

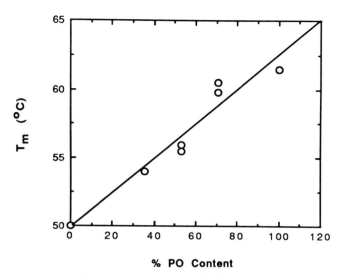

FIG 5. Variation in melting temperature (T_m) with decreasing PS content for the 17-mer anti-β-globin duplexed with an all-PO complement. Note that the T_m decreases with increasing PS content.

faster when the oligonucleotide is complexed with phosphorothioate rather than with normal oligonucleotide (49). By contrast, the target mRNA was more susceptible with the natural (PO) oligomer when rabbit globin mRNA was incubated with both complementary oligomers and *Escherichia coli* RNase H; eighty-five percent of the target was cleaved in the presence of normal oligonucleotide, compared to 50% with phosphorothioate (77). Our results with both human and *E. coli* RNase H, however, demonstrate that the rabbit globin mRNA is hydrolyzed 1.3 to 1.5 times faster when complexed with the all-PS rather than with the all-PO anti-β-globin 17-mer (62a).

B. Inhibition of HIV

The results of the experiments with the S-oligos in the cytopathic assay were dramatic (Fig. 6). The S-oligos effectively and reproducibly inhibited HIV at levels in the 1–10 μM range, with little or no toxicity, whereas the natural phosphodiester and the methylphosphonate oligos were ineffective (15). This work has been described in detail (78); only a brief description is given here for completeness. We found that the inhibitory effect against HIV is not sequence-dependent (Fig. 7), although there was some base-composition dependence in the 14-mers initially tested, but this effect was lost once the oligo was long enough (Fig. 8). Thus, the S-oligos are potent anti-HIV agents, but this is not an antisense effect; it is clearly dependent on the presence of the sulfur atom in the phosphorothioate.

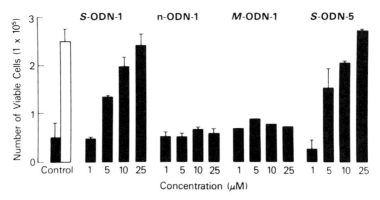

FIG 6. Comparison of inhibition of HIV in the cytopathic ATH8 cell assay using normal (n), phosphorothioate (S), and methylphosphonate (M) analogs of a 14-mer oligo sequence (ODN-1) antisense to the 5′ initiation codon region of the *rev* gene. The solid bars represent viral activity; the open bar represents toxicity control (15).

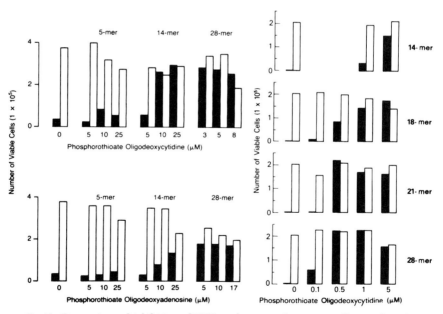

FIG 7. Comparison of inhibition of HIV in the cytopathic ATH8 cell assay by S-homo-oligomers of dA and dC of three lengths (left), and of four lengths of dC (right) (15). The solid bars represent viral activity; the open bars represent toxicity control.

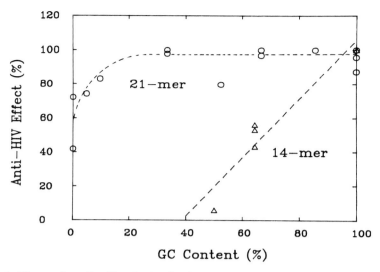

FIG 8. The number of viable ATH8 cells after more than 7 days' incubation is plotted against the S-oligo G·C content for a series of 21-mers (circles) and 14-mers (triangles). Data points were obtained at the S-oligo concentration of 1 μM for the 21-mers and 5 μM for the 14-mers.

Independent studies of reverse transcriptase inhibition revealed that the S-oligo-deoxycytidine 14-mers are potent competitive inhibitors of primer binding of oligo(dT) with a K_I 200 times that of the natural phosphodiester congeners (79). A more extensive study with several lengths and using another primer–template system, namely, oligo(dC) with poly(rI) as the template, showed a very consistent result (80). This seems to indicate that the inhibition of HIV observed with S-oligos arises from the reverse transcriptase interaction (15), although other mechanisms, such as surface interactions inhibiting CD4 binding, are also possible (80a). The results on herpes simplex virus are also consistent with a selective inhibition of polymerase activity (81).

To test for a true antisense inhibition of HIV, it is necessary to have an assay sensitive to the formation of HIV gene products. Such an assay is the chronically infected cell assay using H9 cells and an anti-*gag* antibody. The first study of this kind revealed a classic antisense inhibition (Fig. 9) that exhibited a dose-dependence with the antisense S-oligo 28-mer anti-*rev* sequence (Fig. 10), but not with several other controls tested, including the corresponding S-oligo sense sequence, and the natural oligo of the same antisense sequence (82).

Further studies of HIV in acute cytopathic assays have revealed inhibito-

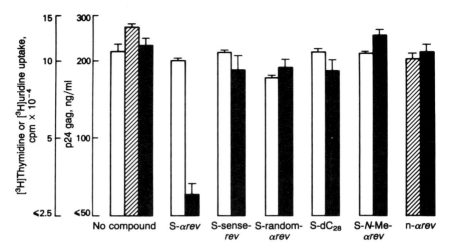

FIG 9. Sequence-specific inhibition of p24 gag protein production in an HIV chronically infected H9 cell assay with a series of oligomers (black bars) at concentrations of 10 μM. Open bars are [³H]thymidine uptake; hatched bars, [³H]uridine uptake (used as a control due to the production of unlabeled threonine from hydrolysis of the natural PO oligomer (82).

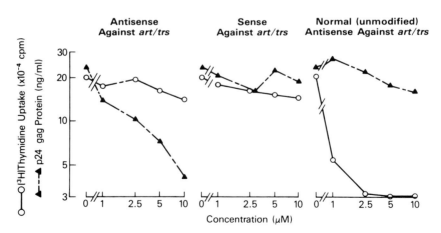

FIG 10. Antisense inhibition of expression of HIV p28 gag protein in chronically infected H9 cells using the phosphorothioate 28-mer anti-*rev* sequence (left), and the absence of inhibition with the sense S-oligo (middle) and the normal antisense 28-mer (the reduction in [³H]thymidine uptake in this case can be attributed to the production of "cold" thymidine due to hydrolysis of the natural PO oligo) (82).

ry activity for natural, phosphorothioate, methylphosphonate, and phosphoramidate analogs (Fig. 1), although the S-oligos were the most effective
inhibitors (16, 83). The modified oligonucleotides inhibit the synthesis of
viral protein (p24) as well as the replication of the virus in a sequence-specific
manner (14). The activity of the phosphoramidates, including phosphomorpholidates, phosphobutylamidates, and phosphopiperazidates, were
comparable to the phosphorothioates in most cases.

Attempts to inhibit other target sites in a chronically infected HIV assay
have been successful, although not at the level of the anti-*rev* results (83).
However, this may result from differences in the assay as well as the length of
the S-oligos used. Whether or not these compounds will have efficacy as
anti-AIDS compounds will depend on other important factors, such as cellular uptake and *in vivo* considerations. (These factors are relevant to any
kind of oligo used as a potential therapeutic compound or informational
drug.)

Selected examples of antisense inhibition of several other viruses by
oligodeoxynucleotide analogs (35) are listed in Table I.

III. Inhibition of Translation in Cell-free Systems

In model systems, the control of gene expression is usually observed by
relative inhibition of translation. This section is concerned with the inhibition of translation by antisense oligonucleotides in cell-free systems. The
process, termed *translation arrest* or *hybridization arrest* (84, 85), requires
specially designed molecules that specifically recognize target sequences of
the selected mRNA and interfere with its normal expression. The design of
an ideal antisense oligonucleotide would require that: (a) its complementary
sequence should be unique in a mammalian genome; (b) it should be long
enough to form a stable hybrid under the ionic and temperature conditions
of the translation experiments; and (c) its target sequence on mRNA should
be single-stranded. However, effective hybridization between the two species is not always followed by translation arrest, as pointed out by Liebhaber
et al. (86), who showed qualitatively that one of their cDNAs remained
hybridized to mRNA even though it did not inhibit translation.

Rabbit globin genes (both α and β) are most frequently used as models to
study the translation in either rabbit-reticulocyte lysates or wheat-germ extracts. The use of rabbit globin mRNA offers several advantages; efficient
translation of the genes can be carried out both *in vitro* (using either of the
extracts) and *in vivo* after injection into *Xenopus* oocytes. Besides, their
primary sequences are well known (87) and information on their secondary
structures is also available (88, 89). Most importantly, the relative selectivity
of inhibition can be monitored, as the globin molecule contains equal

amounts of two different messages with limited primary sequence homologies.

In the presence of antisense oligonucleotides, a selective decrease in translation of the target mRNA is observed in cell-free systems, although the results reported are different for the same oligonucleotide (38, 77, 90) (Table III). The activity is always higher in wheat-germ extract than in the rabbit-reticulocyte system; for example, a 12-mer complementary to the region immediately upstream from the AUG of the β-globin produced 80% inhibition in wheat-germ extracts compared to only 10% in rabbit-reticulocyte lysate at 5-μM concentration (38). The differences observed can be rationalized in terms of the virtual absence of RNase-H activity in the reticulocyte system, and its abundance in the wheat-germ system (75–77). Our recent translation studies with the rabbit-reticulocyte system also confirm the importance of RNase H in this antisense effect (62a). RNase H, present in all actively dividing cells, is presumed to function within the nucleus, but the enzyme is located in the cytoplasm as well (91, 92). An "unwindase"

TABLE III

COMPARISON OF TRANSLATION INHIBITION OF RABBIT GLOBIN MRNA
BY OLIGODEOXYNUCLEOTIDES IN CELL-FREE SYSTEMS

| | | | | % Inhibition[a] | | |
| | | | Concentration | | Wheat | |
Size	Type	Target	(μM)	Reticulocytes	germ	Reference
9-mer	PO	5′ End, β-globin	100	87 (88)	91 (87)	38
8-mer	PO	Initiation codon, β-globin	100	18–30 (25–45)	43–49 (15–30)	
12-mer	PO	Initiation codon, β-globin	25	23 (20)	80 (13)	
		Initiation codon, α-globin	100	97 (96)	100 (100)	
8-mer	PO	Coding region, β-globin	100	20 (8)	66 (70)	
		Coding region, α-globin	100	8 (4)	68 (39)	
15-mer	α-PO	5′ End, β-globin	2	50	70	90
	β-PO	5′ End, β-globin	4	50	100	
	PO	Initiation codon, α-globin	1	0	100	77
	PS	Initiation codon, α-globin	5	~40	100	
	S-dC28	Initiation codon, α-globin	0.2	0	100	

[a]Values in parentheses indicate the percentage of nonspecific inhibition.

activity present in the reticulocyte lysate may also affect the translation by dissociating RNA·DNA duplexes (86, 93).

The specific inhibition by antisense oligonucleotides is influenced by many factors, such as the location of the binding site on the target RNA, the chain length of the oligo, the presence or absence of secondary structure at the binding site, the type of oligonucleotides, and factors promoting hybridization, such as salt content, temperature, and G·C content, and the presence of covalently bound intercalating groups. The results on inhibition of translation from the binding of antisense compounds to target RNA in cell-free systems are confusing. As shown in Table IV, some investigators found activity with oligodeoxynucleotides complementary to the initiation region of mRNA (4, 28, 38, 39, 94, 95), while others concluded that only those binding near the 5′ end are effective (12, 38, 39, 90, 94, 96–98). Those binding to the coding region are usually less effective, but they do work in some cases (4, 38, 39, 76, 77, 94, 99). Hybridization at the 3′ end alone produces no inhibition (100, 101). Boizau and Toulme, using antisense oligonucleotides complementary to either terminal region, observed no specific inhibition in the translation of their target mRNA in reticulocytes (102).

However, when rabbit reticulocytes are used in a cell-free system, there is general agreement that the oligomers complementary to the 5′ end or the initiation-codon regions inhibit translation more effectively than the oligomers binding to the coding region. The susceptible region around the initiator extends for at least eight nucleotides upstream. Oligomers binding between these sites in the 5′ untranslated region or downstream from the initiator coding region show very little activity.

Early work comparing translation arrest in cell-free systems by different oligonucleotides clearly demonstrated the dependence on both chain-length and concentration. The best antisense activity was observed with a chain-length of 14 to 20 bases (77, 94, 95, 98, 99, 103). Increasing the size of the oligomer enhances stability of the duplex and thus its inhibitory effect (17, 104). In cell-free systems in which RNase-H activity is absent, activity increases with increasing chain-length. On the other hand, very long oligonucleotides may decrease specificity by interacting with multiple mRNAs through partial base-pairing involving 5 to 10 contiguous bases within their sequence. This problem can be bypassed by using a mixture of short oligonucleotides complementary to immediately adjacent sites on the target RNA. In fact, several investigators claimed such a synergistic effect with mixtures of oligonucleotides (96, 98, 105, 106). However, others (12) failed to see any such synergistic effect during translation of tobacco mosaic virus mRNA in a rabbit-reticulocyte system.

Chain-length and concentration of oligonucleotides are very much interlinked; lower concentrations (usually in the range of 1–10 μM) are re-

TABLE IV

Effects on Eukaryotic Gene Expression by Antisense Oligodeoxynucleotides Targeted to Different Regions of the Target mRNA

Cell-free system[a]	Target gene	Type	Size (mer)	Concentration (μM)	% Inhibition	Reference
5' End						
WGA (RRL)	Rabbit β-globin mRNA	PO	9	100	97 (87)	38
RRL	Rabbit β-globin mRNA	PMe	9	100	51	39
RRL	Rabbit β-globin mRNA	PO	25	5.2	75	96
			49	2.6	90	
RRL	Rabbit β-globin mRNA	α-PO	15	2	50	90
WGA	Rabbit β-globin mRNA	α-PO	15	0.2	50	
WGA	Rabbit β-globin mRNA	β-PO	15	0.01	50	
RRL	α-tubulin	PO	21	6	100	97
RRL	Tobacco mosaic virus mRNA	PO	51	—	75	12
RRL	Encephalomyocarditis virus mRNA	PO	13	25	55–60	94
Kreb-2	Potato virus X RNA	PO	14	—	68	103
Initiation region						
WGA	Rabbit β-globin mRNA	PO	17	6	95	95
			12	20	98	
			8	20	65	
RRL (WGA)	Rabbit β-globin mRNA	PO	8	100	18–30 (43–49)	38
			12	100	29 (78)	
	Rabbit α-globin mRNA	PO	12	100	96 (100)	

System	mRNA	Modification				
RRL	Rabbit β-globin mRNA	PMe	8	200	8–70	39
		PMe	12	100	50	
	Rabbit α-globin mRNA	PMe	8	100	35	
RRL	Encephalomyocarditis virus	PO	13	25	30–60	94
RRL	BALB-ras p21 mRNA	PO	11	50	0	28
		PS	11	50	98	
		PMe	11	50	44	
RRL	N, NS vesicular stomatitis virus mRNA	PMe	9	100–150	100	4
Coding region						
WGA	Lysozyme mRNA	PO	20	Ratio oligo:mRNA = 1:50	100	99
WGA	Rabbit β-globin mRNA	PS	17	1	100	77
		PO	17	1	100	
RRL	Rabbit β-globin mRNA	PMe	8	100	24–36	39
	Rabbit α-globin mRNA	PMe	8	100	38	
WGA (RRL)	Rabbit β-globin mRNA	PO	8	100	66 (20)	38
	Rabbit α-globin mRNA	PO	8	100	68 (8)	
RRL	L-mRNA of vesicular stomatitis virus	PMe	9	150	60–95	4
RRL	Rabbit β-globin mRNA	PO	20	5.2	20–66	96
3′ Noncoding region						
RRL	Rabbit β-globin mRNA	PO	12	100	0	38
RRL	Encephalomyocarditis virus mRNA	PO	13	25	0	94
RRL	α-Tubulin	PO	21	12	0	97

[a]WGA, Wheat-germ agglutinin; RRL, rabbit-reticulocyte lysate.

quired for oligonucleotides of 17 to 20 bases, compared to oligonucleotides of 10 bases or less. For smaller oligonucleotides, much higher concentrations are needed for activity, and they begin to show nonspecific inhibition due to formation of duplexes at sites of reduced complementarity (38, 39, 77). When the ratio of oligomer to target RNA is considered, the results from different groups seem contradictory. Haeuptle et al. (99) found that ratios of 10:1 for a 20-mer and 50:1 for a 10- to 15-mer are necessary for activity. According to them, a higher ratio is necessary for hybridization arrest, rather than simply hybridization with all target RNA. On the other hand, the ratio to obtain substantial inhibition could be as low as 1.5:1, and there was no further improvement in the inhibition even at higher ratios (12). It was suggested that the hybridization of all target RNA molecules is sufficient for translation arrest.

Another factor that might affect hybridization is the secondary structure of the target RNA (107). Inhibition of translation by the oligonucleoside methylphosphonates was affected by secondary structure, as shown by pre-annealing experiments (39). Preannealing, which opens up the secondary structure and allows the oligonucleotides to bind to the target RNA, improved the activity of an octamer, but was not necessary for a dodecamer, even though they share a common binding site on the target RNA. In another study, the same result was obtained with acridine-labeled unmodified oligomer, in which preannealing was necessary for the activity of a heptamer, but not if the chain-length was increased to 11 (108). These results are consistent with the expected binding interactions of longer versus shorter oligonucleotides to complementary sequences of the target RNA.

Higher G·C content in the antisense molecule (targeted on the coding region) shows higher activity in a cell-free system than do the molecules with low G·C content (cap region), as demonstrated with 17-mers targeted to different regions of rabbit β-globin mRNA (108). In contrast, no correlation was found between the G·C content and translation in another study, but the trend seemed to indicate that regions with a high G·C content are the least sensitive for antisense effect (109). However, a computer calculation of the stability of local hairpins in the target region showed that they decrease with low G·C content.

There are only a few examples of comparing inhibition by modified oligonucleotides in cell-free systems. Modifications of both terminal hydroxyl groups with phenyl isothiocyanate improve antiviral activity, but decreases inhibition of translation of Rous sarcoma virus in what-germ extract (3, 110). Modifications were also made by introducing either a photoreactive group (111, 112) or an intercalating group at the 5′ end of the oligonucleotides (108, 113–115). Such modifications improved the inhibition in cell-free systems, particularly the translation of trypanosome mRNA (114). Cazenave et al.

(*108*), on the other hand, failed to see any significant differences in translation between acridine-labeled and unmodified oligonucleotide.

A class of compound having an unusual glycosyl configuration (the α-oligonucleotides; see Section VI,A) has been compared with the natural β-anomeric oligos for their capacity to inhibit translation of several natural mRNAs in reticulocyte lysates and in wheat-germ cell-free extracts (*77, 116*). In most experiments, 9- to 20-mer α-oligonucleotides were chosen for hybridization with target RNA, but none showed any significant effect in translation, even in the presence of exogenously added RNase H. Similarly, α-oligonucleotides failed to produce any inhibition of vesicular stomatitis virus (VSV) N protein mRNA (*116*), β-globin mRNA (*77*), or *Trypanosoma brucei* mRNAs (P. Verspieren, unpublished) in reticulocyte lysates under experimental conditions in which β-anomeric oligonucleotides are active as inhibitors. The results could be explained by the lack of recognition of the hybrids by RNase H, or inefficient hybridization of this oligonucleotide with its target RNA. However, the only positive results in both cell-free systems were observed when the α-oligonucleotides were targeted toward the 5' untranslated region of the β-globin mRNA immediately downstream from the cap (*90*).

Modification of the ribose-phosphate backbone with a methyl group (methylphosphonate) or with a sulfur atom (phosphorothioate) sometimes generates differences in translation inhibition. This is possibly due to the differences in cleavages of the target mRNA by RNase H, following hybridization with the complementary oligonucleotides. Agrawal *et al.* (*117*), clearly demonstrated that the cleavage of target mRNA by an extract containing RNase H was seen only upon the addition of normal oligonucleotide or the phosphorothioate analog, but was not seen with oligonucleotides containing either methylphosphonates or phosphoramidates. They also demonstrated that the phosphodiester-linked oligonucleotides were more efficient than the phosphorothioate-linked oligonucleotides in producing RNase-H-mediated cleavage of the target mRNA. This results supports the earlier finding (*77*) with respect to susceptibility of the target mRNA by RNase H in the presence of normal and phosphorothiate (17-mer) anti-β-globin mRNA oligonucleotide.

The methylphosphonate oligonucleotides are generally less effective inhibitors of translation in wheat-germ extracts than the phosphodiester oligonucleotides (*39*). The difference does not appear to be due to the inability of the methylphosphonate oligonucleotides to bind adequately with the target RNA at 25°C (temperature for translation in the wheat-germ system). Rather, it can be explained by the lack of activation of RNase H by methylphosphonates (*105, 116*). In the reticulocyte lysate, on the other hand, the results for the two series of compounds are more or less similar,

except that the normal oligonucleotide complementary to the 5' end has slightly more activity (39).

There are only a few examples of comparison of the antisense activity between phosphorothioates and normal oligonucleotides in cell-free systems. In the wheat-germ system, a 17-mer sequence targeted to the coding region of β-globin mRNA is specifically inhibitory when either the normal oligonucleotide or its phosphorothioate analog is used (77). At higher concentration, however, phosphorothioate shows nonspecific inhibition of α-globin. With smaller-size (11-mer) oligonucleotide targeted to the sequence immediately upstream from the AUG codon of β-globin mRNA, all-PS derivatives show specific inhibition of β-globin at low concentration and nonspecific inhibition of α-globin synthesis at higher concentration. But the phosphorothioate derivative is a less efficient inhibitor than the normal oligonucleotide. When the 15-mer oligonucleotide was targeted against the initiation region of α-globin, the normal oligonucleotide showed a much higher activity than does phosphorothioate oligonucleotide in both cell-free systems, but the sensitivity of the assay decreased to 1/100 in rabbit-reticulocyte lysates.

In another study with a series of oligonucleotides having various internucleoside linkages, Chang *et al.* (28) found the superiority of phosphorothioates over other oligonucleotides when compared for their antisense activity in rabbit-reticulosyte lysate. The compounds (11-mer) had all phosphodiester linkages (all-PO), all phosphorothioate (all-PS), all methylphosphonate (all-PMe), or an alternating combination of PO–PMe, and had variable complementarity (80–100%) to the start codon and downstream eight bases of the BALB–ras p21 protein. Although all were active at higher concentration (100–200 μM), only the all-PS showed activity at low concentration (12.5–25 μM). All showed nonspecific effects at higher concentrations, possibly because of the formation of duplexes at sites of reduced complementarity, as discussed earlier.

The phosphorothioates are equally active or sometimes better translation inhibitors than the natural oligonucleotides, even though the former are less active in RNase-H-mediated cleavage of mRNA (77). Further, the phosphorothioate binds less strongly with the target molecule. Therefore, there might be factors other than nuclease resistance, hybrid stability, and RNase-H susceptibility playing roles in the efficacy of oligonucleotides as inhibitors of protein synthesis. In the wheat-germ system, inhibition of translation is observed, albeit to different extents, with oligonucleotides complementary to all three different regions (the 5' end, initiation codon, and coding region) of the target RNA. This could be explained by the endogenous RNase-H activity, which cleaves the RNA part of the RNA·oligonucleotide duplex. For similar reasons, methylphosphonates and α-oligonucleotides are not good inhibitors of translation in this cell-free system, as the compounds do not activate the enzyme (105, 116).

If RNase H is considered solely responsible for such inhibition, then one would not expect to see any translational arrest in cell lines in which this enzyme is absent. The translation arrest in rabbit-reticulocyte lysate by the oligonucleotides complementary to the "cap" or AUG initiation codon region could be explained by the scanning model of Kozak (118–122). According to this model, the small ribosomal subunit attaches itself to the 5′ end of the mRNA along with the initiation factors and initiator tRNA. The whole complex then proceeds to the initiation codon and forms a larger complex with the joining of the larger subunit of the ribosome. Anything that is bound at the cap region or the initiation codon could prevent the translational machinery from forming the appropriate complex required for protein synthesis, whereas anything that binds at other than these regions may fall apart due to the destabilizing activity associated with ribosomes, or could be read-through (86, 93, 123, 124). This possibility was further supported by the activity of α-oligonucleotides in cell-free systems, when the oligonucleotide was complementary to the cap region (90).

Another possible mechanism for inhibition of translation is that binding of an oligonucleotide could cause a conformational change in the target RNA and thus prevent binding of the translational machinery to the mRNA. This possibility is supported by the fact that the efficiency of ribosome binding increases with the decrease of secondary structure of the 5′ end and the initiation codon region (125–127).

Several other RNAs have also been used as models for determining antisense activity in cell-free systems. These include mRNA from mouse globin (74), chicken lysozyme (99), dihydrofolate reductase (98, 105), trypanosomal proteins (128, 129), E. coli protein (130), tubulin (97), and RNAs from encephalomyocarditis virus (94), tobacco mosaic virus (12), and potato virus (103).

IV. Cellular Uptake

It is essential for activity that oligonucleotides be present in either the cytoplasm or the nucleus. Their activity, in other words, depends on how well they can penetrate the cell membrane and reach the designated target areas. As a general rule, plasma membranes of living cells restrict the transportation of large and negatively charged molecules. It might therefore be expected that this membrane would also act as a barrier for polyanionic molecules such as oligonucleotides. In fact, one of the problems that must be overcome before oligonucleotides can be used as therapeutic agents is the difficulty of attaining a high intracellular concentration. We will see from this discussion that a very small percentage of the added oligonucleotide actually penetrates the cell membrane. It is therefore necessary, in order to understand their mechanism(s) of uptake and distribution, to design more efficient antisense-modified oligonucleotides.

To follow cellular uptake, oligonucleotides are generally labeled with either a radioactive or a fluorescent probe. In either case, there are problems and restrictions. Labeling with a fluorescent probe has been discussed in more detail and is usually carried out either at the 3' or 5' end via a linker (112, 113, 141). The yields of such labeled oligonucleotides are very poor, and modification of the method is required to improve yields. One simple approach is to attach the fluorescent group as an already linked synthon, such as a phosphoramidite, to the available 5' end of the oligonucleotides directly in the automatic DNA synthesizer. Besides this, use of fluorescent labeled oligonucleotide raises several unsolved questions, such as (a) the integrity of the labeled molecule following internalization, (b) whether or not the added probe group influences its transportation and distribution following internalization, and (c) whether or not the length of the linker has any effect on cellular uptake. Answers to these questions are currently unavailable.

Labeling with a radioactive atom (particularly ^{32}P) is usually carried out enzymatically at the 5' end of normal oligonucleotides, using T4 polynucleotide kinase. Beside their susceptibilities to nuclease attack, such radiolabeled compounds are also vulnerable to phosphatases (13). Such instability creates problems in estimating the amount of cellular uptake. An alternative approach is by using phosphorothioate oligonucleotide labeled internally with ^{35}S (132). Terminally labeled oligonucleotides disappear more rapidly than do those labeled internally (13), which suggests, as expected, that phosphatase activity is more rapid than endonuclease activity. The most common problem associated with a radiolabeled probe is to differentiate the radioactivity inside the cell from that bound to the outer membrane. However, anything that binds externally should also be considered as cellular uptake, because there is evidence that a membrane-bound analog is gradually internalized following reorientation of the membrane (133, 157, 158).

Cellular uptake of oligonucleotides depends primarily on the type of cells and the experimental conditions used for uptake studies. In most cases, oligonucleotides are taken up very rapidly, with a plateau resulting within 15–120 min, depending on experimental conditions, following the addition of oligonucleotides. Table V lists studies of cellular uptake by different inves-

TABLE V
DISTRIBUTION OF LABELED OLIGONUCLEOTIDES IN CELL FRACTIONS FOLLOWING UPTAKE

System	Oligonucleotide	Probe	Distribution	Reference
HeLa/CEF cells	PO	^{32}P	Nucleus	13
HeLa cella	PO	^{3}H	Nucleus	135
L929 mouse fibroblasts	PO	^{32}P	Cyto/nucleus	136
T-lymphocytes	PO	^{32}P	Intracellular	20
Molt-3 cells	PO	^{32}P	Nucleus	138
CV-1 epithelial cells	PO/PS/PMe	Fluorescent	Nucleus	139
HL-60 cells	PO	Acridine	Cytoplasm	141
Trypanosomes	PO	Acridine	Cytoplasm	114
HL-60 cells	PS	Acridine	Cytoplasm	71
H9/V79 cells	PS	Fluorescent	Nucleus	140
MCF-7 cells	PS	Acridine^{35}S	Cytoplasm	147

tigators using different probes. The first study (13) was carried out in HeLa and CEF cells using a ^{32}P-labeled icosanucleotide complementary to HIV mRNA. Within 15 min, 7–8% of the total radioactivity was found associated with the cell, although it could not be determined that the radioactivity was inside the cell, rather than associated with the membrane. In a different experiment, it was shown that most of the cellular radioactivity was inside, particularly around the nucleus (134). In another study (135) with ^{3}H-labeled oligonucleotide, it was found that the uptake by HeLa cells was complete within 15 min and that most of the radioactivity was localized in the nucleus. Use of normal phosphodiesters in these studies, however, raised the possibility of cellular radioactivity originating from free nucleosides. Yakubov et al. (136) showed degradation of the ^{32}P-labeled oligonucleotide in cells following 2–4 hr of incubation, but others (13, 20) claimed that a significant fraction of the intracellular oligonucleotides is intact even after 3–4 hr.

Transport of oligonucleotides to the nucleus was also confirmed by the inhibition of 70-kDa heat-shock protein transcription (137) and replication of both herpes simplex virus (7) and HIV (13, 138) by antisense oligonucleotides targeted to splice sites of viral precursor RNA, because these activities take place only in the nucleus. Several lines of evidence suggest that the nuclear accumulation of oligonucleotide is not an artifact or a result of oligonucleotide degradation and reincorporation. This was demonstrated (139) by coinjecting fluorescein-labeled oligonucleotide (28-mer) with immunoglobin (which cannot traverse the nuclear membrane) into CV-1 epithelial cells. Nuclear accumulation of fluorescence-labeled oligonucleotides was further supported by the findings of others (140).

In contrast, the uptake of 5'-acridine-labeled oligodeoxythymidylates by HL-60 cells is very slow (plateauing after 50 hr), and most of the fluorescence

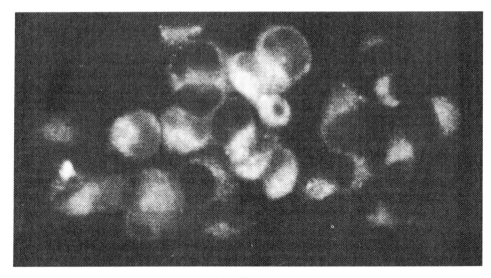

FIG 11. Fluorescence micrograph of cells containing fluorescently linked oligodeoxy-nucleotides; HL-60 cells incubated with Acr-dT$_7$ for 16 hr (*141*).

is in the cytoplasm, rather in the nucleus (*144*) (Fig. 11). A similar study with trypanosomes (*114*) demonstrated that fluorescence can be detected within 2 hr following addition of acridine-linked oligodeoxynucleotide (Acr-dT$_6$) and is spread uniformly throughout the cytoplasm. All these results tend to suggest that the labeling probe may influence the intracellular distribution of the labeled oligonucleotides. However, not enough experiments have been done to fully characterize this effect.

Cellular uptake of oligos varies with size, and is inversely proportional to the length of oligonucleotide. This was clearly demonstrated in HL-60 cells, using oligothymidylate in the range of three to 20 bases (*141*). Another factor that influences the uptake is the nature of the internucleoside linkage. A comparative study of the uptake of 5′-acridine-linked oligodeoxythymidy-lates by HL-60 cells clearly showed that the phosphorothioate oligodeoxy-nucleotide is taken up much more slowly than the corresponding normal oligodeoxynucleotide (*71*). But another study with a 28-mer anti-*rev* sequence labeled with either ^{35}S or a fluorescent probe showed that there is little difference between the rates of uptake of normal and phosphorothioate oligonucleotides by lymphocytes (*140*). The discrepancy may arise from the size (28-mer versus 7-mer), the cell type (HL-60 versus lymphocytes), or the different probes (acridine versus fluorescein) used.

For methylphosphonates, on the other hand, size (between two and nine bases) has very little effect on their uptake (104, 142). An interesting observation regarding the uptake of methylphosphonate by E. coli cells is that, in wild-type cells, uptake is limited to only four bases, but for the mutant variety (ML 308-225), there is no such restriction (130). A methylphosphonate oligomer (18-mer) can be taken up very well by CV-1 epithelial cells and by primary human fibroblasts, and become localized mostly in the nucleus (139). Uptake of methylphosphonate (8-mer) was observed earlier by K. Jayaraman et al. (unpublished) in Syrian hamster cells. Another non-ionic compound, trinucleotide ethyl phosphate triester, is internalized very rapidly in hamster fibroblasts, but following uptake it is de-ethylated and rapidly metabolized (143).

Cellular uptake of oligonucleotides is an energy-dependent process and can be reduced or blocked by treating the cells with dinitrophenol (to inhibit ATP synthesis) (135) or by lowering the temperature (71, 136, 139). The energy-dependence of this process was demonstrated further by the absence of uptake of $5'$-Acr-dT$_{12}$ in dead cells (71). This active transport across the membrane takes place in a temperature-dependent, saturable, and structurally specific manner (141). Using different known inhibitors of endocytosis, several groups (136, 139) have agreed that the uptake is a receptor-mediated endocytotic process. But they differ in determining the actual plasma membrane protein (or receptor) responsible for such uptake.

Loke et al. (141) described the receptor as an 80-kDa protein, while Bennett et al. described a 30-kDa protein responsible for the cellular uptake of large DNA (144). Yakubov et al. (136), on the other hand, found two labeled protein bands on electrophoresis following incubation of their cells with ^{32}P-labeled oligonucleotide. One of them corresponds to that observed by Loke et al. (141). Recently, another protein (34 kDa) from human T cells was purified using oligo(dT)-cellulose and found to be responsible for the inhibition of the binding of [^{32}P]oligonucleotides to T-cells in vivo (145). The possibility that the 30-kDa protein is a receptor was ruled out when oligonucleotides failed to inhibit competitively the binding of high-molecular-weight DNA to this protein (144). Whatever the size of the protein may be, it is almost certain that the uptake takes place via one of these receptors. Approximately 95% of the bound material (both normal and phosphorothioate) could be removed from the cells by glycine treatment (146), which usually removes externally bound material. This suggests that both normal and phosphorothioate oligonucleotides act via a receptor(s). Although phosphorothioates are taken up much more slowly than are normal phosphodiesters (71), binding-displacement experiments revealed that the affinity of phosphorothioate oligonucleotides for the receptor is much higher than that of the normal phosphodiesters.

In other work, (147, 148) it was observed that at least 20% of the total cell-associated radioactivity (^{35}S) was associated with the plasma membrane, and a significant portion of it remained bound even after thorough washing. Only trypsin could remove the tightly bound radioactivity from the membrane, which again suggests the presence of a binding protein on the surface. It also indicates that binding with the phosphorothioate is very tight. Hence, there is need for caution in interpreting the results of cellular uptake, as the oligonucleotides are sometimes associated tightly with the membrane.

The membrane-receptor hypothesis is supported by the finding that phosphorothioate oligonucleotides, but not the methylphosphonates, inhibit the uptake of fluorescence-labeled oligonucleotides (Fig. 12). This suggests that the charge on the phosphorus moiety is important for the uptake mechanism; it has been suggested that, without it, the molecule may be transported by passive diffusion (*149*).

Other approaches have been adopted to improve the transcellular delivery of antisense oligonucleotides. These include inclusion of oligonucleotides into liposomes or attaching them covalently to specific or nonspecific

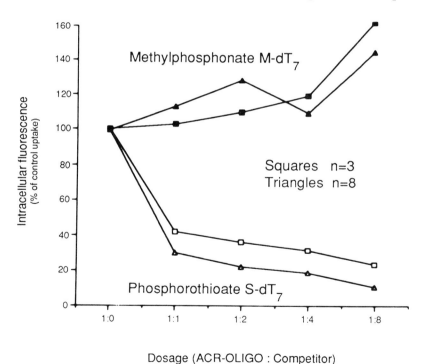

Dosage (ACR-OLIGO : Competitor)

FIG 12. Inhibition of uptake of Acr-dT$_3$ (squares) and Acr-dT$_8$ (triangles) by phosphorothioate dT$_7$ (open symbols), but not methylphosphonate dT$_7$ (solid symbols).

carriers. Liposomes are mono- or multi-layered phospholipid vesicles that can entrap water- or lipid-soluble materials during their formation. The idea of using liposomes as a delivery device for antisense oligonucleotides emerges from earlier studies (150) in which it was found that 2',5'-oligoadenylates incorporated into liposomes were much more active than were the free molecules. However, hardly any attempt has been made to improve the cellular uptake of normal oligonucleotides using liposomes.

Oligonucleotides linked to acridine or benzophenanthridine can be incorporated into neutral liposomes with 50% or greater efficiency (151). Phosphorothioate oligonucleotides were delivered into hematopoietic cells by liposome fusion (22). This method was very efficient and showed an uptake 7.5 to 8 times that of the free material. The use of liposomes is restricted by their short half-life (rapid clearance by the reticuloendothelial system) and their nonspecific distribution. Site-directed targeting, however, can be achieved by attaching ligands to liposomes; an example of this possibility is the recent use of antibody-coated liposomes (pH-sensitive) to deliver DNA to lymphoma cells (152).

The covalent attachment of a nonspecific carrier, such as poly(L-lysine), to antisense oligonucleotides (either the 3' or 5' end) has resulted in superior antisense activity (106, 153–156), although little is known about the mechanism of their improved activity. It is possible that attachment of such polycationic material may improve cellular uptake by better hybridization with the cell, which would explain the improved activity of homo-oligoribonucleotides in tumor cells by poly(L-lysine) (157, 158). This carrier, however, is not absolutely free of drawbacks. Poly(L-lysine) is toxic to most cells (154), and is very "sticky" by nature, which creates problems in estimation of actual concentration (158); most strikingly, this approach does not work in all cells (154).

Another nonspecific carrier reported to improve cellular uptake is cholesterol. There is an increased inhibition of HIV in MOLT cells by cholesterol-conjugated oligonucleotides (80a, 159), which was effective for both normal and phosphorothioate oligonucleotides and independent of the mode of attachment. Another study (160) also demonstrated the superior activity of an alkylating oligonucleotide when conjugated with cholesterol at the 3' end of the oligonucleotide.

For specific carrier-mediated uptake, a ligand is attached to the oligonucleotides in such a way that the receptor (specific for the ligand) on the cell surface can recognize the bound ligand and help the conjugate to penetrate as in receptor-mediated endocytosis. Since ligand–receptor interaction is the basis of such internalization, the ligand of a known receptor will be the choice in this case. Examples of possible ligands are hydrophobic peptides, signal peptide sequences, or peptides that are specifically internalized in a particular group of cells. It is worth mentioning here the finding (*161*) that a double-stranded DNA, when linked to a mitochondrial protein, can be incorporated into mitochondria. The essence of this finding suggests the possibility of using lectin (a sugar-binding protein) for the delivery of oligonucleotides, since most of the cells have glycoproteins on their surface. However, one must be careful about the toxicity sometimes associated with lectins such as ricin or abrin, which are toxins.

V. Oncogene Inhibition

Cancer develops in a stepwise manner (*162*), so that developing a single oligodeoxynucleotide as an anti-cancer therapeutic will be very difficult. A characteristic feature of cancer cells is conversion from paracrine to autocrine stimulation. Thus, oncogenes that may be considered a direct cause of oncogenic growth have genetic precursors, proto-oncogenes, that control normal cellular growth. Since there may be only one or a few differences in the base-sequence due to mutations between them, this presents a challenge to the use of the antisense strategy to differentiate between a proto-oncogene and its oncogene product. It should be pointed out that the ability of a medium-length oligonucleotide to distinguish between a complete match and a single mismatch is the key to the antisense selectivity, and is sufficient to expect this strategy to work, subject to rigorous controls.

It is important to demonstrate that the antisense approach with oligodeoxynucleotides indeed works against oncogenes and proto-oncogenes in mammalian cells *in vitro*. A recent comparative study using natural and phosphorothioate analogs of 15-mer sequences against the *bcl*-2 proto-oncogene is a good example (*33*). This gene is associated with 70% of lymphomas and a large number of leukemias, and represents a suitable target for the antisense strategy. While the efficacy of the S-oligo against a translation-initiation-codon region is slower in developing (4 days) compared to the natural congener (1 day) (Fig. 13), it is much more potent on a relative concentration basis (Fig. 14). As well as cell growth, the selective antisense inhibition of the expression of the *bcl*-2 protein was shown, using an antibody assay (*33*). It should be emphasized that the corresponding sense-sequence was used as a control in all these studies. Thus, the evidence indicates that the strategy of using an oligodeoxynucleotide analog as an antisense compound targeted on a particular proto-oncogene does work. (For further examples of such applications, see Table I.)

A problem is that the normal function of a precursor proto-oncogene can be quite similar to the abnormal function of the transformed oncogene, and a particular target sequence for an oligodeoxynucleotide could be very similar in both cases. Although it should be noted that hybridization *in vivo* does not

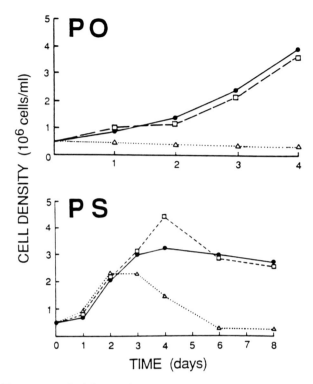

FIG 13. Time course of inhibition of 697 leukemia cell growth by *bcl*-2 antisense 20-mer oligodeoxynucleotides. Triangles represent antisense oligos; squares, sense oligos; circles, controls. (Top) Natural (PO) oligomer; (bottom) phosphorothioate (PS) oligomer (33).

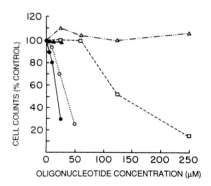

FIG 14. Concentration dependence of inhibition of 697 leukemia cell growth by *bcl*-2 antisense 20-mer oligos. Circles represent antisense PS (two experiments); squares, antisense PO; triangles, sense oligos (solid, PS; open, PO) (33).

occur under stringent conditions, and a few mismatches can have a significant effect, on the other hand, oncogenes are often multiplied or overex-
pressed genes, and therefore any inhibition is likely to affect the normal
proto-oncogene at a lower dose (e.g., for c-*myc*). The selectivity of the antisense oligo strategy is shown by the inhibition by a 15-mer antisense sequence of the N-*myc* gene present as one copy per cell, while expression of
the multiplied c-*myc* gene is unaffected (*163*). This also indicates that the
general strategy can work.

These results and concepts indicate that a suitable target for translation
arrest by oligodeoxynucleotide analogs should be an oncogene that is highly
specific, perhaps due to a chromosomal translocation, such as the *abl* oncogene in the Philadelphia chromosome that results from a chromosomal
translocation (*164*). Other suitable targets relevant to cancer therapy might
be tumor suppressor genes or the development of multi-drug resistance
(mdr). A major cause of mdr is the multi-drug resistance gene (*mdr-1*) that
causes the overexpression of a surface glycoprotein, gp170 (*165*). There is a
great need to circumvent the effects of mdr, and since this is not possible
with the usual anti-cancer drugs, an antisense approach seems appropriate.

Seven oligos were tested against *mdr*-1 in an mdr cell line (*148*); while the

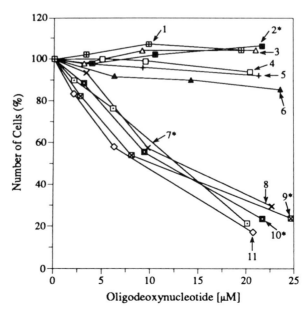

FIG 15. Effects of oligodeoxynucleotides on the growth of MCF-7 ADR cells. The upper
curves (1–6) are the S-oligos; the bottom curves (7–11) are the natural PO congeners (*148*).

natural phosphodiester oligos were toxic to the cells, the S-oligos were not (Fig. 15). Also, only one sequence caused a reduction in cell growth in the presence of Adriamycin, although the antibody assay used for gp170 showed no significant decrease. These experiments represent the first preliminary attempt to inhibit mdr by an antisense approach. In proceeding with this project, the ability to carry out a computer folding of the mdr-1 mRNA should help to direct further efforts (148). Several results indicate the importance of the effect of mRNA folding on target accessibility (107, 166, 167).

Since oligo analogs are very expensive, there is a need for increased potency, which can be achieved by the linking of chemically reactive groups (see Section VI,C). The choice of a suitable cancer target—for example, one that allows bone marrow purging (167a) or topical application, such as melanoma—is also an important feature, although subdural and intracellular absorption may be a problem. However, given the likelihood that these problems can be overcome, oligodeoxynucleotide analogs can be expected to play an important role as combined selective chemotherapeutic agents.

VI. Other Oligodeoxynucleotide Analogs

Many oligodeoxynucleotide backbone modifications can be imagined, as illustrated in Table VI, which lists the possibilities if only S and/or C (methyl, methylene) are substituted for the phosphate oxygens in the backbone

TABLE VI

POSSIBLE SUBSTITUTIONS BY SULFUR AND CARBON OF THE FOUR OXYGENS IN THE PHOSPHODIESTER GROUP OF DNA

Name	Bridging atoms		Nonbridging atoms	
Phosphate	O	O	O^-	O
Phosphorothioate	O	O	S^-	O
Phosphorodithioate	O	S	S^-	O
3'-Alkylthioate	S	O	O	O
5'-Alkylthioate	O	O	O	S
3',5'-Alkyldithioate	S	O	O	S
Methylphosphonate	O	O	CH_3	O
3'-Methylenephosphonate	CH_2	O	O^-	O
5'-Methylenephosphonate	O	O	O^-	CH_2
3',5'-Dimethylene	CH_2	O	O	CH_2
Methylphosphonothioate	O	S	CH_3	O
3'-Methylenethio	CH_2	O	S^-	O
5'-Methylenethio	O	O	S^-	CH_2
3',5'-Dimethylenethio	CH_2	O	S^-	CH_2
3',5'-Dimethylenedithio	CH_2	S	S^-	CH_2

(*168*). But few chimeric analogs have been prepared in sufficient quantity for antisense testing. Of course, there is the possibility of combining different backbone-modified analogs, to produce a specific overall charge, for example, by combining charged and neutral analogs (Fig. 16). Thus, it is possible to make a long oligo with a small net charge. The effect of such combinations on the criteria of hybridization and cell uptake is a matter of some interest, and we are investigating it (*62a*).

Note that in this section we do not discuss base-modified analogs, since the basis of the antisense method is the intactness of the Watson-Crick base-pairing, and one must produce an analog that can hybridize effectively with its complementary target sequence. However, some base modifications might be tolerated, particularly if this allows the attachment of a reactive group (*169*). In addition, it is possible that other chemical structures that base-pair selectively with A, T, G, and U will be developed.

A. Sugar-modified Analogs

Three examples of sugar modifications are shown in Fig. 17. These are used because they confer nuclease-resistance on the oligo analog. Noteworthy is the analog that contains the α-glycosyl configuration.

It was suggested (*170*), on the basis of stereomodels, that an α-oligonucleotide would form a double helix with parallel polarity with its complementary β-strand. Subsequently, it was shown that, of four isomeric dithymidine monophosphates (TpT, αTpT, TpαT, and αTpαT), only the α-anomer exhibited marked stability toward phosphodiesterases, both from snake venom and calf spleen (*171*). These results have provided an impetus

Fɪɢ 16. Possible copolymer structures of oligodeoxynucleotides with chemical modification of the backbone. (A) Alternately modified phosphate groups (X and Y). (B) Block modifications; the blocks can be larger than the XXYYXX copolymer shown.

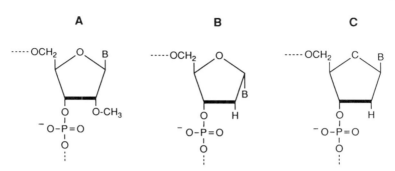

FIG 17. Structures of three modified sugar analogs. (A) 2′-O-methyl substitution; (B) α-configuration of the base at the glycosyl bond; (C) carbocyclic analog of deoxyribose.

to synthesize α-oligonucleotides and to check their activity. The first α-oligonucleotides synthesized (hexamers) used αdC and αT (*172*); later, all four α-anomeric deoxynucleotides (*173*) were used with the classical triester method.

α-Oligonucleotides can form duplexes with β-RNA and DNA by forming Watson–Crick base-pairs. Due to the opposite configuration of the base, they are expected to result in parallel, rather than the usual anti-parallel, strand orientation (*173–176*). However, in some cases, anti-parallel orientations have also been observed (*177*). The resulting hybrids are more stable than the hybrids formed between the two β-strands (*178, 179*). However, detailed thermodynamic studies of complexes between α·β and β·β analogs suggest that the stability of the duplexes depends on the nature of the bases (*179*). When the α-strand consists of α-purines, the stability of the α·β duplex is lower than that of the β·β duplex.

α-Oligonucleotides show remarkable stability against various nucleases. The half-lives of α- (16-mer) and β- (17-mer) single-stranded oligonucleotides following injection in *Xenopus* oocytes are 45 to 50 times more stable than those of the β-variety (*180*). Compared to the short half-lives (15–90 min) of 5′-labeled β-oligonucleotides, the 5′-labeled α-oligonucleotides have a half-life of around 24 hr in various biological fluids as well as in rabbit-reticulocyte lysates (*182*). With respect to the stability against various nucleases, there are striking differences between the oligomers (*173, 183, 184*). Under conditions in which almost 90–99% of β-oligonucleotides were hydrolyzed, the α-oligonucleotide remained almost intact.

In spite of their hybridizing abilities and great stabilities toward various nucleases, α-oligonucleotides have had very limited success in translation arrest. In cell-free systems, no significant inhibition in the translation of the target mRNA by α-oligonucleotides even with different sizes of oligonucleo-

tides (9- to 20-mer) has been seen (77, 116). A 20-mer α-anomeric oligonucleotide complementary to the initiation region of IL-6 mRNA failed to
inhibit the synthesis of a 26-kDa protein in a rabbit-reticulocyte system even
in the presence of excess oligo or externally added RNase H (116). Similarly,
no significant inhibition was observed in the translation of viral proteins by
an α-oligonucleotide targeted to the initiation region of VSV mRNA (116).

In intact cells, the results with α-oligonucleotides have also been negative. There was no antiviral activity following treatment of cells with poly(L-
lysine)-conjugated oligonucleotides (154). The inability of α-oligonucleotides
to inhibit protein synthesis both in cellular and cell-free systems may be
explained by the lack of cleavage of the target mRNA by RNase H following the complexation of the target mRNA with the complementary α-oligonucleotides. This was further proved by showing that the hybrids between
α-[d($G_2T_{12}G_2$)] and r(A_{12}) are not degraded by E. coli RNase H under conditions in which the duplexes containing the corresponding β-anomer are
hydrolyzed (116). There is only one positive result using α-oligonucleotides
in the inhibition of protein synthesis (90); this is discussed in Section III.
Combined α-phosphorothioate oligos gave no greater activity against HIV
than the β-S-oligo, indicating no correlation with RNase H (184a).

α-Oligonucleotides have also been used for the formation of triplexes
(175), forming a third strand in the major groove of the DNA duplex (see
Section VI,A). Whether or not this use of these analogs will be effective is
unclear. (The extra cost of such analogs must always be borne in mind in
devising potential therapeutic uses for them.)

The susceptibilities of normal oligonucleotides to nucleases have led to
the synthesis of other classes of compound with the modification at the 2'
position of the ribose moiety. The 2'-O-methyl-substituted oligo is one such
compound; it has attracted attention for various reasons. The synthesis of its
monomers has been described (185). They are much less expensive than the
deoxy analogs because the starting material is much cheaper. Also, there is
increased thermal stability of the hybrid between 2'-O-methylribonucleo-
tides and the complementary RNA compared to that of the DNA·RNA duplexes (65). The 2'-O-methyl oligonucleotides are more stable toward various DNA- and RNA-cleaving enzymes (186). With P1 nuclease and
micrococcal nuclease (an endonuclease), the 2'-O-methyl oligonucleotides
were hydrolyzed 1/10, and 1/100 as fast as DNA, respectively. With snake
venom phosphodiesterase (a 3'–5' exonuclease), however, there was no difference in the hydrolysis rates between 2'-O-methyl oligonucleotides and
DNA.

In spite of the stability toward different nucleases of the 2'-O-methyl
analogs and their ability to form stable complexes with complementary
RNAs, their use to inhibit translation has been very limited, which could be

explained by their inability to activate RNase H. However, there is a specific cleavage of the complementary RNA by RNase H when it forms a complex with a "chimeric oligonucleotide" analog containing four 2'-deoxyribo- and six flanking 2'-O-methylribonucleotides (37). A similar approach for the development of an antisense compound against HIV showed that a 20-mer 2'-O-methyloligoribonucleotide, containing five and three phosphorothioate linkages at the 5' and 3' ends, respectively, was almost as active as the corresponding all-PS against HIV *in vitro* (16).

Other unusual structures considered are the carbocyclic analog of D-ribose (189) (Fig. 17C) and the L-2'-deoxyribose isomer analog (189a).

B. Phosphodiester-modified Analogs

In view of the focus on phosphorothioate analogs in the above discussion, this section is devoted to a brief description of several of the other backbone-modified analogs that have been synthesized. Several examples of non-phosphorus-containing oligonucleotide analogs have been examined (2, 149). Many of these are neutral, and in some respects may be simpler and cheaper to synthesize than the corresponding phosphodiesters. In a few cases, their ability to hybridize with a target sequence of natural RNA or DNA has been reported (190), although the results are usually poor. This presumably results from the steric and charge interactions, which differ from natural DNA.

Methylphosphonates, which contain a methyl group linked to phosphorus (Fig. 1), were among the first oligo analogs used. They have been used in many experiments (9). In this context, it is important to stress that these analogs are neutral, and consequently are more hydrophobic than natural phosphodiesters. For example, they elute later in HPLC, and are less water-soluble. Above a length of about eight, it is usual to terminate their synthesis with a 5'-phosphodiester to increase aqueous solubility.

Phosphorodithioates have been synthesized partly in order to overcome the problem of chirality in the monothio analogs and the methylphosphonates. The synthesis is usually via the thiophosphoramidite (191–193), although other synthetic approaches have also been used (194). These compounds usually contain at least 10% of the monothio analog following purification; this can be observed readily by ^{31}P NMR. Methylphosphonothioate is another analog that has been synthesized (M. H. Caruthers, personal communication), although its properties have not been described in detail.

Phosphoramidates and phosphomorpholidates have been synthesized (150, 195), and have been applied as antisense oligos against HIV (14). The di- and trinucleotide alkyl phosphoramidate derivatives of adenine form stable complexes with poly(thymidylic acid); the stabilities of the complexes increase with the increasing chain-length of N-alkylphosphoramidate substituents (187). Inhibition of transforming growth factor (TGF-β) and inhibition of cell transformation (epithelial → mesenchymal) can be brought about by a phosphoramidate oligonucleotide complementary to TGF-β mRNA (188). Unmodified oligonucleotide controls to TGF-β mRNA, on the other hand, failed to show any inhibition of protein synthesis or transformation. The anti-HIV activity of a series of phosphoramidates was observed earlier (14) and it was shown that, in most cases, their activities are comparable with those of the phosphorothioates (discussed in Section II,B). However, they are generally more sterically hindered than the phosphorothioates and methylphosphonates, and have the same disadvantages—namely, chirality and neutrality,—so they may not be expected to be very useful analogs. Isosteric 3'-methylenephosphonates have been synthesized (196); a recent study of a singly substituted sequence (197) showed no significant differences from phosphodiester geometry.

C. Oligonucleotide Conjugates

It is, of course, possible to make conjugates of oligonucleotides with groups attached at either the 3' or 5' terminus or within the chain. This topic has recently been reviewed extensively (198), so only a brief discussion is included here. The group can be attached (a) to block exonucleases, (b) to increase the stability of duplex formation by intercalation, (c) to act as a fluorescent probe, or (d) to attach to or destroy the complementary strand. While many different chemical groups have been attached to oligos, only a few attempts have been made to increase specifically the activity of an anti-sense effect by these means (113, 114). The attachment of multiple groups—for example, one at each end—to confer increased cellular uptake and reactivity at the target site, is another versatile aspect of the antisense oligodeoxynucleotide approach that has yet to be fully realized. Peptide-conjugate oligos also have been made to improve cellular uptake (34) and to increase hydrolysis of target mRNA by RNase-like activity (169).

VII. Other Approaches

Two other approaches often lumped together as "antisense applications" are (a) triplex formation between DNA duplexes and oligodeoxynucleotides and (b) antisense catalytic ribo-oligomers, or "ribozymes."

A. Triplex Formation

The strategy of preventing transcription might be more effective than translation inhibition because one molecule of an oligo could prevent the expression of a greater number of protein products than by inhibiting the

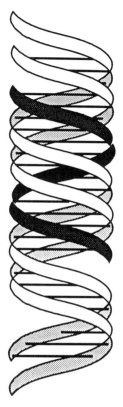

Fɪɢ 18. Structure of a triplex with an oligonucleotide (shaded) bound in the major groove of duplex DNA.

mRNA. This approach has been termed "gene targeting." It has been known for some time that polynucleotides form triple-strand helices (*199, 200*), called *triplexes* (Fig. 18), and this could form the basis of an effective strategy for *transcription arrest*. The binding and subsequent selective cleavage of duplex DNA by pyrimidine-containing oligomers with a reactive group attached have been demonstrated (*201, 202*). The transcription of c-*myc* DNA into mRNA was inhibited in a cell-free system by T·G-containing oligomers (*203*). Thus, the potential for the development of an efficient means of transcription arrest is there, and it could be useful against the integrated double-strand DNA stage of HIV. A major factor in determining the relative effectiveness of the strategy of using an oligo for duplex formation with mRNA or for triplex formation with DNA will be the relative degree of uptake into the cytoplasm and the nucleus of the cell. Up to this point, the results for such distribution studies seem to depend largely on the nature of the reporter groups used (see Section IV).

B. Ribozymes

Another form of antisense oligonucleotide that has been described is the self-splicing element of mRNAs (204), which has been characterized (205) and termed a ribozyme (Fig. 19). The mechanism of the enzymatic action is a trans-esterification that requires the 2'-hydroxyl group of the RNase-active guanosine residue (206, 207). The length of the first ribozyme was 39 nucleotides, but shorter ones have been described (208). The effect of chemical modification on the activity of such an oligo-*ribo*nucleotide is only just being investigated. It should be emphasized that the problem of nuclease susceptibility of oligo-*ribo*nucleotides is even more stringent than that of oligo-*deoxy*ribonucleotides because of the presence of RNases; these can be inhibited by addition of a 2'-O-methyl group (209). But the same problems of DNase susceptibility, cellular uptake, and intracellular distribution apply to these novel catalytic oligos as to those discussed above.

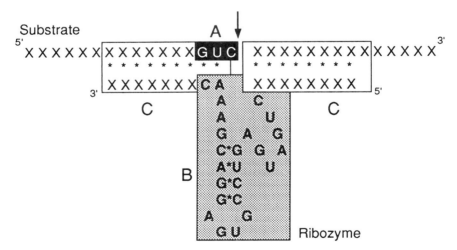

FIG 19. Structure of a catalytic RNA, or ribozyme. The three structural domains are (A) the target sequence in mRNA substrate adjacent to the site of cleavage; (B) the highly conserved sequence in the ribozyme; and (C) the flanking sequences that comprise the antisense segments (205).

VIII. Conclusion

There are several barriers to the exploitation of oligodeoxynucleotide analogs as therapeutic agents. Some that have been considered and discussed in this article are nonspecific interactions, cellular uptake, and hybridization capability. Other unresolved questions include drug delivery, toxicity, pharmacokinetics, and cost of production (58). We address each of these topics in turn, but at this point we can provide only partial answers.

Drug delivery is a problem with every kind of drug, including oligomers. Attempts have been made to use liposomes (22, 210), and it is likely that further attempts will be made to use specifically labeled liposomes. But these have other problems in terms of primary hepatic processing; this is beyond the scope of the present article.

Toxicity and pharmacokinetics have been addressed in a number of preliminary studies (211–213), but detailed results have not yet been published. However, certain conclusions can be drawn from the results so far, namely, that both normal and phosphorothioate oligos are cleared in mice with two half-lives, one fast (about 10 min) and the other slow (about 2 hr). The latter pool of oligos enables them to be absorbed by the tissues. The phosphorothioate oligos were not found to be very toxic; only a small degree of liver enlargement has been observed (213). These results in general make the prospects for the use of oligos *in vivo* look promising. Of course, use in humans must await further tests.

At present, the cost of synthesizing an oligodeoxynucleotide by automatic synthesis using the phosphoramidite method is about $500 per 10 mg. For the amounts needed for a Phase II trial, the cost appears prohibitive. But there are two factors that mitigate this situation. First, there are constant attempts to devise newer and more potent forms of oligo-drugs by using different approaches and attaching reactive groups to them. Second, the cost of synthesis of oligos has been coming down very rapidly over the past few years; with the current interest, it is likely to decrease even more rapidly, although the basic costs of raw materials will always make oligos expensive as drugs.

It may be noted that penicillin was originally very rare and expensive. This may not be a good example for oligodeoxynucleotides, as penicillin is a natural product produced by fermentation. However, with the rapid development of biotechnology, it is not unlikely that, if these compounds are effective against intractable human diseases, less expensive methods will be developed for their large-scale production. Recent results showing antisense inhibition in elucidating complex stages of embryological development (181), and extending the life span of human epithelial cells by inhibiting programmed cell death (apoptosis) (214), indicate the wide range of biological applications now being demonstrated using oligodeoxynucleotides. Future therapeutic applications to a range of human diseases can be anticipated.

REFERENCES

1. J. S. Cohen, ed., "Oligodeoxynucleotides: Antisense Inhibitors of Gene Expression." CRC Press, Boca Raton, Florida, 1989.
2. E. Uhlmann and A. Peyman, *Chem. Rev.* **90,** 543 (1990).
3. P. C. Zamecnik and M. L. Stephenson, *PNAS* **75,** 280 (1978).
4. C. H. Agris, K. Blake, P. Miller, M. Reddy and P. O. P. Ts'o, *Bchem* **25,** 6268 (1986).
5. M. Lemaitre, B. Bayard and B. Lebleu, *Bchem* **84,** 648 (1987).
6. E. L. Wickstrom, T. A. Bacon, A. Gonzalez, D. L. Freeman, G. H. Lyman and E. Wickstrom, *PNAS* **85,** 1028 (1988).
6a. K. G. Draper, M. E. Konertz and L. J. Sturzenbecker, *Antiviral Res.* **13,** 151 (1990).
7. C. C. Smith, L. Aurelian, M. P. Reddy, P. S. Miller and P. O. P. Ts'o, *PNAS* **83,** 2787 (1986).
8. P. Westermann, B. Gross and G. Hoinkis, *Biomed. Biochim. Acta* **48,** 85 (1989).
9. P. S. Miller, C. Agris, L. Aurelian, K. Blake, A. Murakami, M. Reddy, S. Spitz and P. O. P. Ts'o, *Biochimie* **67,** 769 (1985).
10. A. Zerial, N. T. Thuong and C. Helene, *NARes* **15,** 9909 (1987).
11. K. C. Gupta, *JBC* **262,** 7492 (1987).
12. C. Crum, J. D. Johnson, A. Nelson and D. Roth, *NARes* **16,** 4569 (1988).
13. P. C. Zamecnik, J. Goodchild, Y. Taguchi and P. Sarin, *PNAS* **83,** 4143 (1986).
14. S. Agrawal, J. Goodchild, M. P. Civeira, A. H. Thornton, P. S. Sarin and P. C. Zamecnik, *PNAS* **85,** 7079 (1988).
15. M. Matsukura, K. Shinozuka, G. Zon, H. Mitsuya, M. Reitz, J. Cohen and S. Broder *PNAS* **84,** 7706 1987).
16. S. Shibahara, S. Mukai, H. Morisawa, H. Nakashima, S. Kobayashi and N. Yamamoto, *NARes* **17,** 239 (1989).
17. P. S. Sarin, S. Agrawal, M. P. Civeira, J. Goodchild, T. Ikeuchi and P. C. Zamecnik, *PNAS* **85,** 7448 (1988).
18. J. A. Zaia, J. J. Rossi, G. J. Murakawa, P. A. Spallone, D. A. Stephens, B. E. Kaplan, R. Eritja, R. B. Wallace and E. M. Cantin, *J. Virol.* **62,** 3914 (1988).
19. R. Heikkila, G. Schwab, E. Wickstrom, S. L. Loke, D. H. Pluznik, R. Watt and L. M. Neckers, *Nature* **328,** 445 (1987).
20. A. Harel-Bellan, D. K. Ferris, M. Vinocour, J. T. Holt and W. L. Farrar, *J. Immunol.* **140,** 2431 (1988).
21. J. T. Holt, R. L. Redner and A. W. Nienhuis, *MCBiol* **8,** 963 (1988).
22. S. L. Loke, X. H. Zhang, C. A. Stein, M. Avigan, J. S. Cohen and L. M. Neckers, *Curr. Top. Microbiol. Immunol.* **141,** 282 (1988).
23. M. S. Kindy and I. M. Verma, *in* "Antisense RNA and DNA" (D. A. Melton, ed.), p. 129. *CSHLab*, Cold Spring Harbor, New York, 1988.
24. A. M. Gewirtz and B. Calabretta, *Science* **242,** 1303 (1988).
25. N. Sagata, M. Oskarsson, T. Copeland, J. Brumbaugh and G. F. Vande Woude, *Nature* **335,** 519 (1988).
26. R. S. Paules, R. Buccione, R. C. Moschel, G. F. Vande Woude and J. J. Eppig, *PNAS* **86,** 5395 (1989).
27. S. M. Tidd, P. Hawley, H. M. Warenius and I. Gibson, *Anti-Cancer Drug Design* **3,** 117 (1988).

28. E. H. Chang, Z. Yu, K. Shinozuka, G. Zon, W. D. Wilson and A. Strekowska, *Anti-Cancer Drug Design* **4**, 221 (1989).
29. D. Jaskulski, K. deRiel, W. E. Mercer, B. Calabretta and R. Baserga, *Science* **240**, 1544 (1988).
30. G. Tortora, H. Yokozaki, S. Pepe, T. Clair and Y. S. Cho-Chung, *PNAS* **88**, 2011 (1991).
31. Y. S. Cho-Chung, G. Tortura, H. Yokozaki, S. Meissner, K. I. Urkami and K. Miki, *Proc. Am. Assoc. Cancer Res.* **31**, 308 (Abstr. 171) (1990).
32. C. O'Connell, M. Sparks, M. Beckwith, C. Ferre, D. Longo and W. Urba, *in* "Oligodeoxynucleotides as Antisense Inhibitors of Gene Expression: Therapeutic Implications." Rockville, Maryland, 1989.
33. J. C. Reed, C. A. Stein, C. Subasinghe, S. Haldar, C. M. Croce, S. Yum and J. S. Cohen, *Cancer Res.* **50**, 6565 (1990).
34. R. Colomer, R. Lupu and E. P. Gelmann, *Proc. Am. Assoc. Cancer Res.* **31**, 308 (Abstr. 1825) (1990).
35. J. S. Cohen, *Med. Virol.* **10**, 247 (1991).
36. P. J. Green, O. Pines and M. Inouye, *ARB* **55**, 569 (1986).
37. H. Inoue, Y. Hayse, S. Iwai and E. Ohtsuka, *FEBS Lett.* **215**, 327 (1982).
37a. G. W. Krystal, B. C. Armstrong and J. F. Battey, *MCBiol* **10**, 4180 (1990).
38. K. Blake, A. Murakami and P. S. Miller, *Bchem* **24**, 6132 (1985).
39. K. Blake, A. Murakami, S. Spitz, S. Glave, M. Reddy, P. O. P. Ts'o and P. Miller, *Bchem* **24**, 6139 (1985).
40. H. Mitsuya, T. Shirasaka and S. Broder, *in* "Design of Anti-AIDS Drugs" (E. De Clerq, ed.), Vol. 14, p. 25. Elsevier, Amsterdam, 1990.
41. E. Wickstrom, *J. Biochem. Biophys. Methods* **13**, 97 (1986).
42. M. B. Feinberg, R. F. Jarrett, A. Aldovini, R. C. Gallo and F. Wong-Staal, *Cell* **46**, 807 (1986).
43. D. A. Usher, E. S. Erenrich and F. Eckstein, *PNAS* **69**, 115 (1972).
44. F. Eckstein, *ARB* **54**, 367 (1985).
45. W. J. Stec, G. Zon, V. Egan and B. Stec, *JACS* **106**, 6077 (1984).
46. L. A. LaPlanche, T. L. James, C. Powell, W. D. Wilson, B. Uznanski, W. J. Stec, M. F. Summers and G. Zon, *NARes* **14**, 9081 (1986).
47. S. Roy, V. Sklenar, E. Appella and J. S. Cohen, *Biopolymers* **26**, 2041 (1987).
48. J. Ott and F. Eckstein, *Bchem* **26**, 8237 (1987).
49. C. A. Stein, K. Shinozuka, C. Subasinghe and J. S. Cohen, *NARes* **16**, 3209 (1988).
50. B. C. Froehler, P. G. Ng and M. D. Mateucci, *NARes* **14**, 5399 (1986).
51. M. Matsukura, G. Zon, K. Shinozuka, C. A. Stein, H. Mitsuya, J. S. Cohen and S. Broder, *Gene* **72**, 343 (1988).
52. E. De Clerq, F. Eckstein, H. Sternbach and T. C. Morgan, *Virology* **42**, 421 (1970).
53. P. A. Bartlett and F. Eckstein, *JBC* **257**, 8879 (1982).
54. P. M. J. Burgers and F. Eckstein, *Bchem* **18**, 592 (1978).
55. P. M. J. Burgers and F. Eckstein, *JBC* **254**, 6889 (1979).
56. B. V. L. Potter, B. A. Connolly and F. Eckstein, *Bchem* **22**, 1369 (1983).
57. B. V. L. Potter, P. J. Romaniuk and F. Eckstein, *JBC* **258**, 1758 (1983).
58. G. Zon, *Pharm. Sci.* **5**, 539 (1988).
59. W. Saenger, *in* "Principles of Nucleic Acid Structure," p. 192. Springer-Verlag, New York, 1984.
60. R. C. Weast, *in* "CRC Handbook of Chemistry and Physics (1986–87)," p. 161. CRC Press, Boca Raton, Florida, 1988.
61. F. Eckstein, *Angew. Chem., Int. Ed. Engl.* **14**, 160 (1975).

62. F. Eckstein, *Acc. Chem. Res.* **12**, 204 (1979).
62a. M. K. Ghosh, K. Ghosh and J. S. Cohen, unpublished results, 1991.
63. C. Oefner and D. Suck, *JMB* **192**, 605 (1986).
64. L. J. P. Latimer, K. Hampel and J. S. Lee, *NARes* **17**, 154 (1989).
65. H. Inoue, Y. Hayse, A. Imura, S. Iwai, K. Miura and E. Ohtsuka, *NARes* **15**, 6131 (1987).
66. P. J. Romaniuk and F. Eckstein, *JBC* **257**, 7684 (1982).
67. T. M. Jovin, J. H. van de Sande, D. A. Zarling, D. J. Arndt-Jovin, F. Eckstein, H. H. Fuldner, I. Greider, E. Hamori, Kalisch, L. P. McIntosh and M. Robert-Nicoud, *CSHSQB* **47**, 143 (1983).
68. T. M. Jovin, L. P. McIntosh, D. J. Arndt-Jovin, D. A. Zarling, M. Robert-Nicoud, J. H. van de Sande and K. F. Jorgensen, *J. Biomol. Struct. Dyn.* **1**, 21 (1983).
69. R. Cosstick and F. Eckstein, *Bchem* **24**, 3630 (1985).
70. W. B. T. Cruse, S. A. Salisbury, T. Brown, R. Cosstick, F. Eckstein and O. Kennar, *JMB* **192**, 891 (1986).
71. C. A. Stein, K. Mori, S. L. Loke, C. Subasinghe, K. Shinozuka, J. S. Cohen and L. M. Neckers, *Gene* **72**, 333 (1988).
72. F. Eckstein and T. M. Jovin, *Bchem* **22**, 4546 (1983).
73. J. W. Suggs and D. A. Taylor, *NARes* **13**, 5707 (1985).
74. R. Y. Walder and J. A. Walder, *PNAS* **85**, 5011 (1988).
75. P. Dash, I. Lotan, M. Knapp, E. R. Kandel and P. Goelet, *PNAS* **84**, 7896 (1987).
76. J. Minshull and T. Hunt, *NARes* **14**, 6433 (1986).
77. C. Cazenave, C. A. Stein, N. Loreau, N. T. Thuong, L. M. Neckers, C. Subasinghe, C. Helene, J. S. Cohen and J.-J. Toulme, *NARes* **17**, 4255 (1989).
78. J. S. Cohen, in "Design of Anti-AIDS Drugs"(E. De Clerq, ed.), Vol. 14, p. 195. Elsevier, Amsterdam, 1990.
79. C. Majumdar, C. A. Stein, J. S. Cohen, S. Broder and S. H. Wilson, *Bchem* **28**, 1340 (1989).
80. K. Molling, T. Schulze, C. Subasinghe and J. S. Cohen, in "Oligodeoxynucleotides as Antisense Inhibitors of Gene Expression: Therapeutic Implications." Rockville, Maryland, 1989.
80a. C. A. Stein, R. Pal, K. L. De Vico, G. Hoke, O. Kinstler, M. G. Sarngadharan and R. L. Letsinger, *Bchem* **30**, 2439 (1991).
81. W.-Y. Gao, R. N. Hanes, M. A. Vasquez-Padua, C. A. Stein, J. S. Cohen and Y.-C. Cheng, *Antimicrob. Agents Chemother.* **34**, 808 (1990).
82. M. Matsukura, G. Zon, K. Shinozuka, M. Robert-Guroff, T. Shimada, C. A. Stein, H. Mitsuya, F. Wong-Staal, J. S. Cohen and S. Broder, *PNAS* **86**, 4244 (1989).
83. D. Kinchington, S. Galpin, J. Jaroszewski, C. Subasinghe and J. S. Cohen, *Antiviral Res.* in press (1991).
84. B. M. Paterson, B. E. Roberts and E. L. Kuff, *PNAS* **74**, 4370 (1977).
85. N. D. Hastie and W. A. Held, *PNAS* **75**, 1217 (1978).
86. S. A. Liebhaber, F. E. Cash and S. H. Shakin, *JBC* **259**, 15597 (1984).
87. A. Efstratiadis, F. C. Kafatos and T. Maniatis, *Cell* **10**, 571 (1977).
88. G. N. Pavlakis, R. E. Lockard, N. Vamvakopoulos, L. Rieser, U. L. Rajbhandari and J. Vournakis, *Cell* **19**, 91 (1980).
89. G. Albrecht, A. Krowczynska and G. Brawerman, *JMB* **178**, 881 (1984).
90. J. R. Bertland, J.-L. Imbach, C. Paoletti and C. Malvy, *BBRC* **164**, 311 (1989).
91. R. C. Haberken and G. L. Cantoni, *Bchem* **12**, 2389 (1973).
92. K. Tsukada, Y. Sawau, J. Saito and F. Sako, *BBRC* **85**, 280 (1978).
93. T. G. Lawson, B. K. Ray, J. J. Dodds, J. A. Grifo, R. D. Abramson, W. C. Mernick, D. F. Betsch, H. L. Weith and R. E. Thach, *JBC* **261**, 13979 (1986).

94. S. Sabita, K. C. Cheah and A. G. Porter, *EJB* **184**, 39 (1989).
95. C. Cazenave, N. Loreau, N. T. Thuong, J.-J. Toulme and C. Helene, *Biochimie* **68**, 1063 (1986).
96. J. Goodchild, E. Caroll III and J. R. Greenberg, *ABB* **263**, 401 (1988).
97. A. T. Weinber, U. Z. Litthauer and I. Ginzburg, *Gene* **72**, 297 (1989).
98. L. M. Maher III and B. J. Dolnick, *ABB* **253**, 214 (1987).
99. M. T. Haeuptle, R. Frank and B. Dobberstein, *NARes* **14**, 1427 (1986).
100. D. A. Melton, *PNAS* **82**, 144 (1985).
101. H. M. Kronenberg, B. E. Robbert and A. Efstratiadis, *NARes* **6**, 153 (1979).
102. C. Boizau and J.-J. Toulme, *Bioconjugate Chem.* in press (1991).
103. N. A. Miroshnichenko, O. V. Karpova, S. Y. Morozov, N. P. Rodionova and J. G. Atabekov, *FEBS Lett.* **234**, 65 (1988).
104. C. J. Marcus-Sekura, A. M. Woerner, K. Shinozuka, G. Zon and G. V. Quinnan, *NARes* **15**, 5749 (1987).
105. L. J. Maher III and B. J. Dolnick, *NARes* **16**, 3341 (1988).
106. M. Lemaitre, C. Bisbal, B. Bayard and B. Lebleu, *Nucleosides Nucleotides* **6**, 311 (1987).
107. E. Wickstrom, W. S. Simonet, K. Medlock and I. Ruiz-Robles, *Biophys. J.* **49**, 15 (1986).
108. C. Cazenave, N. Loreau, N. T. Thuong, J.-J. Toulme and C. Helene, *NARes* **15**, 4717 (1987).
109. P. F. Cavanaugh, Jr., and W. F. Pilgermayer, Jr., *Proc. Am. Assoc. Cancer Res.* **30**, 417 (1989).
110. M. L. Stephenson and P. C. Zamecnik, *PNAS* **75**, 285 (1978).
111. J. M. Kean, A. Murakami, K. R. Blake, C. D. Cushman and P. S. Miller, *Bchem* **27**, 9113 (1988).
112. D. Praseuth, T. Le Doan, M. Chassingol, J.-L. Decout, N. Habhoub, J. Lhomme, N. T. Thuong and C. Helene, *Bchem* **27**, 3031 (1988).
113. K. Mori, C. Subasinghe and J. S. Cohen, *FEBS Lett.* **249**, 213 (1989).
114. P. Verspieren, A. W. C. A. Cornelissen, N. T. Thuong, C. Helene and J.-J. Toulme, *Gene* **61**, 307 (1987).
115. P. Verspieren, A. W. C. A. Cornelissen, N. T. Thuong and C. Helene, *in* "Current Communications in Molecular Biology: Antisense RNA and DNA" (D. A. Melton, ed.), p. 53. CSHLab, Cold Spring Harbor, New York, 1988.
116. C. Gagnor, J.-R. Bertrand, S. Thenet, M. Lemaitre, F. Morvan, B. Rayner, C. Malvy, B. Lebleu, J.-L. Imbach and C. Paoletti, *NARes* **15**, 10419 (1987).
117. S. Agrawal, S. H. Mayrand, P. C. Zamecnik and T. Pederson, *PNAS* **87**, 1401 (1990).
118. M. Kozak, *Cell* **15**, 1109 (1978).
119. M. Kozak, *Cell* **22**, 7 (1980).
120. M. Kozak, *Curr. Top. Microbiol. Immunol.* **93**, 81 (1981).
121. M. Kozak, *NARes* **9**, 5233 (1981).
122. M. Kozak, *Microbiol. Rev.* **47**, 1 (1983).
123. M. Kozak, *PNAS* **83**, 2850 (1986).
124. S. H. Shakin and S. A. Liebhaber, *JBC* **261**, 16018 (1986).
125. M. Kozak, *Cell* **19**, 79 (1980).
126. K. A. W. Lee, D. Guertin and N. Sonenberg, *JBC* **258**, 707 (1983).
127. M. A. Morgan and A. J. Shatkin, *Bchem* **19**, 5960 (1980).
128. A. W. C. A. Cornelissen, P. Verspieren, J. Toulme, B. Swinkles and P. Borst, *NARes* **14**, 5605 (1986).
129. J. A. Walder, P. S. Eder, D. M. Engman, S. J. Brentano, R. Y. Walder, D. S. Knutzon, D. M. Dorfman and J. E. Donelson, *Science* **233**, 569 (1986).
130. K. Jayaraman, K. McParland, P. Miller and P. O. P. Ts'o, *PNAS* **78**, 1537 (1981).

131. A. Bielinska, R. A. Shivdasani, L. Zhang and G. J. Nabel, *Science* **250**, 997 (1990).

132. C. A. Stein, P. L. Iversen, C. Subasinghe, J. S. Cohen, W. J. Stec and G. Zon, *Anal. Biochem.* **188**, 11 (1990).

133. E. L. Wickstrom, T. A. Bacon, A. Gonzales, D. L. Freeman, G. H. Lyman and E. Wickstrom, *PNAS* **85**, 1028 (1988).

134. P. Zamecnik, *in* "Oligodeoxynucleotides as Antisense Inhibitors of Gene Expression: Therapeutic Implications." Rockville, Maryland, 1989.

135. J. Goodchild, *in* "Conference on Antisense RNA and DNA." St. John's College, Cambridge, England, 1989.

136. L. A. Yakubov, E. A. Deeva, V. F. Zarytova, E. M. Ivanova, A. S. Ryte, L. V. Yurchenko and V. V. Vlassov, *PNAS* **86**, 6454 (1989).

137. J. Shuttleworth and A. Colman, *EMBO J.* **7**, 427 (1988).

138. J. Goodchild, S. Agrawal, M. P. Civeira, P. S. Sarin, D. Sun and P. C. Zamecnik, *PNAS* **85**, 5507 (1988).

139. D. J. Chin, G. A. Green, G. Zon, F. Szoka and R. M. Straubinger, *New Biologist* **2**, 1091 (1990).

140. G. E. Marti, G. Zon, W. Egan, P. Noguchi, M. Matsukura and S. Broder, *in* "Oligodeoxynucleotides as Antisense Inhibitors of Gene Expression: Therapeutic Implications." Rockville, Maryland, 1989.

141. S. L. Loke, C. A. Stein, X. H. Zhang, K. Mori, M. Nakanishi, C. Subasinghe, J. S. Cohen and L. M. Neckers *PNAS* **86**, 3474 (1989).

142. P. S. Miller, K. B. McParland, K. Jayaraman and P. O. P. Ts'o, *Bchem* **20**, 1874 (1981).

143. P. S. Miller, L. T. Braiterman and P. O. P. Ts'o, *Bchem* **16**, 1988 (1977).

144. R. M. Bennett, G. T. Gabor and M. J. Morritt, *J. Clin. Invest.* **76**, 2182 (1985).

145. G. Goodarzi and K. Wataba, *in* "International Conference on Nucleic Acid Therapeutics." 1991.

146. L. M. Neckers, *in* "Oligodeoxynucleotides: Antisense Inhibitors of Gene Expression" (J. S. Cohen, ed.), p. 211. CRC Press, Boca Raton, Florida, 1989.

147. J. W. Jaroszewski, C. Subasinghe, P. J. Faustino and J. S. Cohen, *in* "Oligodeoxynucleotides as Antisense Inhibitors of Gene Expression: Therapeutic Implications." Rockville, Maryland, 1989.

148. J. W. Jaroszewski, O. Kaplan, J.-L. Syi, M. Sehested, P. J. Faustino and J. S. Cohen, *Cancer Commun.* **2**, 287 (1990).

149. P. S. Miller, *in* "Oligodeoxynucleotides: Antisense Inhibitors of Gene Expression" (J. S. Cohen, ed.), p. 79. CRC Press, Boca Raton, Florida, 1989.

150. B. Bayard, L. D. Lesserman, C. Bisbal and B. Lebleu, *EJB* **151**, 319 (1985).

151. H. L. Weith, E. Darbishire, M. Cushman, C. Pidgeon, S. R. Byrn, J. K. Chen, J. G. Stowell, K. Ray and D. Carlson, *in* "Oligodeoxynucleotides as Antisense Inhibitors of Gene Expression: Therapeutic Implications." Rockville, Maryland, 1989.

152. C. Y. Wang and L. Huang, *PNAS* **84**, 7851 (1987).

153. M. Lemaitre, B. Bayard and B. Lebleu, *PNAS* **84**, 648 (1987).

154. J.-P. Leonetti, B. Rayner, M. Lemaitre, C. Gagnor, P. G. Milhaud, J.-L. Imbach and B. Lebleu, *Gene* **72**, 323 (1988).

155. M. Stevenson and P. L. Iverson, *J. Gen. Virol.* **70**, 2673 (1989).

156. G. Degols, J.-P. Leonetti, C. Gagnor, M. Lemaitre and B. Lebleu, *NARes* **17**, 9341 (1989).

157. P. L. Schell, *BBA* **340**, 323 (1974).

158. P. L. Schell, *BBA* **240**, 472 (1971).

159. R. L. Letsinger, G. Zhang, D. K. Sun, T. Ikeuchi and P. S. Sarin, *PNAS* **86**, 6553 (1989).

160. A. S. Boutorin, L. V. Guikova, E. M. Ivanova, N. D. Kobetz, V. F. Zarytova, A. S. Ryte, L. V. Yurchenko and V. V. Vlassov, *FEBS Lett.* **254**, 129 (1989).

161. D. Vestweber and G. Schatz, *Nature* **172,** 289 (1989).

162. R. A. Weinberg, *Cancer Res.* **49,** 3713 (1989).

163. A. Rosolen, L. Whitesell, N. Ikegaki, R. H. Kennet and L. M. Neckers, *Cancer Res.* **50,** 6316 (1990).

164. C. Szczylik, T. Skorski, N. C. Nicolaides, L. Manzella, L. Malaguarnera, D. Venturelli, A. M. Gerwitz, and B. Calabretta, *Science* **253,** 562–565 (1991).

165. I. Pastan and M. M. Gottesman, *in* "Important Advances in Oncology" (V. T. DeVita, S. Hellman, and S. A. Rosenberg, eds.), p. 3. Lippincott, Philadelphia, Pennsylvania, 1988.

166. Y. Daaka and E. Wickstrom, *Oncogene Res.* **5,** 267 (1990).

167. P. Verspieren, N. Loreau, N. T. Thuong, D. T. Shire and J.-J. Toulme, *NARes* **18,** 4711 (1990).

167a. B. Calabretta, R. B. Sims, M. Valteri, D. Caracciolo, C. Szyczylik, D. Venturelli, M. Ratajczak, M. Beran, and A. M. Gerwitz, *PNAS* **88,** 2351–2355 (1991).

168. J. S. Cohen, *Trends Pharmacol. Sci.* **10,** 435 (1989).

169. J. K. Bashkin, J. K. Gard and A. S. Modak, *J. Org. Chem.* **55,** 5125 (1990).

170. U. Sequin, *Experientia* **29,** 1059 (1973).

171. U. Sequin, *Helv. Chim. Acta* **57,** 68 (1974).

172. F. Morvan, B. Rayner, J.-L. Imbach, D.-K. Chang and J. W. Lown, *NARes* **14,** 5019 (1986).

173. F. Morvan, B. Rayner, J.-L. Imbach, M. Lee, J. A. Hartley, D.-K. Chang and J. W. Lown, *NARes* **15,** 7027 (1987).

174. D. Praseuth, M. Chassignol, M. Tekasugi, T. LeDoan, N. T. Thuong and C. Helene, *JMB* **196,** 939 (1987).

175. J. Sun, U. Asseline, D. Rouzand, T. Montenay, N. T. Thuong, and C. Helene, *NARes* **15,** 6149 (1978).

176. C. Gagnor, B. Rayner, J.-P. Leonetti, J.-L. Imbach and B. Lebleu, *NARes* **17,** 5107 (1989).

177. J.-S. Sun, J.-C. Francois, R. Lavery, T. Saison, T. Montenay, N. T. Thuong and C. Helene, *Bchem* **27,** 6039 (1988).

178. M. Durand, J. C. Maurizot, N. T. Thuong and C. Helene, *NARes* **16,** 5039 (1988).

179. J. Paoletti, D. Bazile, F. Morvan, J.-L. Imbach and C. Paoletti, *NARes* **17,** 2693 (1989).

180. C. Cazenave, M. Cheverier, N. T. Thuong and C. Helene, *NARes* **15,** 10507 (1987).

181. J. Cherfas, *Science* **250,** 33 (1990).

182. T. A. Bacon, F. Morvan, B. Rayner, J.-L. Imbach and E. Wickstrom, *J. Biochem. Biophys. Methods* **16,** 311 (1988).

183. U. Sequin and C. Tamm, *Helv. Chim. Acta* **55,** 1196 (1972).

184. F. Morvan, B. Rayner, J.-L. Imbach, S. Thenet, J. R. Betrand, J. Paoletti, C. Malvy and C. Paoletti *NARes* **15,** 3421 (1987).

184a. B. Rayner, M. Matsukura, F. Morvan, J. S. Cohen and J.-L. Imbach, *C. R. Hebd. Seances Acad. Sci.* **310,** 61 (1990).

185. Y. Furukawa, K. Kobayashi, Y. Kanai and M. Honjo, *Chem. Pharm. Bull.* **13,** 1273 (1965).

186. B. S. Sproat, A. I. Lamond, B. Beijer, P. Neuner and U. Ryder, *NARes* **17,** 3373 (1989).

187. A. Jäger, J. M. Levy and S. M. Hecht, *Bchem* **27,** 7237 (1988).

188. J. D. Potts, J. M. Dagle, J. A. Walder, D. L. Weeks and R. B. Runyan, *PNAS* **88,** 1516 (1991).

189. M. Perbost, M. Lucas, C. Chavis, A. Pompon, H. Baumgartner, B. Rayner, H. Griengl and J.-L. Imbach, *BBRC* **165,** 742 (1989).

189a. M. J. Damha, P. A. Giannaris, P. Marfey and L. S. Reid, *Tetrahedron Lett.* **23,** 2573 (1991).

190. M. Mateucci, *Tetrahedron Lett.* **31,** 2385 (1990).

191. B. H. Dahl, K. Bjergarde, V. B. Sommer and O. Dahl, *Acta Chem. Scand.* **43,** 896 (1989).

192. N. Farschtschi and D. G. Gorenstein, *Tetrahedron Lett.* **29**, 6843 (1988).

193. W. K.-D. Brill, E. K. Yau and M. H. Caruthers, *Tetrahedron Lett.* **30**, 6621 (1989).

194. J. Neilsen, W. K.-D. Brill and M. H. Caruthers, *Tetrahedron Lett.* **29**, 5517 (1988).

195. B. C. Froehler, *Tetrahedron Lett.* **274**, 5575 (1986).

196. M. Morr, L. Ernst and L. Grotjahn, Z. *Naturforsch. B* **38B**, 1665 (1983).

197. U. Heinmann, L.-N. Rudolph, C. Alings, M. Morr, W. Heikens, R. Frank and H. Blöcker, *NARes* **19**, 427 (1991).

198. J. Goodchild, *Bioconjugate Chem.* **1**, 165 (1990).

198a. S. Agrawal and P. C. Zamecnik, *NARes* **18**, 5419 (1990).

199. G. Felsenfeld, D. R. Davies and A. Rich, *JACS* **79**, 2023 (1957).

200. S. L. Broitman, D. D. Im and J. R. Fresco, *PNAS* **84**, 5120 (1988).

201. C. Helene and J.-J. Toulme, *in* "Oligodeoxynucleotides: Antisense Inhibitors of Gene Expression" (J. S. Cohen, ed.), p. 137. CRC Press, Boca Raton, Florida, 1989.

202. P. B. Dervan, *in* "Oligodeoxynucleotides: Antisense Inhibitors of Gene Expression" (J. S. Cohen, ed.), p. 197. CRC Press, Boca Raton, Florida, 1989.

203. M. Cooney, G. Czernuszewicz, E. H. Postel, S. J. Flint and M. E. Hogan, *Science* **241**, 456 (1988).

204. T. R. Cech, *Cell* **44**, 207 (1986).

205. J. Haseloff and W. L. Gerlach, *Nature* **334**, 585 (1988).

206. J. A. McSwiggen and T. R. Cech, *Science* **244**, 679 (1989).

207. J. Rajagopal, J.A. Doudna and J. W. Szostak, *Science* **244**, 692 (1989).

208. A. C. Jeffries and R. H. Symons, *NARes* **17**, 1371 (1989).

209. S. Shibahara, S. Mukai, T. Nishihara, H. Inouye, E. Ohtsuka and H. Morisawa, *NARes* **15**, 4403 (1987).

210. A. Thierry, A. Dritschilo and A. Rahman, *Proc. Am. Assoc. Cancer Res.* **31**, 445 (Abstr. 2642) (1990).

211. D. G. Knorre, V. V. Vlassov, and V. F. Zarytova, *in* "Oligodeoxynucleotides: Antisense Inhibitors of Gene Expression" (J. S. Cohen, ed.), p. 173. CRC Press, Boca Raton, Florida, 1989.

212. P. Iversen, J. Mata and G. Zon, *J. Pharmacol. Exp. Ther.* in press (1991).

213. S. Agrawal, J. Temsamani and J. Y. Tang, *PNAS* **88**, 7595 (1991).

214. J. A. M. Maier, P. Voulalas, D. Roeder and T. Maciag, *Science* **249**, 1570 (1990).

5,6-Dihydropyrimidine Adducts in the Reactions and Interactions of Pyrimidines with Proteins[1]

KATHRYN M. IVANETICH
AND DANIEL V. SANTI

Department of Biochemistry and
    Biophysics and
Department of Pharmaceutical Chemistry
and the Biomolecular Resource Center
University of California, San Francisco
San Francisco, California 94143

Enzymes that catalyze certain reactions of pyrimidine metabolism may share a common mechanistic feature: nucleophilic attack at position 6 of the pyrimidine heterocycle to form transient 5,6-dihydropyrimidine intermediates ("Michael adducts") (1–3). A Michael adduct is the product formed after addition of a nucleophile to the β-carbon of an α,β-unsaturated carbonyl (Fig. 1). The original basis for the proposal of such intermediates in enzymic reactions of pyrimidines was that relevant chemical counterparts are greatly facilitated by this mechanism. It was rationalized that reactions that appear difficult for the parent pyrimidine may be facile on dihydropyrimidines or intermediates derived from them, and that dihydropyrimidines readily form

[1] Abbreviations used: TS, thymidylate synthase; DCMT, DNA-cytosine methyltransferase; RUMT, RNA-uracil methyltransferase; AdoMet, S-adenosylmethionine; Ado-Hcy, S-adenosylhomocysteine; H_2folate, dihydrofolate; CH_2H_4folate, 5,10-methylenetetrahydrofolate; NO_2-dUMP, 5-nitrodeoxyuridine monophosphate; CF_3-dUMP, 5-trifluoromethyldeoxyuridine monophosphate; F-dUMP, 5-fluorodeoxyuridine monophosphate; E-dUMP, 5-ethynyldeoxyuridine monophosphate; BV-dUMP, 5-(2-bromovinyl)deoxyuridine monophosphate; BrUrd, 5-bromouridine; SDS–PAGE, sodium dodecyl sulfate/polyacrylamide gel electrophoresis; QSAR, quantitative structure–activity relationship.

127

Progress in Nucleic Acid Research
and Molecular Biology, Vol. 42

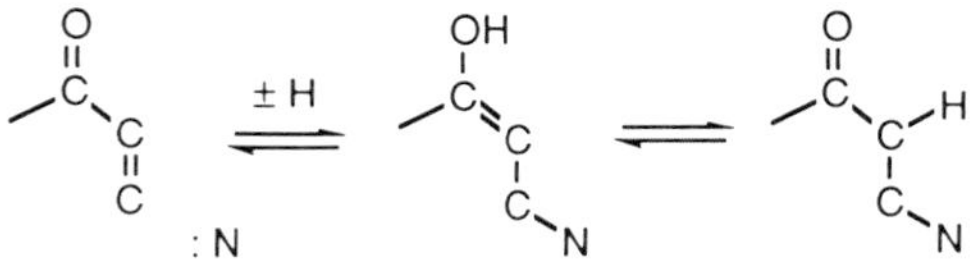

FIG. 1. Basic mechanism of Michael adduct formation. N, Nucleophile.

by addition of a nucleophile to carbon 6 of the pyrimidine. In short, Michael adducts can modify the reactivity of pyrimidines. In addition, reversible Michael adducts may play a role in protein–nucleic acid interactions. Here, after formation of a reversible complex, a Michael adduct between a protein and a pyrimidine component of the nucleic acid would provide an additional dimension of specificity and binding, the magnitude of which would be dependent on the system.

As depicted in Fig. 2, there are at least three types of reactions in pyrimidine metabolism that, from chemical evidence, are facilitated by or require nucleophilic attack at position 6 of the heterocycle to form transient 5,6-dihydropyrimidine intermediates.

First, enzyme-catalyzed electrophilic substitution of the 5-H of 1-substituted pyrimidines appears to require this pathway. An enzyme would have

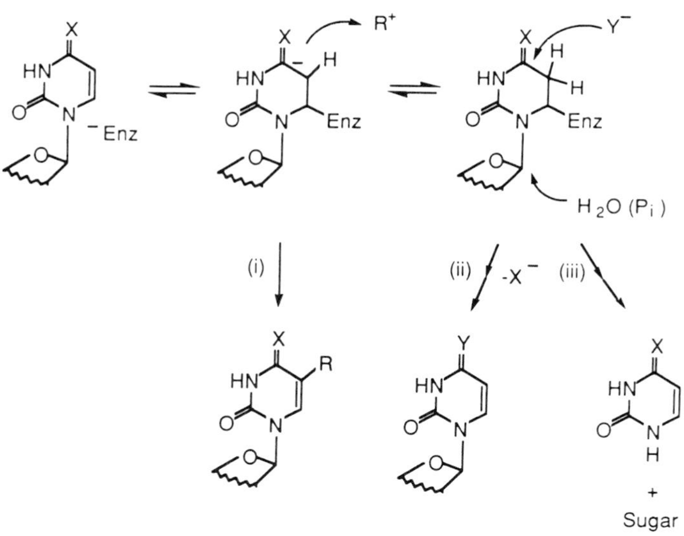

FIG. 2. Three types of reactions of pyrimidines that may involve Michael adduct formation: (i) electrophilic displacement at C-5; (ii) nucleophilic displacement at C-4; (iii) glycosyl bond cleavage.

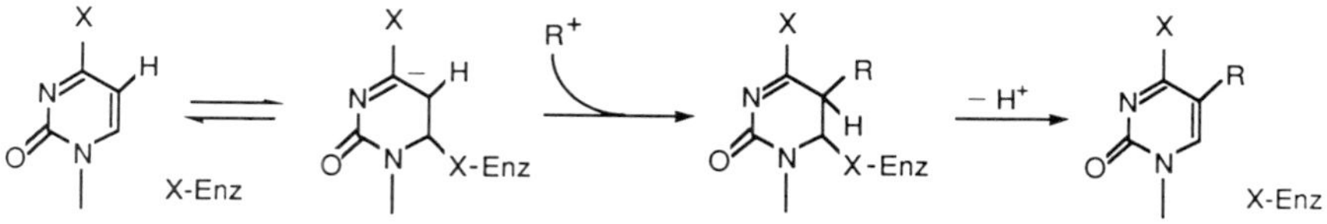

FIG. 3. General mechanism for electrophilic substitution at position 5 of pyrimidines. X, OH or NH_2.

difficulty facilitating the direct abstraction of the weakly acidic vinylic proton at C-5 of the parent pyrimidine ($pK_a > 50$); the pathway shown in Fig. 3 provides an easily accessible route to activating the 5-carbon for reactions with electrophiles. The general mechanism shown in Fig. 3 has been demonstrated for five enzymes (TS, dUMP hydroxymethylase, dCMP hydroxymethylase, DNA-cytosine methyltransferase, and tRNA-uracil methyltransferase), and it is probably the primary pathway for all enzyme-catalyzed electrophilic displacement reactions at position 5 of pyrimidines.

The second reaction type is nucleophilic displacement of the 4-substituent of the pyrimidine heterocycle, as in the the deamination of cytidine and related nucleotides. The basis for this proposal is that such adducts of cytidine are easily formed, and that displacement of the 4-amino group proceeds much faster on dihydropyrimidines than on the parent pyrimidines. The chemical evidence is as follows. A variety of nucleophiles catalyze the deamination of cytidine by adding to position 6, with the reaction proceeding through the dihydropyrimidine adduct (4–6). Further, hydrolytic deamination of 5,6-dihydrocytidine proceeds at least 10^4 times faster than the deamination of cytidine, and both cytidine and 5,6-dihydrocytidine are substrates for cytidine deaminase (7). Although the mechanism appears justified by these observations, studies to date indicate that cytidine deaminase does *not* proceed via the dihydropyrimidine adduct, but rather by direct displacement of the 4-amino group on the parent pyrimidine (8). However, there are other enzymes in this class, and the chemical precedent is sufficiently strong to warrant continued search for Michael adducts in this type of reaction.

The third reaction that may involve intermediacy of 5,6-dihydropyrimidines is the cleavage of glycosyl bonds, by such enzymes as pyrimidine nucleoside hydrolases and pseudouridine synthase. Here, the argument again rests upon chemical studies. Acid-catalyzed hydrolysis of the glycosyl bond of 5,6-dihydrouridine proceeds approximately 2000 times faster than glycosyl bond hydrolysis of uridine, and the dihydrouridine adduct forms easily. Indeed, acid-catalyzed hydrolysis of uridine proceeds through addition of water across the 5,6 double bond to form a 5,6-dihydrouridine intermediate (9, 10).

In both enzyme-catalyzed reactions and protein–nucleic acid interactions involving nucleophilic attack at the C-6 of pyrimidines, Michael adducts may be be difficult to detect, since they are transient and reversible. Gradually, various tools have been developed to detect transient or unstable Michael adducts of pyrimidines. The verification of the validity of such tools in a particular reaction has justified their use in other reactions. Similarly, once a system has been shown to proceed via a Michael adduct, it serves to develop new approaches and tools. These tools have also served as important probes for other aspects of the mechanism of enzymic reactions that form Michael adducts to facilitate catalysis. In this article, we describe first the approaches developed to detect Michael adducts in the interaction of pyrimidines and proteins. Then, we describe various systems in which these adducts have been demonstrated or proposed, attempting to focus on how the tools were used.

I. Approaches to Detect Michael Adducts of Pyrimidines

The approaches used to detect Michael adducts of pyrimidines have been validated by model chemical studies and by studies with TS, an enzyme whose mechanism is well known, and several other enzyme systems.

A. Exchange of the 5-H of a Pyrimidine for a Proton of Water

Addition of a nucleophile to position 6 of a pyrimidine generates a carbanion equivalent (enol or enolate) at position 5 that, upon protonation by water, gives the 5,6-dihydropyrimidine adduct (Fig. 4). Reversal of this reaction can lead to exchange of the 5-H of the pyrimidine for a water proton. This hydrogen-exchange has been observed in numerous chemical reactions that serve as models for enzymic reactions involving the formation of such intermediates (1, 3).

Stereochemical consequences of the 5-H exchange reaction are of interest (11). Since most enzymes are stereospecific, if position 5 of one face of the pyrimidine were protonated to form the adduct, the same proton would be removed upon reversal, and no exchange would be observed. The fact that exchange does occur with several enzymes may be explained by one of two mechanisms. (i) Both faces of the pyrimidine may be accessible to solvent, albeit to different degrees, and the protonation and deprotonation may be non-stereospecific. Here, the observed rate of exchange will be slower than the true rate of formation/reversal of the dihydropyrimidine adduct. (ii) The reaction may be a direct counterpart of the enzymic reaction, in which the stereochemical addition of the entering solvent proton mimics that of the normal electrophile of the reaction, and the proton removed emanates from the original 5-H of the pyrimidine. That is, the solvent proton always enters

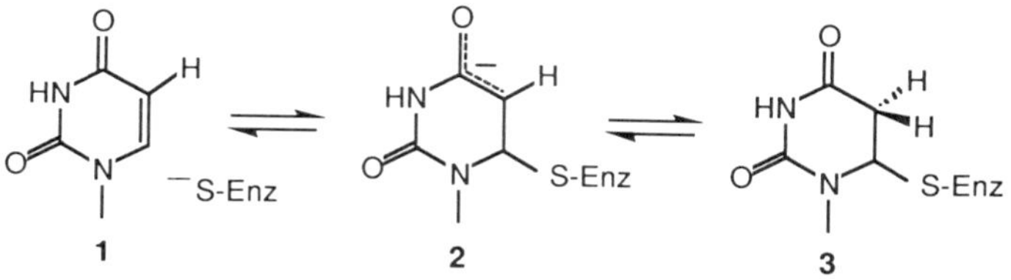

FIG. 4. Mechanism of exchange of the 5-H of pyrimidines for protons of water.

from one face of the pyrimidine, and the outgoing proton is always removed from the other. Here, the rate of exchange could equal that of dihydropyrimidine formation/reversal, and the stereochemistry of the normal reaction would be maintained.

Detection of 5-H exchange is straightforward (11–13). One starts with the 5-tritiated pyrimidine, and monitors loss of radioactivity from the substrate and/or release of radioactivity into the solvent. For the former, it is convenient to also incorporate ^{14}C into the substrate so the $^3H/^{14}C$ ratio can be used to monitor ^3H loss from the substrate. The precaution should be taken to verify that 5-H exchange rather than displacement by some exogenous electrophile has occurred, which usually requires demonstration that no other products are formed, and that the specific activity of the substrate diminishes over the course of the reaction.

B. α-Hydrogen Secondary Isotope Effects

6α-Hydrogen isotope effects have been used to detect transient Michael adducts of pyrimidines (14). Upon formation of the dihydropyrimidine adduct, the sp²-hybridized C-6 of the pyrimidine rehybridizes to sp³. If a heavy hydrogen isotope is attached to C-6, an equilibrium isotope effect of up to 25% may be observed ($K_T/K_H \simeq 1.25$) with tritium enrichment in the adduct. Further, reaction of the labeled pyrimidine can proceed faster than molecules with hydrogen, and an inverse kinetic isotope of as high as $k_T/k_H \simeq 1.25$ can be observed. In the simplest case, the maximum kinetic isotope effect may be seen if rehybridization occurs before the rate-determining step, or at a rate-determining step with a late transition state; a smaller effect can be seen if rehybridization occurs at the rate-determining step; and no isotope effect is seen if it occurs very early in the transition state of the rate-determining step, or if the hybridization change is post-rate-determining.

Demonstration of a large isotope effect is good evidence for rehybridization at C-6, but the absence of a kinetic isotope effect does not rule out rehybridization and Michael adduct formation; the rehybridization may occur with an early transition state or be post-rate-determining, so it need not be manifested in a kinetic isotope effect. If measurement of the equilibrium isotope effect is experimentally feasible, an unequivocal demonstration of rehybridization at C-6 is possible.

Secondary isotope effects are conveniently measured using a doubly labeled substrate, such as 6-^{3}H and ^{14}C in some remote part of the molecule. The isotope effect between sp^2 and sp^3 hybridized species is then assayed by a change in the ^{3}H/^{14}C ratio of reactants or products, and the data are fitted to appropriate equations to calculate the magnitude of the isotope effect (14).

C. Dehalogenation of 5-Bromo- and 5-Iodopyrimidines

5-Bromo and 5-iodouracils and cytosines (but not the fluoro derivatives) can undergo dehalogenation in the presence of thiols, as shown below (15, 16).

$$5\text{-X-dUMP} + 2\text{RSH} \rightarrow \text{dUMP} + (\text{RS})_2 + \text{HX} \quad (\text{X} = \text{Br or I})$$

The mechanism, as elucidated by chemical and enzymic studies, is shown in Fig. 5. The reaction is initiated by attack of thiolate nucleophilic catalyst at carbon 6 to form the 5-halo-6-alkylthio-5,6-dihydropyrimidine intermediate. The most likely mechanism then involves abstraction of Br$^+$ or I$^+$ by an exogenous thiol to provide a carbanion intermediate and a sulfenyl halide (17). The latter would react rapidly with another thiol to give the disulfide plus halide products, and the intermediate would undergo β-elimination to form the 5-H pyrimidine and unmodified nucleophilic catalyst.

It is of interest that exogenous thiols may also directly displace the halide from Michael adducts of 5-halopyrimidines to give, after β-elimination, the 5-thiolpyrimidine as product (15, 16). This partitioning of the dihydropyri-

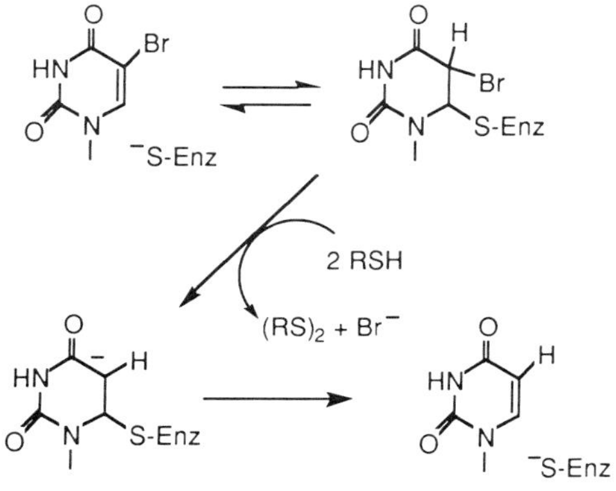

FIG. 5. Mechanism of thiol-dependent dehalogenation of 5-bromouracil derivatives.

midine intermediate (viz. the Michael adduct) between dehalogenation and nucleophilic displacement provides good evidence for its existence.

D. Isolation of Covalent Adducts

It may be possible to trap dihydropyrimidine adducts of substrates or analogs that are covalently bound to proteins as Michael adducts by rapid denaturation of the protein. This is possible because reversal of the dihydropyrimidine adduct is also catalyzed by the native protein, and—providing that denaturation and analysis are performed under conditions in which the denatured product is chemically stable—the covalent adduct may be isolated. A good example of this is the F-dUMP–CH_2H_4folate–TS adduct (see Section II,A,4), which is slowly reversible in the native state but very stable when denatured. It has also been reported that the TS–dUMP adduct is sufficiently stable to be isolated under conditions that denature the protein and thus inhibit enzyme-catalyzed reversal of the Michael adduct (18). In contrast, the TS–NO_2-dUMP complex is stable in the native state, but rapidly dissociates upon denaturation (19). The important point is that the success of isolating stable covalent complexes depends on the chemical stability of the adduct in the denatured protein that must be assessed for the particular system of interest.

E. Mechanism-based Inhibitors and Alternate Substrates

These refer to pyrimidine substrate analogs that undergo one or more reactions characteristic of the substrate to form covalent complexes between a nucleophile of the enzyme and the 6-position of the heterocycle. The important features of such inhibitors are that they are intrinsically stable in solution, they form specific reversible complexes with the enzyme, and they undergo covalent adduct formation with the catalytic nucleophile. After adduct formation, depending on the system, two different courses may be followed to form the inhibitory covalent complex. First, the initially formed covalent complex may itself be stable, or may react with an additional component of the reaction, such as a cofactor, to form a stable complex; examples include the interaction of TS with NO_2-dUMP and F-dUMP (see Section II,A,4 and 7). Often, in these cases, the complex is stable but is still capable of reversal and dissociation. Second, the formation of the dihydropyrimidine may activate a latent chemical group at position 5 to form a chemically reactive intermediate on the protein surface. This reactive chemical group may react either with a nucleophile on the enzyme to form an inhibitory covalent adduct, or with components of the solvent (water or buffer), which destroys the inhibitor and releases the active enzyme. The latter case, in effect, describes alternate substrates. Examples include the TS reactions with CF_3-, E-, and BV-dUMP (see Section II,A,5, 6, and 8).

II. Enzyme Systems That Form Michael Adducts

In this section, we provide examples of proteins that may form Michael adducts. Salient experiments using the aforementioned tools are briefly described.

A. Thymidylate Synthase

TS catalyzes the conversion of dUMP and CH_2H_4folate to dTMP and H_2folate. In this reaction, the 6-H of the folate cofactor is transferred as a hydride to the incipient methyl group of dTMP (20). Once it was shown that nucleophilic attack at the 6-carbon of the uracil heterocycle occurs readily, it was straightforward to generate chemical models that mimick partial reactions of TS, and to construct a complete mechanism (1, 3, 21–23). The mechanism proposed originally has withstood the test of time and experiments, and is generally accepted today, albeit with embellishment. The minimal mechanism is shown in Fig. 6. After formation of a reversible binary dUMP–TS complex, the cofactor is converted to its 5-iminium ion, the thiol

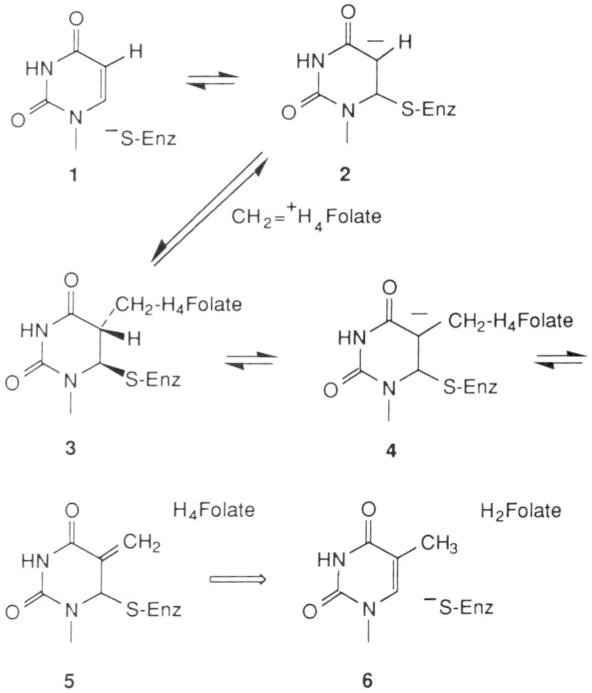

FIG. 6. Minimal mechanism of thymidylate synthase.

group of a cysteine residue adds to position 6 of the heterocycle to generate a nucleophilic center (carbanion equivalent) at position 5, and the ternary covalent complex 3 is formed. In this key intermediate, position 6 of dUMP is covalently linked to the enzyme, and position 5 of dUMP is attached to the one-carbon unit of the cofactor. Next, a proton is removed from position 5, and β-elimination of H$_4$folate gives the covalently bound exocyclic intermediate 5. The exocyclic 5-carbon of intermediate 5 has a pronounced carbonium ion character, and can readily accept a hydride ion from H$_4$folate. Finally, β-elimination of the enzyme and dissociation provide the products of the reaction, dTMP and H$_2$folate.

Many important aspects of the TS mechanism were elucidated by use of the aforementioned tools. Further, once features of the mechanism were elaborated, credence was given to the use of these tools in establishing similar mechanistic features for related reactions. The following describes how the mechanism of TS was elucidated, as well as other aspects of the reaction.

1. 1.5-H EXCHANGE OF dUMP: EVIDENCE FOR COVALENT MICHAEL ADDUCTS

TS catalyzes exchange of the 5-H of dUMP and solvent protons in the presence of cofactor (24). A very slow enzyme-catalyzed 5-H exchange occurs in the absence of cofactor, the rate of which can be increased in the presence of folic acid, which is incapable of the one-carbon transfer (11). Since 5-H exchange in chemical models requires the addition of a nucleophile to C-6, this result was considered evidence for the TS-catalyzed formation of the carbanion equivalent intermediate 2 and the dihydropyrimidine adduct 3 in Fig. 4. The reaction is quite slow, and the formation of 3 (Fig. 4), as measured by exchange, is not competent kinetically as an intermediate in the formation of dTMP. However, as noted above, this exchange could be artifactually slow for reasons involving the stereochemistry of proton addition to or removal from C-5. Further, although intermediate 2 (Fig. 4) is on the reaction path to dTMP, the dihydropyrimidine adduct 3 is not, so the rate of formation of intermediate 2 may be much faster than that of 3.

Independent evidence for the presence of the adduct 3 verified this interpretation. This evidence includes: NMR studies of the corresponding covalent binary complex between TS and F-dUMP (25); isolation of the TS–dUMP binary complex by acid precipitation (26); isolation of and UV-difference spectroscopic evidence for TS–NO$_2$-dUMP adducts as transition-state analogs of intermediate 2 in Fig. 4 (19); and UV-difference spectroscopic evidence for a covalent TS-dUMP adduct in the presence of cofactor analogs (27). Finally, there is the crystal structure of a TS–dUMP–folate complex, showing that dUMP is covalently linked to TS, as indicated in intermediate 3 of Fig. 4 (28, 29). Taken together, the evidence strongly supports the existence of the covalent TS–dUMP intermediates, and the validity of using 5-H exchange as a probe for Michael adduct formation.

2. DEHALOGENATION OF 5-BROMO- AND 5-IODO-dUMP

TS catalyzes a facile dehalogenation of 5-bromo- and 5-iodo-dUMP in the presence of thiols according to Fig. 5 (15). The evidence for the mechanism is as follows: (i) the reaction is directly analogous to the chemical reactions in which the analogous mechanisms have been elucidated; (ii) 5-alkylthio-dUMP is a by-product of the TS-catalyzed dehalogenation of Br-dUMP (but not I-dUMP), which can only form by displacement of a 5-bromo dihydro intermediate followed by elimination, viz. partitioning of the covalent intermediate; (iii) the dehalogenation reactions of 6-^{3}H derivatives proceed with a large secondary isotope effect ($k_T/k_H = 1.23$), which confirms sp^3 rehybridization of C-6 during the course of the reaction.

3. ISOLATION OF COVALENT TS-dUMP COMPLEXES

TS–dUMP complexes can be isolated from *L. casei* by acid precipitation (26). Likewise, stable nonproductive TS–dUMP binary complexes are formed on one of the two subunits of the *Leishmania* TS (30). Although direct structural proof that these are covalent complexes is lacking, the proposed complexes are consistent with the formation of Michael adducts such as intermediate 3 in Fig. 4. Model systems of such adducts suggest that the adducts may be sufficiently stable for isolation (9, 10).

4. INTERACTION OF F-dUMP WITH TS

Studies of the interaction of F-dUMP with TS provide a substantial amount of information about the mechanism of the enzyme; indeed, FdUMP has been the single most important tool contributing to our current understanding of TS and related reactions. Such studies were central to the determination of several intermediates of the pathway, identification of the catalytic thiol of TS, elucidation of the role of the cofactor in such interactions, and characterization of other mechanistic aspects. As such, F-dUMP serves as a paradigm for mechanism-based inhibitors of TS and mechanistically related enzymes. Further, an understanding of the mechanism of inhibition of TS by F-dUMP has contributed directly to improved use of the drug in chemotherapy (31).

Some aspects of how our current understanding of this inhibitor was achieved are worth reviewing. 5-Fluorouracil was first synthesized 1957, and shown to be active as an anti-neoplastic agent (31). The drug is metabolized to nucleotides in much the same way as is uracil. The cytotoxic effects of fluorouracil are a result of two effects: (1) incorporation into RNA, which is poorly understood, and (2) inhibition of TS by F-dUMP. It remains contro-versial as to which of these effects predominates in a given cell line or situation; probably both occur and probably both are important. For the present discussion, we focus on aspects of TS inhibition by F-dUMP.

In the 1960s, a major mechanism for F-Ura anti-neoplastic activity was shown to involve the inhibition of TS by F-dUMP. However, the mechanism of inhibition was controversial. Some workers observed competitive inhibi-tion, others noncompetitive, and yet others observed competitive inhibition changing to noncompetitive (32). With the proposed mechanism of TS from model chemical reactions, and the known chemical susceptibility of the C-6 of F-dUMP toward nucleophiles, it was reasonable to suspect that covalent adduct formation of F-dUMP is an important aspect of its inhibition; the controversy regarding the type of inhibition could then be explained by the time-dependent nature of inhibition, and the differing times after initiation of the reaction that rate measurements were made. Within several years, the mechanism of F-dUMP inhibition of TS was elucidated, and the solution provided solid evidence for many of the salient features of the mechanism of catalysis of TS.

The currently accepted mechanism of F-dUMP inhibition of TS is shown in Fig. 7. F-dUMP binds to the enzyme, followed by CH_2H_4folate binding to form a reversible ternary complex. Activation of each of the two bound

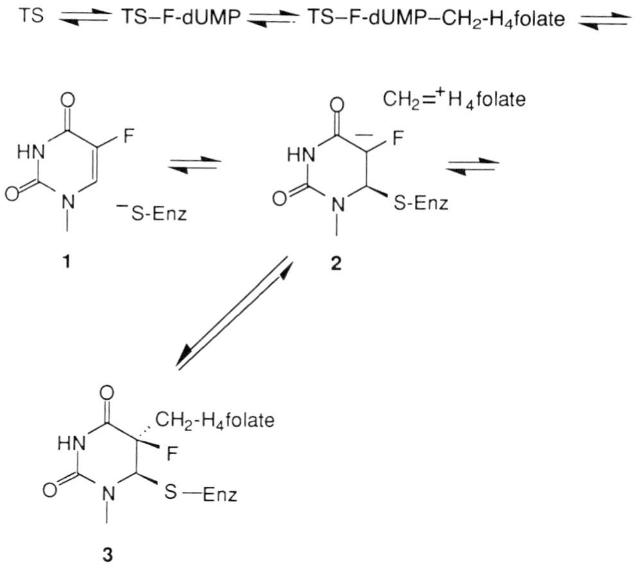

$$TS \rightleftharpoons TS\text{--}F\text{-}dUMP \rightleftharpoons TS\text{--}F\text{-}dUMP\text{--}CH_2\text{-}H_4folate \rightleftharpoons$$

FIG. 7. Mechanism of interaction of thymidylate synthase with F-dUMP.

ligands then occurs. First, the CH_2H_4folate is converted to the reactive 5-iminium ion, converting the one-carbon unit into a highly reactive electrophilic center. Second, the sulfhydryl of an active site cysteine residue (Cys-198 in *L. casei* TS) adds to the 6-position of F-dUMP to generate a carbanion equivalent at C-5. With the two reactants activated, the 5-carbon of the pyrimidine condenses with the one-carbon unit of the cofactor to give the covalent ternary complex **3**. This adduct is directly analogous to a steady-state intermediate formed in the normal enzymic reaction, except that the 5-H is replaced by F (cf. structures **3** in Figs. 4 and 6). In the normal reaction, the subsequent step is removal of the 5-H as a proton; since the C–F bond of the inhibitory complex cannot be broken, the reaction proceeds no further, and the covalent ternary complex accumulates.

Many studies provide the basis of our understanding of the mechanism of F-dUMP interaction with TS. In our opinion, some of the key initial observations that led to the understanding of the basic features of F-dUMP inhibition of TS are as follows. F-dUMP forms a stable covalent complex with TS which requires CH_2H_4folate (33). The complex is shown to be reversible under native conditions, but essentially irreversible when the protein is denatured. The properties of the covalent complex were subsequently elucidated (34, 35), and the role of the cofactor was substantiated. The structure of the covalent complex has been confirmed by UV spectral and ^{19}F NMR analysis of an active-site peptide isolated following proteolysis of the complex (36, 37). Evidence for the location of the one-carbon bridge at the N-5 position of the cofactor, rather than at N-10, was provided by the stability of the cofactor on this peptide (37) (substitution at N-5 is necessary to protect against oxidation), and this was later confirmed by oxidation studies of the ternary complex (38). The sulfhydryl of cysteine was shown to be the nucleophile attached to F-dUMP by sequence analysis of the F-dUMP peptide (36, 39, 40) and by differential labeling studies of thiol residues of TS (41).

NMR studies with ^{19}F of the F-dUMP–CH_2H_4folate–peptide showed that the enzyme nucleophile and the cofactor added across the 5,6 C = C of F-dUMP in a *trans* manner (25, 36, 42, 43). In the normal enzymic reaction, if the formation of the analogous dUMP–CH_2H_4folate–TS intermediate (**3** in Fig. 6) also proceeds by *trans* addition, subsequent elimination of the 5-H and thiol must proceed by an overall *cis* elimination to provide the products. This has interesting implications in regard to the possible conformational changes of bound intermediates during a turnover, which suggests complementary conformational changes of the enzyme (36). The initial addition of the thiolate to position 6 should be perpendicular to the plane of the ring, so the incipient carbanion at C-5 can be delocalized through the carbonyl system. Likewise, the approach of CH_2H_4folate to the sp^2 5-carbon will be with maximal orbital overlap, and perpendicular to the opposite face of the ring.

Consequently, the covalent adduct formed initially will contain the 6-thiol and the 5-CH_2H_4folate in *trans* pseudoaxial positions, whereas the 5- and 6-hydrogens will be *trans* pseudoequatorial. To remove the 5-H from the intermediate and form a delocalized carbanion at C-5, a conformational change would first have to occur to convert the cofactor to pseudoequatorial, and the 5-hydrogen to the axial position. Once the 5-H is removed and the carbanion is formed, subsequent reactions could readily occur. Thus, the stereochemistry of the covalent F-dUMP–CH_2H_4folate–peptide, together with basic chemical considerations, place the occurrence of a conformational change of the ligands–enzyme complex after formation of the adduct but before proton abstraction of 3 in Fig. 6. Crystal structures of TS–ligand complexes are in accord with these deductions (28, 29, 44).

Studies of α-secondary hydrogen isotope effects in the interaction of F-dUMP, CH_2H_4folate, and TS have confirmed aspects of the enzyme mechanism and revealed new information (14, 45). [6-^{3}H]F-dUMP has been used to demonstrate the rehybridization of the 6-C in the interaction of F-dUMP with TS, and to position this rehybridization in the reaction pathway. Theoretically, a maximal tritium isotope effect of about 23% is calculated for interconversion of [6-^{3}H]F-dUMP and the Michael adduct at equilibrium, with enrichment of the heavy isotope in the Michael adduct (45). When TS, [2-^{14}C, 6-^{3}H]F-dUMP, and CH_2H_4folate were equilibrated, the complex was enriched in tritium, and a K_T/K_H of 1.24 was determined. Depending on where the rehybridization occurs with respect to the rate-determining step, this large equilibrium isotope effect could be manifested as a kinetic inverse isotope effect ($k_T > k_H$) in formation of the adduct, in a normal isotope effect in reversal of the adduct, or in both directions. No kinetic isotope effect was seen in the formation of the complex, so adduct formation was either very early in the transition state of the rate-determining step, or post-rate-determining. A large normal isotope effect ($K_H/K_T = 1.23$) was seen in dissociation of the ternary complex, which was equal to the equilibrium isotope effect. Thus, in the direction of dissociation of the covalent complex, rehybridization occurs before the rate-determining step (pre-equilibrium) or late in the transition state of the rate-determining step. The isotope-effect data show that, in formation of the complex, adduct formation occurs very early in the transition state of the rate-determining step, or after the rate-determining step.

Danenberg and Danenberg (46) exploited the kinetics of dissociation of the F-dUMP–CH_2H_4folate–TS complex to ascertain the order of addition of the ligands to TS. Their approach is generally applicable to analogous isolable ternary complexes. Using the [6-^{3}H]F-dUMP–CH_2H_4folate–TS complex, they monitored the rate of dissociation of [6-^{3}H]F-dUMP as a function of CH_2H_4folate concentration. It can be seen in Fig. 8 that in an ordered

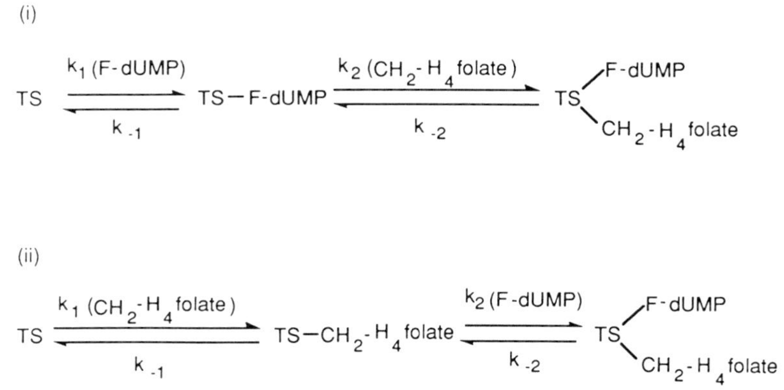

(i)

$$\text{TS} \underset{k_{-1}}{\overset{k_1\ (\text{F-dUMP})}{\rightleftharpoons}} \text{TS}-\text{F-dUMP} \underset{k_{-2}}{\overset{k_2\ (\text{CH}_2\text{-H}_4\text{folate})}{\rightleftharpoons}} \text{TS} \Big\langle \begin{matrix} \text{F-dUMP} \\ \text{CH}_2\text{-H}_4\text{folate} \end{matrix}$$

(ii)

$$\text{TS} \underset{k_{-1}}{\overset{k_1\ (\text{CH}_2\text{-H}_4\text{folate})}{\rightleftharpoons}} \text{TS}-\text{CH}_2\text{-H}_4\text{folate} \underset{k_{-2}}{\overset{k_2\ (\text{F-dUMP})}{\rightleftharpoons}} \text{TS} \Big\langle \begin{matrix} \text{F-dUMP} \\ \text{CH}_2\text{-H}_4\text{folate} \end{matrix}$$

Fig. 8. Ordered mechanisms for F-dUMP and CH_2H_4folate binding to thymidylate synthase (TS); (i) F-dUMP binding first, (ii) cofactor binding first.

mechanism with F-dUMP released from the ternary complex first, CH_2H_4folate would have no effect on the rate of dissociation of F-dUMP; in an ordered mechanism with CH_2H_4folate released first, the rate of dissociation of $[6\text{-}^3\text{H}]$F-dUMP would be suppressed, with no net release at infinite CH_2H_4folate concentration; with a random mechanism, the rate of $[6\text{-}^3\text{H}]$F-dUMP release would be suppressed, but not completely, at infinite concentrations of cofactor. Of course, the mechanism of association is the microscopic reverse of dissociation, so the order of addition of ligands can be deduced by these simple experiments on the rates of dissociation. Application of this approach to the F-dUMP–CH_2H_4folate–TS complex showed that an infinite concentration of CH_2H_4folate completely suppresses dissociation of F-dUMP. Thus, the mechanism is ordered with F-dUMP binding first, and cofactor last.

5. Interaction of CF_3-dUMP with TS

CF_3-dUMP is another inhibitor of TS discovered in the 1960s. Because it causes noncompetitive inhibition of the enzyme, and CF_3-Ura can acylate amines in neutral media, CF_3-dUMP was thought to act by irreversibly acylating some functional group of the enzyme (47). At the time, the C–F bond was considered stable under such conditions, and it was not obvious how acylation of TS might occur. Chemical model systems demonstrated that nucleophilic attack at C-6 can generate a carbanion at C-5 (Fig. 9), which would activate the C–F bonds and convert the CF_3 moiety to the exocyclic difluoromethylene intermediate, thus rendering the CF_3 group a reactive acylating agent (48). When TS is treated with CF_3-dUMP, there is a time-dependent loss of enzyme activity and loss of fluoride ion from the nu-

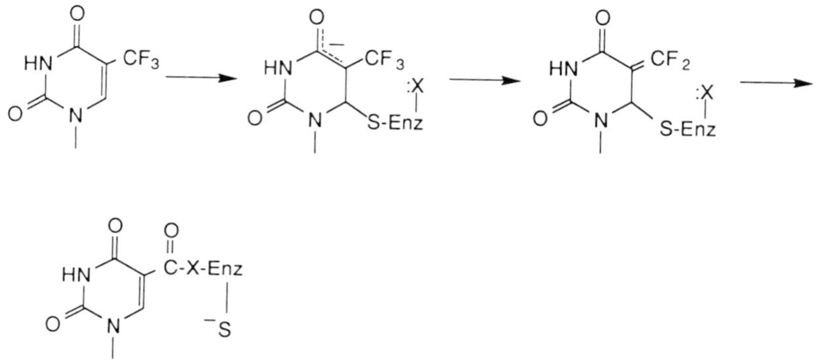

FIG. 9. Interaction of CF_3-dUMP with thymidylate synthase.

cleotide (49). It is probable that CF_3-dUMP acylates TS by the mechanism shown in Fig. 9, but the molecular aspects of the reaction remain unknown.

6. INTERACTION OF E-dUMP WITH TS

β,γ-Acetylenic carbonyl compounds have received much attention in the design of "suicide" inhibitors of enzymes (50). Although β,γ-acetylenic carbonyl compounds are normally inert, enzyme-catalyzed generation of a carbanion on the α-carbon can generate a conjugated allene; the latter is a good Michael acceptor, and if a nucleophile of the enzyme is juxtaposed to the reactive β-carbon, covalent bond formation can occur:

$$-\overset{\overset{\displaystyle O}{\|}}{C}-CH_2-C{\equiv}CH \rightleftharpoons -\overset{\overset{\displaystyle O}{\|}}{C}-\bar{C}H-C{\equiv}CH$$

$$\rightleftharpoons -\overset{\overset{\displaystyle O}{\|}}{C}-CH{=}C{=}CH_2$$

Consideration of the properties of TS toward dUMP analogs, and of the chemistry of β,γ-acetylenic carbonyl compounds, suggested that TS might catalyze the conversion of E-dUMP to a reactive allene (Fig. 10); nucleophilic attack at C-6 would generate the requisite carbanion at the α position, and protonation of the terminal acetylene carbon would result in the allene. Model studies show that such a reaction occurs readily with 2-mercaptoethanol, in which a thiol reacts with both the 6-position of the heterocycle to generate the allene and with reactive carbons of the allene intermediate (51). In the absence of CH_2H_4folate, TS catalyzes attack of the catalytic thiol at the 6-position of E-dUMP and formation of the expected

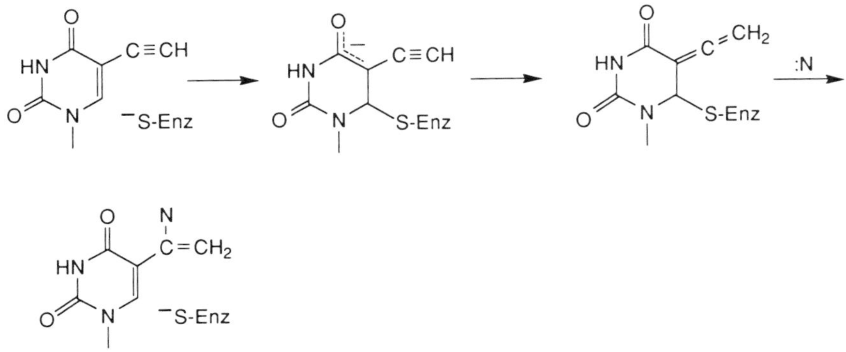

FIG. 10. Interaction of E-dUMP with thymidylate synthase. N, Nucleophile.

allene (51). However, the allene does not capture an enzyme nucleophile, but rather reacts with thiols or other nucleophiles in the medium, and regenerates active enzyme. That is, without cofactor, E-dUMP acts as an alternate substrate. Interestingly, in the presence of CH_2H_4folate, E-dUMP and related analogs cause time-dependent inhibition of the enzyme and form stoichiometric soluble E-dUMP–CH_2H_4folate–TS complexes (52). Although the chemical nature of these complexes has not been elucidated, they probably arise from Michael adducts between TS and E-dUMP.

7. INTERACTION OF NO$_2$-dUMP WITH TS

A QSAR study of 5-substituted dUMP analogs as reversible inhibitors of TS led to the prediction that NO_2-dUMP would be a potent reversible inhibitor of TS with a $K_i \simeq 10^{-8}\ M$ (53). Further, the known susceptibility of the 6-position of 1-substituted 5-nitrouracil toward nucleophiles led us to believe that NO_2-dUMP would form a covalent adduct with TS. Both of the suppositions proved correct. NO_2-dUMP was a potent competitive inhibitor of TS with a $K_i \simeq 10^{-8}\ M$, quite close to the value predicted by QSAR. Several observations demonstrated that NO_2-dUMP is also a mechanism-based inhibitor of TS (19). Incubation of TS plus NO_2-dUMP leads to a time-dependent loss of enzyme activity. Using labeled NO_2-dUMP, and UV spectral titrations, it was shown that complexes with a stoichiometry of one NO_2-dUMP per monomer of enzyme were formed, which could be isolated on nitrocellulose filters. Dissociation of the [2-^{14}C, 6-^{3}H]NO_2-dUMP from the enzyme proceeded with a large secondary isotope effect ($k_H/k_T > 1.2$), suggesting that the C-6 was sp^3 hybridized within the complex. Further, the UV spectrum was characteristic of an adduct of a thiol to the 6-position of NO_2-dUMP. Interestingly, there was no evidence that the cofactor participated in complex formation. These observations suggest that the interaction

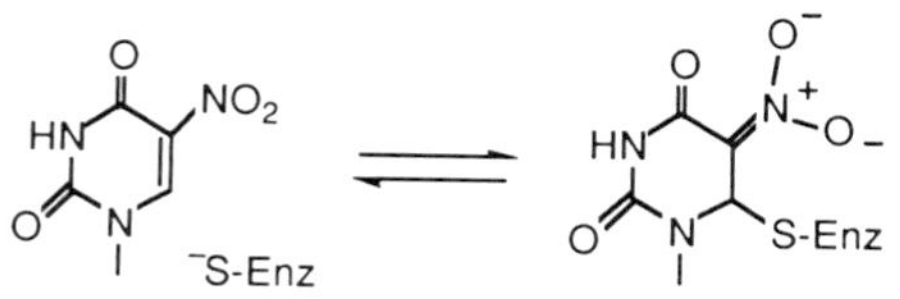

FIG. 11. Interaction of NO_2-dUMP with thymidylate synthase.

is as shown in Fig. 11, where the covalent complex arises from addition of the catalytic thiol of TS to position 6 of NO_2-dUMP. The adduct is stabilized by resonance forms of the 5-nitro group, which explains why a ternary complex with cofactor (which would be destabilized) does not form.

8. INTERACTION OF BV-dUMP WITH TS

5-(2-Bromovinyl)dUrd shows activity as an antiviral agent, particularly for HSV-1. It was proposed (54) that, upon addition of a nucleophile to position 6 of BV-dUMP, a carbanion would be generated at position 5 that could lead to rearrangement of the bromovinyl group to a conjugated allylic bromide, with reactive electrophilic centers at both the α and β positions (Fig. 12). We surmised that if such an intermediate was generated at the active site of TS, covalent reaction between either one of the generated electrophilic sites and a nucleophile of the enzyme could give irreversible inhibition. When BV-dUMP was allowed to react with TS in the presence of mercaptans but in the absence of cofactor, there was no time-dependent inhibition (54). Instead, BV-dUMP was a substrate of TS, forming products in which sulfhydryl or water added to the α and β positions of the transient dihydropyrimidine adduct (Fig. 12). It appears that nucleophiles of TS are not suitably juxtaposed to the activated carbons of BV-dUMP in the binary

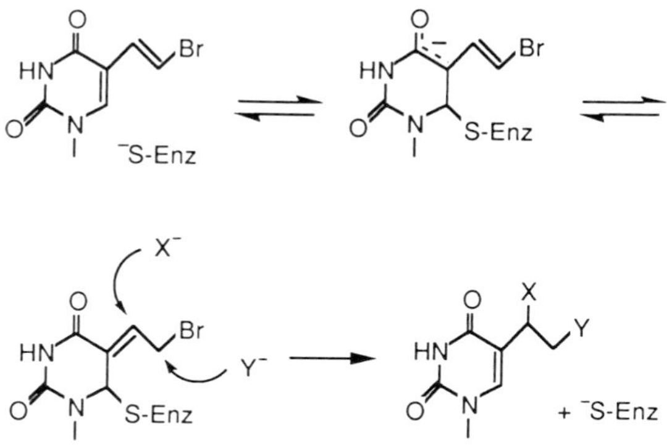

FIG. 12. Interaction of BV-dUMP with thymidylate synthase.

complex to react with them. Nevertheless, the observed chemistry strongly suggests the intermediacy of Michael adducts in the pathway.

9. SECONDARY α-HYDROGEN ISOTOPE EFFECTS AT C-6

These isotope effects have been observed with several dUMP analogs that serve as alternative substrates or mechanism-based inhibitors of TS (14). As such, they convincingly show that C-6 undergoes the sp^2-to-sp^3 rehybridizations required to form the proposed covalent enzyme intermediates or stable complexes. In many cases, these analogs have provided independent evidence for the mechanism, which, together with other observations, strongly supports the existence of Michael adducts in these reactions. The technology for detecting such secondary α-hydrogen isotope effects uses the appropriate [6-^{3}H]dUMP analog labeled elsewhere with ^{14}C, and monitors the ^{3}H/^{14}C ratio in the product or dissociated ligand. The TS reactions studied using α-secondary isotope effects include dehalogenation of Br-dUMP (15), conversion of E-dUMP to 5-acetyl-dUMP (51), dissociation of the TS–F-dUMP–CH$_2$H$_4$folate complex (45), and dissociation of the TS–NO$_2$-dUMP complex (19).

B. dUMP and dCMP Hydroxymethylases

dUMP hydroxymethylase catalyzes the hydroxymethylation of position 5 of dUMP using 5,10-CH$_2$H$_4$folate as cofactor, and yields 5-hydroxymethyl-dUMP and H$_4$folate as products. The enzyme is found in *Bacillus subtilis* infected with certain bacteriophage such as *SPO1* (55). dCMP hydroxymethylase catalyzes a similar reaction with dCMP as substrate, and is found in *E. coli* infected with T-even phage (56). Formally, the reactions are analogous to the TS reaction, except that there is no redox step involving reduction of the one-carbon unit and oxidation of H$_4$folate. The reactions are believed to occur by a mechanism analogous to TS up to and including formation of the putative exocyclic intermediate **5** (Fig. 6). At this stage, the electrophilic carbon of the exocyclic intermediate reacts with water (instead of the hydride from H$_4$folate, as in TS) to generate the 5-hydroxymethyl nucleotides. The evidence for the mechanisms of these enzymes is as follows:

dUMP hydroxymethylase catalyzes the 5-H exchange of [5-^{3}H]dUMP in the presence or absence of CH_2H_4folate. In the presence of cofactor, exchange of the 5-H of dUMP for protons of water proceeds at about one-third the rate of hydroxymethylation (57). In the absence of cofactor, the 5-H exchange of [5-^{3}H]dUMP occurs at a rate about 6% of that in the presence of CH_2H_4folate (i.e., about 2% of the rate of hydroxymethylation). These data require a 5,6-dihydro intermediate containing two hydrogens at C-5, which can undergo non-stereospecific proton abstraction; as previously described for the analogous reaction of TS (Fig. 6), this intermediate must form from protonation of a steady-state intermediate and is not on the normal reaction path.

dUMP hydroxymethylase is inhibited by F-dUMP in the presence of CH_2H_4folate (57). Stable complexes containing F-dUMP, CH_2H_4folate, and dUMP hydroxymethylase can be isolated under native or denaturing (SDS) conditions, demonstrating that the enzyme is covalently complexed to both F-dUMP and CH_2H_4folate. The covalent complex of F-dUMP, CH_2H_4folate, and dUMP hydroxymethylase is believed to be analogous to that formed with TS (57).

Considering what is known of the TS reaction and model chemical counterparts, we are reasonably confident that a mechanism analogous to that in Fig. 6 applies to the dUMP hydroxymethylase reaction. In the future, dUMP hydroxymethylase should be cloned and expressed in heterologous systems, so that sufficient amounts of enzyme are available for detailed studies. We anticipate that the enzyme will show high structural homology with TS and share many common features. The three-dimensional structure will be particularly interesting, since it may reveal information as to how the hydride transfer of TS and the hydrolysis step of dUMP hydroxymethylase differ.

In addition to the normal hydroxymethylation reaction, dCMP hydroxymethylase catalyzes an exchange of the 5-H of dCMP for protons of water in the absence of CH_2H_4folate (58), and the debromination of 5-bromo-dCMP (59). As previously described, both of these reactions indicate the intermediacy of 5,6-dihydropyrimidine adducts, which form upon Michael addition. However, although 5-fluoro-dCMP is a competitive inhibitor of dCMP hydroxymethylase, a covalent complex between the enzyme, 5-fluoro-dCMP, and CH_2H_4folate was not demonstrated (12). Several possible explanations are consistent with this in the context of the proposed mechanism for dCMP hydroxymethylase, but the actual reason remains unresolved. The dCMP hydroxymethylase from T4 phage has recently been cloned, sequenced, and expressed (60). Interestingly, but perhaps not unexpectedly, dCMP hydroxymethylase shows high homology with TS.

C. DNA-Cytosine Methyltransferase

DCMTs catalyze the sequence-specific methylation of cytosine residues of DNA using AdoMet to give 5-methyl-C residues and AdoHcy. The DCMTs are widespread in Type II restriction-modification systems of prokaryotes, serving to protect host DNA from destruction by partner restriction endonucleases. In mammalian cells, methylation of C residues of DNA by DCMT is believed to be important in cell differentiation and regulation.

Based on what was known of the chemistry of methylation of position 5 of pyrimidines, the effects of certain inhibitors of DCMT, and the mechanism of TS, a minimal mechanism for catalysis of DCMT has been proposed (61). As indicated previously in Fig. 3 (where R = CH_3 and X = NH_2), the key step is attack of an enzyme nucleophile at C-6 of the target C residue to form a reactive dihydropyrimidine intermediate; subsequent steps involves reactions analogous to the TS reaction, except that AdoMet, rather than the folate cofactor, serves as the methyl donor, and carbon transfer is irreversible. Evidence for this mechanism was obtained using approaches established for TS (13, 62, 63) and is detailed below.

First, HhaI methylase, a bacterial DCMT, catalyzes the exchange of the 5-H of target C residues in DNA in the absence of AdoMet (13), which provides strong evidence for a covalent Michael adduct. Interestingly, the k_{cat} of the exchange reaction is about 7-fold that of methylation; similar exchange reactions catalyzed by other enzymes described here (TS, dUMP hydroxymethylase, and RUMT) are invariably slower than methylation. The addition of AdoMet suppresses the exchange reaction and, at saturating concentrations, loss of protons from carbon 5 of the substrate is completely accounted for by release during methylation. Likewise, the product AdoHcy completely suppresses the 5-H exchange reaction; only the binary enzyme–DNA complex, not the ternary complex containing AdoMet or AdoHcy, undergoes 5-H exchange. Second, with DNA containing 5-azacytidine, several bacterial methylases form covalent complexes that are stable to denaturants (63); the enzyme–DNA linkages show sequence specificity expected of the methylases. From the known susceptibility of the 6-carbon of 5-azacytidine to nucleophiles, it was surmised that a covalent adduct was formed between the enzyme and azaC residues in the target sequences. Third, in the presence of AdoMet, poly(FdC–dG) causes a time-dependent loss of enzyme activity, with concomitant formation of a covalent (i.e., stable to SDS) complex containing enzyme, polynucleotide, and the methyl group of AdoMet (62). We surmised that this complex is analogous to the F-dUMP–CH_2H_4folate–TS complex (3 in Fig. 7).

The identity of the nucleophile that adds to position 6 is not known.

However, based on chemical precedent and the sensitivity of *Hha*I methylase to thiol reagents, it has been proposed that a sulfhydryl group of a cysteine residue is the nucleophilic catalyst (*13*). Further, it has been proposed that Cys-81 of *Hha*I methylase is the nucleophilic catalyst, since it is conserved as a proline–cysteine doublet in all DCMTs sequenced to date (*13*; see *64* and references therein).

The studies on the interaction of the DCMTs with DNA containing 5-azaC or F–C also provide information on why incorporation of these analogs into DNA has such profound inhibitory effects on methylation of DNA: They result in stoichiometric, essentially irreversible inhibition of the DCMT.

An interesting and possibly important idea was spawned (*13*) by the dual observations that (i) the interaction of *Hha*I methylase, DNA, and AdoHcy proceeds by an ordered mechanism, with DNA binding first, and (ii) that saturating concentrations of AdoHcy completely inhibit the 5-H exchange reaction of poly(dC–dG). The proposal is that dissociation–reassociation, or processivity of DNA, is inhibited in the ternary complex, and only occurs in the binary complex. One can envision this as follows. For exchange to occur, the enzyme must relocate to a new tetranucleotide recognition site, either by lateral diffusion along DNA in the binary complex, or by dissociation–reassociation of the binary complex. The ordered binding prevents this from occurring in the ternary complex. That is, at saturating concentration of AdoHcy, the E–DNA complex is completely partitioned toward the ternary complex, and neither processivity nor dissociation is permitted. Thus, the presence of high concentrations of a second ligand in an ordered reaction prevents dissociation of the first, and "locks" the enzyme on a specific sequence, permitting neither processive movement along DNA nor dissociation. The importance of this apparently obvious phenomenon in biological systems has not received significant attention.

The generalization to be made is that after addition of DNA to a protein, binding of another molecule in an ordered mechanism to form a dead-end ternary complex can inhibit dissociation or lateral movement of the protein along DNA. Thus, a protein can be "stalled" at a nucleotide sequence simply by specific binding of another ligand; in such a manner, the half-life and specificity of a protein–DNA complex could be regulated by the concentration of the second binding ligand. This property could have important consequences in regulatory DNA–protein complexes, but is limited to those systems that form ternary complexes by strictly ordered mechanisms.

$$
\begin{array}{ccccc}
k_1\ (\text{DNA}) & & k_2\ (\text{AdoHcy}) & & \\
\text{E} \quad \rightleftharpoons & & \text{E—DNA} \quad \rightleftharpoons & & \text{E—DNA—AdoHcy} \\
k_{-1} & & k_{-2} & &
\end{array}
$$

D. tRNA-Uracil Methyltransferase

RUMT catalyzes the AdoMet-dependent methylation of a specific uridine residue in the T-loop of tRNA to give the 5-methyl-Urd found in most tRNAs. The similarity of this enzyme to others that catalyze one-carbon transfer reactions to C-5 of pyrimidines suggested that they share mechanistic features (65). The mechanism of RUMT is shown in Fig. 13. In the absence of AdoMet, RUMT catalyzes 5-H exchange between the target uracil, labeled as [5-^{3}H]Ura-tRNA, and protons of water at a rate that is 1% of the methylation rate (65), providing evidence for a Michael adduct. Further, in the presence of AdoMet and F-Ura-substituted tRNA, a covalent complex is formed containing enzyme, F-Ura-tRNA, and the methyl group of the cofactor. It was surmised that the complex was analogous to the other covalent adducts described for TS, F-dUMP, and CH_2H_4folate (Fig. 7). Recently, Cys-324 of RUMT was identified as the nucleophile covalently attached to F-Ura-tRNA and is therefore concluded to be the catalytic nucleophile (J. T. Kealey and D. V. Santi, unpublished).

In more recent studies, it was shown that small oligoribonucleotides corresponding to the T-arm stem–loop structure served as substrates of RUMT (66). The minimal structure contained the seven-base loop and two adjacent base-pairs of the stem, and a consensus sequence that defined permissible bases in the minimal structure has been established (X. Gu and D. V. Santi, unpublished). These oligoribonucleotides provide more manageable substrates than intact tRNA for studies of enzyme mechanism and inhibition.

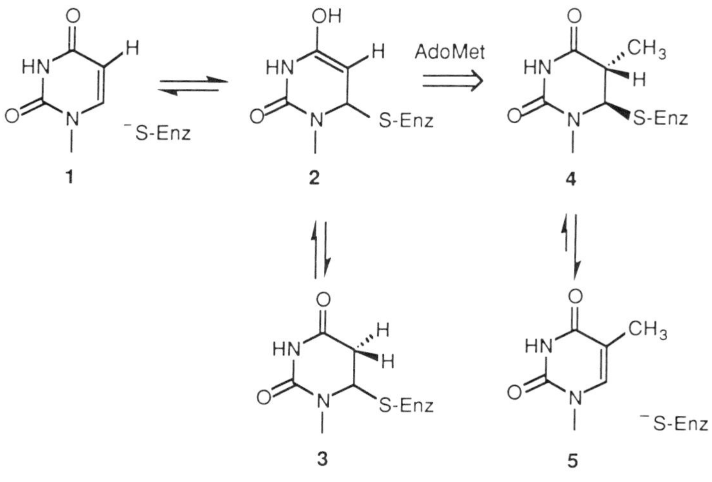

FIG. 13. Mechanism of tRNA-uracil methyltransferase.

In the absence of AdoMet, RUMT and unmodified tRNA also formed a binary complex stable to SDS–PAGE (X. Gu and D. V. Santi, unpublished). The covalent complex had an apparent molecular mass of about 54 kDa on SDS–PAGE, well resolved from the native enzyme with a molecular mass of 42 kDa. Similar complexes were formed between RUMT and the small T-arm substrates (but not nonsubstrates). Interestingly, when AdoMet was added to such complexes, the covalent complex disappeared and methylated tRNA was formed. We concluded that a binary covalent complex was an intermediate, or derived from an intermediate, in the reaction pathway. The most reasonable candidate for the stable complex is a covalent Michael adduct between the nucleophilic catalyst and position 6 of the heterocycle, which can turn over to product. The first-formed adduct in the reaction path would be a carbanion equivalent, such as an enol, which can undergo methylation by AdoMet; however, such structures are unstable and would be expected to undergo tautomerization to the 5-dihydro derivative 3 upon denaturation (Fig. 13). Since the enzyme catalyzes exchange of the 5-H of the target uracil residue (65), the dihydro intermediate can be formed on the enzyme, although this intermediate is not directly on the methylation pathway. Thus, the product we isolate by SDS–PAGE is most likely intermediate 3 of Fig. 13.

It has been reported that in crude extracts of *E. coli* containing an expressing plasmid for RUMT, the enzyme is found both in its native form with an apparent molecular mass of 42 kDa and in a form with an apparent molecular mass of about 54 kDa (67). The high-molecular-mass form contains tightly bound RNA, and the complex is stable to SDS–PAGE. We have made similar observations in *E. coli* cells containing another expression vector, which produces about 5% of total protein as RUMT; in crude extracts, almost half the enzyme is bound to RNA (68). Neither the identity nor the function of the RNA species bound to RUMT is currently established. However, the fact that the complex is so prominent suggests that such protein–nucleic acid complexes exist *in vivo*, and underlines the importance of Michael adducts in protein–nucleic acid complexes (see Section II,G).

E. Cytidine Deaminase

Cytidine deaminase and dCMP deaminase catalyze the deamination of the respective substrates to uridine and dUMP. The basis for believing that such reactions may occur via dihydropyrimidine adducts relied on model chemical counterparts, which indicate that a variety of nucleophiles catalyze the deamination of cytidine by adding to position 6 of the heterocycle, and that the resultant 5,6-dihydrocytosines are quite susceptible to deamination (6, 7). However, it has been shown convincingly that cytidine deaminase proceeds by a direct displacement of water on the 4-amino group of the

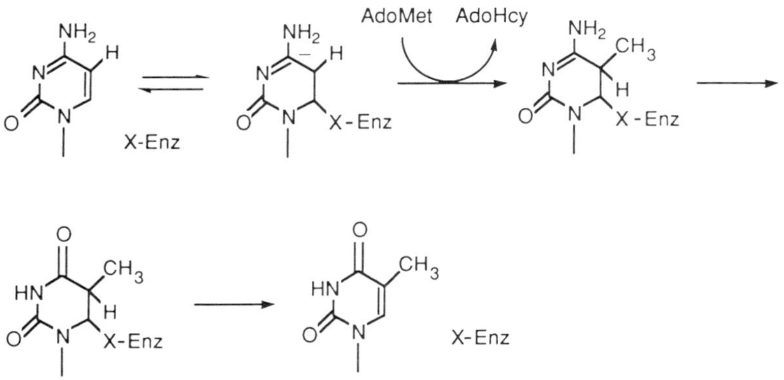

FIG. 14. Mechanism of methylation/deamination in repeat-induced point mutation.

parent pyrimidine (8). Nevertheless, chemical precedent for Michael adducts in such reactions is strong, and continued investigations in other systems are warranted.

Recently (69), it has been suggested that an enzyme involved in changes of cytosine to thymine in premeiotic mutation of *Neurospora crassa* DNA may involve both methylation and deamination in a process termed "repeat-induced point mutation." Further, it was suggested that the conversion may involve both methylation and deamination from a common Michael adduct. In this reaction, the Michael adduct would form at the target cytidine residue to allow methylation at C-5 as in the DCMT reaction; the 5-methyl-5,6-dihydropyrimidine adduct formed would undergo deamination while still bound to the enzyme, and β-elimination would result in the observed products (Fig. 14). If correct, this example illustrates the economy inherent in the use of a Michael adduct in both protein–nucleic acid recognition and enzyme catalysis.

F. tRNA-Pseudouridine Synthase

Pseudouridine synthase catalyzes the post-transcriptional conversion of a uridine residue of tRNA to pseudouridine. This interesting reaction involves (a) cleavage of the glycosyl bond, (b) repositioning the substrates so that C-5 of the uracil is juxtaposed with the reactive carbon-1 of the ribose moiety, and (c) formation of the C-1′ to C-5 carbon–carbon bond. As described elsewhere, dihydropyrimidine intermediates can facilitate both of these reactions: cleavage of the glycosyl bond and electrophilic displacement (carbon–carbon bond formation) at C-5 of a uridine residue. Based on this reasoning, we proposed a mechanism to explain conversion of uridine in tRNA to pseudouridine (2) (Fig. 15). If a nucleophile of the enzyme adds to

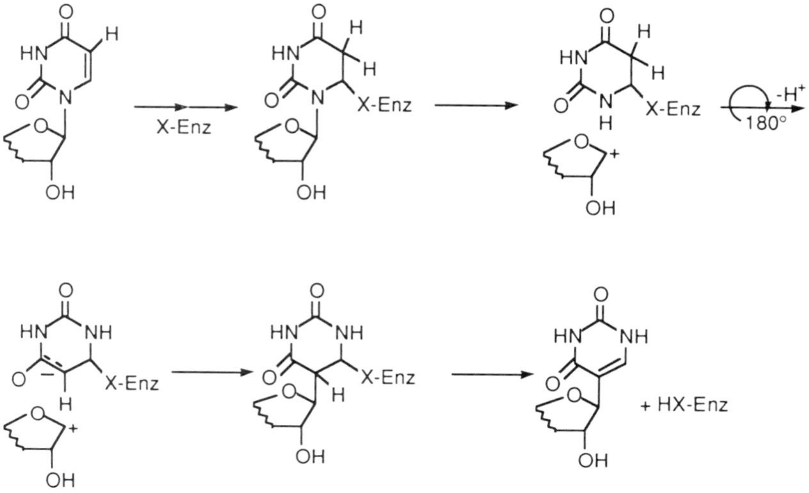

FIG. 15. Mechanism of pseudouridine synthase.

carbon 6 of the target uridine to form a Michael adduct, the glycosyl bond should be more susceptible to cleavage; the carbonium ion at C-1 of the ribose could be held in waiting as a covalent adduct with the enzyme or water. After rotation of the H_2-Ura ring 180° about the axis intersecting the covalently bound C-6 and N-3, the 5-carbon of the pyrimidine would be juxtaposed with the C-1′ of the ribose. After proton abstraction at C-5, coupling with a ribosyl carbonium ion could occur, and a β-elimination reaction would generate free enzyme and product. The important aspect of this mechanism is that through one simple transformation (viz. formation of a covalent Michael adduct), complicated biochemical conversions can readily be explained in terms of individual reactions that have chemical precedent.

In early studies, we were unable to demonstrate covalent complexes upon denaturation of unmodified tRNA and pseudouridine synthase (L. Hardy and D. V. Santi, unpublished). Recently, Kammen et al. (70) purified E. coli pseudouridine synthase of the HisT operon and showed tight binding to tRNA; however, they could not demonstrate covalent adducts by denaturation of binary enzyme–tRNA complexes. However, the failure to isolate covalent adducts directly by denaturation does not disprove the mechanism; in fact, since such adducts would be steady-state intermediates, it is not surprising that they are difficult to isolate. We remain optimistic about the validity of the proposed mechanism of pseudouridine synthase, and feel that other approaches described here to detect dihydropyrimidine intermediates are worth pursuing with this system.

G. Michael Adducts in Protein–Nucleic Acid Interactions

In Section II,A, C, and D, we discussed such enzymes as DCMT and RUMT, which bind polynucleotide substrates and form Michael adducts during catalysis. Reversible Michael adducts may also play important roles in binding interactions of proteins and nucleic acids per se. There are several advantageous features of such interactions. (i) Since adducts would only form within a certain sequence context, they could add a dimension of specificity for recognition. An example of this is the aforementioned RUMT–tRNA interaction, where Michael adducts require a two-base stem and a seven-base loop with a certain "consensus" sequence, and form an extremely tight covalent complex. (ii) The adduct could provide binding affinity, the magnitude of which is determined by the system. For example, the covalent adduct of TS with various nucleotides may increase binding affinity up to 10^5-fold, depending on the nucleotide. (iii) The adduct may modify the kinetics of the system, and effectively control the occupancy time of the sequence by the protein. One can imagine benefits of controlling the occupancy time of a protein at sequences such as promoters or enhancers, which would allow appropriate timing of other necessary events. A special example of this is DCMT, which, as previously described, is held fast to its recognition sequence by the product of the reaction, AdoHcy (13).

There are several reported proposals of Michael adducts in protein–nucleic acid complexes which are not steady-state intermediates of enzyme reactions. For example, it has been proposed that aminoacyl-tRNA synthetases form a Michael adduct at U-8 of tRNA (71, 72). The evidence is that the enzyme catalyzes exchange between the 5-H of U-8 in cognate tRNAs and water, and undergoes putative covalent bond formation with position 6 of BrUrd. It has also been suggested that bacteriophage R17 coat protein undergoes covalent bond formation with a 21-nucleotide RNA hairpin containing a specific binding site for that protein, as well as 5-bromopyrimidine nucleosides (73). A transient covalent adduct stable to SDS–PAGE has been proposed to occur between a 50-kDa protein and a stem–loop structure in the 5′ noncoding region of poliovirus (74). Finally, as cited above, in the absence of AdoMet, RUMT undergoes reversible Michael adduct formation with U-54 of tRNA and oligoribonucleotide analogs of the T-arm, and the adducts are sufficiently stable to allow isolation. The reaction is also inhibited by BrUrd and analogs (X. Gu and D. V. Santi, unpublished).

Covalent Michael adducts between proteins and nucleic acids may be difficult to demonstrate. The adducts are reversible, so there is no evidence in the dissociated components that the interaction has occurred. Approaches to detecting such complexes rely on experience with analogous systems of enzyme and small molecules. The following are approaches we feel are best suited to the task.

(i) Ideally, the complex could be physically isolated under protein denaturing conditions that disrupt noncovalent interactions (e.g., SDS–PAGE). The caveat is that many such complexes reverse during dissociation, so a negative result does not provide an answer to the question.

(ii) Exchange of the 5-H of [5-^{3}H]U or [5-^{3}H]C in nucleic acids would provide good evidence for a Michael adduct. However, the substrate may not undergo isotope exchange because of stereochemical or kinetic constraints, so lack of exchange does not rule out the intermediate.

(iii) One of the mechanism-based inhibitors or alternate substrates described for TS may be incorporated into the oligonucleotide (e.g., CF$_3$-dUMP, Br-dUMP, and ethynyl-dUMP). Upon formation of the Michael adduct, the 5-substituent may undergo activation and subsequent reaction. Conversion of the normally unreactive analog to an appropriate product would suggest a covalent Michael adduct.

(iv) Utilization of an analog that forms a more stable covalent adduct may facilitate isolation and identification. For example, fluorouracil seems to form more stable covalent complexes than uracil or thymine, and fluorine NMR could distinguish covalent and noncovalent complexes. Of course, large quantities of well-defined relatively small components are required for NMR experiments, so this approach is limited.

(v) Finally, inhibition of the interaction by BrUrd and related analogs has been used as evidence for such covalent complexes. The idea is that a covalent protein–BrUrd adduct would inhibit the formation of the natural adduct by forming a stable protein–BrUrd adduct. As described, the method has presumably been successful with three known interactions: aminoacyl-tRNA synthetase–tRNA, RUMT–tRNA, and bacteriophage R17 coat protein–RNA.

Although the use of BrUrd has pointed toward the formation of Michael adducts, we are skeptical about the mechanism and thus cautious about its use and interpretations. First, the BrUrd analog must be used in multi-millimolar concentrations to display the effect, and it is difficult to envision how the analog can specifically and productively compete with the target residue of the nucleic acid, which usually binds at low concentrations. Second, the properties of the putative BrUrd complexes do not parallel those of model chemical or enzymic systems studied in detail. In the model systems, thiols result in dehalogenation of the adduct and production of Urd. In the cases examined, the adduct is reversed by treatment with mercaptans, with release of the unchanged BrUrd residue (72, 73). This requires that added thiols mediate the cleavage of the thiol ether bond of the adduct, and this reaction has no chemical precedent. Without resolution of these discrepancies or alternative supporting evidence, one should be conservative in interpreting results of BrUrd analog interactions with nucleic acid-binding proteins.

It is our opinion that Michael adducts of pyrimidines will prove to be important intermediates for a subset of protein–nucleic interactions. The interaction provides a simple solution to issues such as high affinity and specificity, and has been demonstrated in several cases. The fact that it has not been observed more frequently may simply reflect the difficulty of the analysis. With the availability of more suitable systems and approaches, we will learn how widespread such interactions are.

ACKNOWLEDGEMENTS

The authors wish to acknowledge the support of USPHS Grants CA14394 and AI19358. We thank present and previous students and post-doctoral fellows who have contributed to D.V.S.'s laboratory on the topics covered in this review.

REFERENCES

1. A. L. Pogolotti and D. V. Santi, in "Bioorganic Chemistry" (E. E. Van Tamelen, ed.), p. 277. Academic Press, New York, 1977.
2. D. V. Santi, Y. Wataya and A. Matsuda, in "Enzyme-Activated Irreversible Inhibitors" (N. Seiler, M. J. Jung, and J. Koch-Weser, eds.), p. 291. Elsevier/North-Holland, New York, 1978.
3. D. V. Santi and P. V. Danenberg, in "Folates and Pteridines" (R. L. Blakeley and S. J. Benkovic, eds.), p. 343. Wiley, New York, 1984.
4. R. Shapiro and R. S. Klein, Bchem 6, 3576 (1967).
5. T. E. Notari, J. Pharm. Sci. 56, 804 (1967).
6. M. Sono, Y. Wataya and H. Hayatsu, JACS 95, 4745 (1973).
7. B. F. Evans, G. N. Mitchell and R. Wolfenden, Bchem 14, 621 (1975).
8. L. Frick, C. Yang, V. E. Marquez and R. Wolfenden, Bchem 28, 9423 (1989).
9. J. J. Prior and D. V. Santi, JBC 259, 2429 (1984).
10. J. J. Prior, D. V. Santi and J. Maley, JBC 259, 2422 (1984).
11. A. L. Pogolotti, C. Weill and D. V. Santi, Bchem 18, 2794 (1979).
12. R. Subramaniam, Y. Wang, C. K. Mathews and D. V. Santi, ABB 274, 11 (1989).
13. J. C. Wu and D. V. Santi, JBC 262, 4778 (1987).
14. T. W. Bruice and D. V. Santi, in "Isotope Effects in Enzyme Mechanisms" (P. Cook, ed.), p. 457, Ch. 19. CRC Press, Boca Raton, Florida, 1991.
15. C. Garrett, Y. Wataya and D. V. Santi, Bchem 18, 2798 (1979).
16. Y. Wataya and D. V. Santi, JACS 99, 4535 (1977).
17. F. A. Sedor and E. G. Sander, JACS 98, 2314 (1976).
18. R. J. Cisneros and R. B. Dunlap, BBA 1039, 149 (1990).
19. Y. Wataya, A. Matsuda and D. V. Santi, JBC 255, 5538 (1980).
20. M. Friedkin, FP 18, 230 (1959).
21. D. V. Santi and A. L. Pogolotti, Bchem 13, 456 (1974).
22. D. V. Santi and C. F. Brewer, JACS 90, 6236 (1968).
23. D. V. Santi and C. F. Brewer, Bchem 12, 2416 (1973).
24. M. I. Lomax and G. R. Greenberg, JBC 242, 109 (1967).

25. R. A. Byrd, W. H. Dawson, P. D. Ellis and R. B. Dunlap, *JACS* **99**, 6139 (1977).
26. R. J. Cisneros and R. B. Dunlap, *Anal. Biochem.* **186**, 202 (1990).
27. A. L. Pogolotti, P. V. Danenberg and D. V. Santi, *J. Med. Chem.* **29**, 478 (1986).
28. W. R. Montfort, K. M. Perry, E. B. Fauman, J. S. Finer-Moore, G. F. Maley, L. Hardy, F. Maley and R. M. Stroud, *Bchem* **29**, 6964 (1990).
29. D. A. Matthews, J. E. Villafranca, C. A. Janson, W. W. Smith, K. Welsh and S. Freer, *JMB* **214**, 937 (1990).
30. E. P. Garvey and D. V. Santi, *JBC* **262**, 9068 (1987).
31. S. G. Arbuck, *Cancer* **63**, 1036 (1989).
32. R. L. Blakeley, "The Biochemistry of Folic Acid and Related Pteridines." Elsevier, New York, 1969.
33. D. V. Santi and C. S. McHenry, *PNAS* **69**, 1855 (1972).
34. P. V. Danenberg, R. J. Langenbach and C. Heidelberger, *Bchem* **13**, 926 (1974).
35. D. V. Santi, C. S. McHenry and H. Sommer, *Bchem* **13**, 471 (1974).
36. T. L. James, A. L. Pogolotti, K. M. Ivanetich, Y. Wataya, S. S. Lam and D. V. Santi, *BBRC* **72**, 404 (1976).
37. H. Sommer and D. V. Santi, *BBRC* **57**, 689 (1974).
38. A. M. Pellino and P. V. Danenberg, *JBC* **260**, 10996 (1985).
39. A. L. Pogolotti, K. M. Ivanetich, H. Sommer and D. V. Santi, *BBRC* **70**, 972 (1976).
40. R. L. Bellisario, G. F. Maley, J. H. Galivan and F. Maley, *PNAS* **73**, 1848 (1976).
41. G. F. Maley, F. Maley and C. M. Baugh, *ABB* **216**, 551 (1982).
42. R. A. Byrd, W. H. Dawson, P. D. Ellis and R. B. Dunlap, *JACS* **100**, 7478 (1978).
43. C. A. J. Lewis, P. D. Ellis and R. B. Dunlap, *Bchem* **20**, 2275 (1981).
44. D. A. Matthews, K. Appelt, S. J. Oatley and N. H. Xuong, *JMB*, **214**, 923 (1990).
45. T. W. Bruice and D. V. Santi, *Bchem* **21**, 6703 (1982).
46. P. V. Danenberg and K. D. Danenberg, *Bchem* **17**, 4018 (1978).
47. P. Reyes and C. Heidelberger, *Mol. Pharmacol.* **1**, 14 (1965).
48. D. V. Santi and T. T. Sakai, *Bchem* **10**, 3598 (1971).
49. D. V. Santi, A. L. Pogolotti, T. L. James, Y. Wataya, K. M. Ivanetich and S. M. Lam, *ACS Symp. Ser.* **28**, 57 (1976).
50. R. R. Rando, *in* "Methods in Enzymology" (W. B. Jakoby and M. Wilchek, eds.), Vol. 46, p. 158. Academic Press, New York, 1977.
51. P. J. Barr, M. J. Robins and D. V. Santi, *Bchem* **22**, 1696 (1983).
52. P. J. Barr, P. A. Nolan, D. V. Santi and M. J. Robins, *J. Med. Chem.* **24**, 1385 (1981).
53. Y. Wataya, D. V. Santi and C. Hansch, *J. Med. Chem.* **20**, 1469 (1977).
54. P. J. Barr, N. J. Oppenheimer and D. V. Santi, *JBC* **258**, 13627 (1983).
55. H. E. Hemphill and H. R. Whiteley, *Bacteriol. Rev.* **39**, 257 (1975).
56. J. G. Flaks and S. S. Cohen, *BBA* **25**, 667 (1957).
57. M. G. Kunitani and D. V. Santi, *Bchem* **19**, 1271 (1980).
58. Y.-C. Yeh and G. R. Greenberg, *JBC* **242**, 1307 (1967).
59. A. K. Basak, M. Gautam-Basak and E. G. Sander, *J. Cell Biol.* **107**, 401 (1988).
60. N. Lamm, Y. Wang, C. K. Mathews and W. Ruger, *EJB* **172**, 553 (1988).
61. D. V. Santi, C. E. Garrett and P. J. Barr, *Cell* **33**, 9 (1983).
62. D. G. Osterman, G. D. DePillis, J. C. Wu, A. Matsuda and D. V. Santi, *Bchem* **27**, 5204 (1988).
63. D. V. Santi, A. Norment and C. E. Garrett, *PNAS* **81**, 6993 (1984).
64. S. Klimasauskas, A. Timinskas, S. Menkevicius, D. Butkiene, V. Butkus and A. Janualaitis, *NARes* **17**, 9823 (1989).
65. D. V. Santi and L. Hardy, *Bchem* **26**, 8599 (1987).
66. X. Gu and D. V. Santi, *Bchem* **30**, 2999 (1991).

67. T. Ny, P. Lindstrom, T. Hagervall and G. Bjork, *EJB* **177,** 467 (1988).
68. X. Gu and D. V. Santi, *DNA Cell Biol.* **9,** 273 (1990).
69. E. U. Selker *ARGen* **24,** 579 (1990).
70. H. O. Kammen, C. C. Marvel, L. Hardy and E. E. Penhoet, *JBC* **263,** 2255 (1988).
71. H. J. P. Shoemaker and P. R. Schimmel, *Bchem* **16,** 5454 (1977).
72. R. M. Starzyk, S. W. Koontz and P. Schimmel, *Nature* **298,** 136 (1982).
73. P. J. Romaniuk and O. C. Uhlenbeck, *Bchem* **24,** 4239 (1985).
74. I. Najita and P. Sarnow, *PNAS* **87,** 5846 (1990).

NOTE ADDED IN PROOF. Recently, the active site nucleophile of a DCMT was directly identified [L. Chen, A. M. MacMillan, W. Chang, K. Ezaz-Nikpay, W. S. Lane and G. L. Verdine, *Bchem* **30,** 11018 (1991)]. A methylated covalent complex between *M. Hae*III and an oligonucleotide containing FC was isolated and subjected to proteolysis. Sequence analysis of the DNA-bound peptides showed covalent attachment at the Cys residue (Cys 71 in *M. Hae*III) in the conserved Pro-Cys doublet.

RNA Replication of Plant Viruses Containing an RNA Genome

CHANTAL DAVID,[1] RADHIA
GARGOURI-BOUZID[2] AND
ANNE-LISE HAENNI

*Institut Jacques Monod
75251 Paris Cedex 05, France*

I. Overview

Within the plant kingdom, the number of viruses possessing an RNA genome far surpasses those with a DNA genome, and the genome of most RNA-containing viruses is single-stranded and of (+)-polarity; about 80% of plant viruses are of this latter type (*1*). The reasons for this bias in favor of RNA-containing viruses are unknown. In any event, it is essentially because of their predominance in nature that plant RNA viruses have been more extensively studied than DNA viruses. The present review therefore concentrates on plant RNA viruses.

Multiplication of RNA viruses within the host cell involves four fundamental steps that overlap chronologically. These are: (1) decapsidation,

---

[1] Present address: Institut des Sciences Végétales, CNRS, 91190 Gif-sur-Yvette, France.

[2] Present address: Center of Biotechnology of Sfax, Route de Soukka km 4, 3038 Sfax, Tunisia.

Progress in Nucleic Acid Research
and Molecular Biology, Vol. 42

which liberates the nucleic acid and makes it available for the other processes; (2) translation, during which the viral RNA serves as messenger
RNA, producing the structural and nonstructural proteins coded by the viral
RNA; (3) replication of the viral genome, yielding progeny RNA molecules;
and (4) encapsidation of these progeny RNA strands.

The details of the molecular mechanisms leading to decapsidation and
encapsidation within the cell are incompletely understood. Yet it is known
that, *in vitro*, certain virions disassemble during translation, association with
ribosomes favoring decapsidation (2, 3). Moreover, structures resembling
those observed *in vitro* have been isolated from newly infected cells, supporting this concept (4). This cotranslational/disassembly process could represent one of the early events of virus multiplication. The fact that, in (+)-
stranded RNA viruses, the RNA genome serves directly as messenger RNA
for the synthesis of the virus-coded proteins explains the vast body of data
that has accumulated on the translation strategies used by such viruses. As
for the study of replication of viral RNAs, it has only recently become accessible, in particular since the pioneering work of Hardy *et al.* (5) on the
RNA-dependent RNA polymerase (RdRp)[3] of brome mosaic virus (BMV).

In this essay, we discuss our present knowledge of viral RNA replication.
Both *in vivo* and *in vitro* data are presented. However, we have restricted
our attention to those viruses for which an RdRp complex has been isolated,
irrespective of whether the enzyme requires exogenous RNA for its activity
and thus initiates as well as elongates complementary RNA chains, or
whether it still retains RNA molecules (whose synthesis was initiated *in vivo*)
and thus only elongates these RNA chains. RNA replication of viruses with a
tripartite RNA genome, such as BMV, cowpea chlorotic mottle virus
(CCMV), cucumber mosaic virus (CMV), and alfalfa mosaic virus (AlMV), is
described first, followed by replication of viruses with a monopartite genome, such as turnip yellow mosaic virus (TYMV) and tobacco mosaic virus
(TMV), then cowpea mosaic virus (CPMV) with a bipartite genome. RNA
replication of velvet tobacco mottle virus (VTMoV) appears last due to the

---

[3] Abbreviations: *Viruses and corresponding family:* AlMV = alfalfa mosaic virus (ilarvirus);
BMV = brome mosaic virus (bromovirus); CCMV = cowpea chlorotic mottle virus (bromovirus); CcTMV = cowpea strain of TMV (tobamovirus); CGMMV = cucumber green mottle
virus (tobamovirus); CMV = cucumber mosaic virus (cucumovirus); CPMV = cowpea mosaic
virus (comovirus); TMV = tobacco mosaic virus (tobamovirus); TYMV = turnip yellow mosaic
virus (tymovirus); VTMoV = velvet tobacco mottle virus (sobemovirus).

Others: RI = replicative intermediate; RF = replicative form; kDa = kilodalton; ORF =
open reading frame; GDD = Gly–Asp–Asp; NTP = nucleoside triphosphate; sat-RNA = satellite RNA; ER = endoplasmic reticulum; *ts* mutant = temperature-sensitive mutant; CAT=
chloramphenicol acetyltransferase; ICR = internal control region; DI RNA = defective interfering RNA; VPg = virus protein, genome-linked; RdRp = RNA-dependent RNA polymerase.

limited information available on the replication mechanism of its RNA. The enzymes isolated from the first five viruses presented (BMV, CCMV, CMV, AlMV, and TYMV) are capable not only of elongating but also of initiating (−)-RNA strand synthesis, since they are devoid of endogenous RNA; the RdRp's of the last three viruses (TMV, CPMV, and VTMoV) are only capable of elongating chains whose synthesis was initiated *in vivo*. Further information may be found in other reviews on viral RNA replication (6–12).

It has been reported that, in whole plants, multiplication of certain viruses, such as BMV, AlMV, and TMV, is not continuous, but rather cyclical (reviewed in 9), virus concentration rising, then decreasing over a period of time that depends on the virus and the host. The mechanisms that limit virus multiplication and then lead to reduction in virus concentration are not understood, although it has been suggested that depletion of the pool of amino acids and/or nucleic acids, and degradation of virus particles by host proteinases and nucleases may be involved. In any event, a subtle equilibrium must be maintained by the virus to allow its efficient multiplication, yet avoid premature death of the host.

Cells infected with certain viruses present characteristic cytopathic structures known as inclusion bodies, whose nature is either crystalline or amorphous. Multiple vesicles generally also appear, and in some cases they are part of the inclusions. In certain cases, it has been demonstrated that the fibrillar material often detected in these vesicles is composed of double-stranded RNA; hence, vesicles may be the site of viral RNA replication (reviewed in 8 and 12). Numerous vesicles have also been reported to be associated with animal cells infected with certain RNA viruses (13), and there is evidence that the vesicles in arbovirus-infected cells are the site of viral RNA replication (14).

By analogy with the mechanism of genome replication of RNA bacteriophages, the complete replication cycle of the genome of eukaryotic viruses possessing single-stranded RNA of (+)-polarity involves the synthesis of complementary (−)-RNA strands on the (+)-strand template, and subsequently the synthesis (+)-strand progeny RNA molecules on the (−)-strand template. Replication of the RNA begins at the 3′ end of the template and does not require a primer. During the course of RNA replication, replicative intermediates (RIs) are produced; these are branched chains usually composed of full-length (−)-RNA strands to which are bound partially synthesized (+)-strands that are being elongated. Replication forms (RFs) are composed of full-length double-stranded RNA molecules; they most likely correspond to artifacts formed by phenol deproteinization during RNA extraction (15). A bona fide RNA replicase must be specific to the virus, and it must be capable of faithfully producing full-length (−)- and (+)-RNA chains. In most cases, however, it is not the replicase that has been described, but rather an RdRp, an enzyme that produces full-length (−)-RNA, but not full-length progeny (+)-RNA chains.

Early attempts at isolating the enzyme responsible for the production of progeny viral RNA molecules were considerably hampered by the presence within plants of a host RdRp. This enzyme, whose function in the plant remains elusive, is present in uninfected tissue (16), and its activity is enhanced by various types of traumatizations (reviewed in 9); its activity is markedly enhanced upon virus infection, such as by CCMV (17), CMV (18), AlMV (19), TMV (20, 21), and CPMV (22, 23). It was therefore postulated that this enzyme might represent the viral RdRp (24). However, it is now well established that the host enzyme is distinct from the viral RdRp (25; reviewed in 7). Indeed, the host enzyme is soluble, whereas the viral enzyme is nearly always membrane-bound. The host enzyme is composed of one protein subunit of about 120 kDa (kilodaltons), has no template specificity, initiates RNA synthesis anywhere along the template, and produces only short RNA chains (reviewed in 7). Clearly, it does not comply with the definition of a viral replicase as given above.

Based on previous work performed on RNA bacteriophages (26), it is generally assumed that the replicase of all viruses containing an RNA genome of (+)-polarity is composed of both virus- and host-coded proteins.

Candidates for the virus-coded proteins are to be found among the nonstructural proteins. The ease with which viral RNA can be retrieved from isolated virion and the small size of viral genomes have made it possible to sequence a large number of plant viral RNA genomes and thereby to deduce the sequence of the proteins corresponding to the various open reading frames (ORFs). These studies have revealed the presence of conserved domains that are believed to reflect the participation of the corresponding protein in RNA replication (27–29). One of these domains contains the amino-acid sequence Gly–Asp–Asp (GDD) as part of the consensus sequence. It is encountered in the poliovirus RdRp (a nonstructural protein) as well as in one of the nonstructural proteins of all (+)-strand RNA viruses examined to date (reviewed in 30 and 31). It is generally assumed that the nonstructural protein harboring this motif is part of the viral replicase; this GDD-containing domain is also referred to as the "polymerase domain." Another consensus sequence commonly found in one of the nonstructural proteins of both animal and plant RNA viruses is a nucleoside triphosphate (NTP) motif. This motif is characteristic of many NTP-utilizing enzymes and it has been proposed that the viral protein harboring this sequence might perform some function in viral RNA replication, such as anchoring of the replication complex to cell membranes, initiation of RNA synthesis, and NTP hydrolysis, or act as helicase during RNA replication. Therefore, in investigating which viral nonstructural proteins could be involved in the replication process, specific attention has been paid to viral proteins containing the polymerase domain and the NTP motif.

The observation of the presence of these conserved domains among bacterial, plant, and animal viruses implies that fundamentally similar strategies underlie RNA replication of all these viruses. However, the mode of expression of these nonstructural proteins can be quite different, depending on the virus. For instance, in viruses containing a monopartite genome, the two motifs may be located on the same protein or on different proteins as a result of readthrough of a termination codon, as in the case of TMV, or as a result of post-translational cleavage, as in TYMV. In viruses with a tripartite genome, such as BMV, CCMV, CMV, and AlMV, the two motifs are located on distinct polypeptides that are synthesized from their respective genomic RNAs.

Another consequence of the comparison of the strategies used by different plant and animal RNA viruses has been the proposal that these viruses could be classified in at least two large supergroups (reviewed in 30 and 32–35): the "poliovirus-like supergroup," of which poliovirus is the prototype, and the "Sindbis virus-like supergroup," with Sindbis virus as prototype. It has also led to the suggestion that plant and animal RNA viruses might have evolved from a common ancestor (32).

Information concerning the nature of the host-coded subunit of the viral enzyme is still fragmentary due to difficulties in obtaining pure, soluble, and active enzyme preparations; only in the case of CMV, AlMV, and TYMV have specific host proteins been earmarked as forming an intrinsic part of the enzyme. In no instance has the function of the host-coded protein within the cell been established.

In addition to examining the mechanism governing the synthesis of progeny viral RNA, attention has also been focused on the replication of two other types of viral RNAs: subgenomic RNAs and satellite RNAs (sat-RNAs).

In virtually all cases described, the genome of eukaryotic RNA viruses is functionally monocistronic, even though it is structurally polygenic: Only the 5′-proximal cistron is translated from the genomic RNA, whereas translation of internal cistrons is produced by subgenomic RNAs where they occupy a 5′-proximal position. Subgenomic RNAs are thus direct copies of the 3′ part of genomic RNAs. The strategy of subgenomic RNA synthesis is very commonly used by RNA viruses of the Sindbis virus-like supergroup. Three mechanisms can reasonably be considered to explain how subgenomic RNAs are produced: (1) internal initiation of replication on full-length (−)-strand RNA; (2) premature termination of (−)-strand synthesis followed by autonomous replication of the subgenomic RNA; or (3) post-transcriptional processing of the full-length (+)-RNA. The last mechanism can most likely be discarded, since it implies the loss of an important part of the message;

moreover, the 5′ RNA fragment that would result from such cleavage has not been detected in infected tissues. Rather, the evidence from *in vivo* and *in vitro* experiments accumulated to date with various RNA viruses clearly tends to favor the first mechanism. Since subgenomic RNAs contain at their 3′ end the elements required for the production of complementary subgenomic RNA chains, various explanations have been put forward to account for the lack of autonomous replication of subgenomic RNAs. These are that (1) the sequence contained within the subgenomic RNA is insufficient for replication of the subgenomic RNA; (2) the subgenomic RNA, which is frequently a highly efficient mRNA, may not be available for replication; and (3) the subgenomic RNA would be produced late in infection or at a time when (−)-strand synthesis has ceased. The first explanation is certainly the most likely one, as will become clear from experiments described further in this article (Sections II–VI).

Certain viruses are often accompanied by sat-RNAs, small single-stranded RNAs that depend entirely on the helper virus for their multiplication, but are not required for multiplication of the helper virus; they are encapsidated in the helper viral capsid (reviewed in 36 and 37). They frequently alter the symptoms produced by the helper virus, either attenuating or enhancing them, depending on the host. Since they have no significant sequence homologies with the helper genome, the mechanism of their replication presents an interesting challenge for plant virologists, as exemplified below (Sections IV and IX) for the sat-RNAs of CMV and VTMoV.

A novel aspect of viral RNA replication concerns the possibility of interfering with virus multiplication based on the replicating enzyme. It has long been known that if a plant is inoculated with a mild virus strain (inducer virus), it becomes resistant to subsequent inoculation by a related severe strain (challenger virus); this phenomenon is known as "cross-protection" (reviewed in 38 and 39). Several models have been proposed to explain cross-protection, the most favored being that the coat protein of the inducer is involved in cross-protection either by competing with the challenger for specific sites on the cell surface, or by inhibiting uncoating of the challenger virus. Consequently, most experiments aimed at rendering plants resistant to virus infection have focused on the production of transgenic plants expressing a viral coat protein. Compared to normal plants, such transgenic plants present delays in symptom development when inoculated with challenger virus (reviewed in 40 and 41). Nevertheless, other strategies of plant protection can be considered (42). These are presented here concerning the viruses discussed, insofar as they are in some manner related to RNA replication. As discussed below, an intriguing result has been reported in which a fragment of the cDNA of TMV RNA, the region whose corresponding protein contains the polymerase domain, has been introduced into plants, which then become entirely resistant to subsequent TMV infection (43). This opens the field to further studies in which other regions of viral genomes could be inserted into host plants in the hope of obtaining resistance to viral infection, and it again raises the question of the mechanisms involved in cross-protection.

II. Replication of Brome Mosaic Virus RNA

Brome mosaic virus (BMV) the type-member of the bromovirus group, infects monocotyledonous plants, more specifically, cereals. It possesses a tripartite genome, three separately encapsidated RNAs, designated RNA1 (3234 nucleotides), RNA2 (2865 nucleotides), and RNA3 (2114 nucleotides). The entire sequences of these BMV RNAs have been established (44–46). A subgenomic RNA derived from the 3' region of RNA3 and designated RNA4 (876 nucleotides) is encapsidated together with RNA3; it codes for the viral coat protein. All four RNAs possess "cap" structures at their 5' extremities and tRNA-like structures that can be acylated by tyrosine at their 3' ends. Multiple copies of the coat protein are assembled to form the icosahedral nucleocapsid.

A. Intracellular Location of BMV RNA Replication

BMV infection induces a number of disturbances in the cytoplasmic membranes of the host, with proliferation and accumulation of endoplasmic reticulum (ER) adjacent to the nucleus (47). Round vesicles containing electron-dense material resembling nucleic acids are formed and accumulate in the cytoplasm. They may result from blebbing of ER cisternae, inducing the formation of inclusion bodies. Similar nucleic acid-containing vesicles have been identified in localized dilations of the nuclear envelope. These vesicles originate from the nuclear membrane and are released into the cytoplasm as virus infection progresses (47, 48).

B. Expression of BMV RNA

The two largest BMV RNAs are monocistronic and encode proteins of 109 and 94 kDa, designated proteins 1a and 2a. RNA3 is dicistronic. It encodes a 32-kDa protein (protein 3a) presumably involved in cell-to-cell movement. The 3' ORF of RNA3, corresponding to the coat-protein gene, remains "silent." Synthesis of the coat protein (20 kDa) occurs via RNA4. The four BMV proteins have been detected in cell-free translation systems as well as in tissues of infected plants (49, 50). The genome organization of BMV is illustrated in Fig. 1. It correspond to the general genome organization of all tricornaviridae.

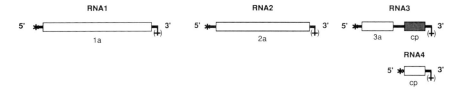

FIG. 1. General genome organization of such tricornaviruses as the bromoviruses, the cucumoviruses, and the ilarviruses. The three genomic RNAs (RNAs 1, 2, and 3) as well as the subgenomic RNA4 are presented. The boxes on the RNAs (black line) correspond to the ORFs. The box is open when the ORF is translated from the corresponding RNA; it is shaded when the ORF cannot be translated from the RNA. *"Cap" structure; inverted cross, tRNA-like structure. The cross is in brackets since the tRNA-like structure is absent from ilarviruses. Designation of the nonstructural proteins and the structural coat protein (cp) is indicated below the corresponding ORF. The nonstructural proteins are designated 1a, 2a, and 3a in BMV, CCMV, and CMV; they are designated P1, P2, and P3 in AlMV.

C. BMV RdRp

1. PURIFICATION AND CHARACTERIZATION OF BMV RdRp

Several experimental data demonstrate that BMV RNAs 1 and 2 together, but not separately, are necessary for RNA replication in barley protoplasts (51–54). Neither RNA3 nor RNA4 is required for RNA replication. An RdRp has been isolated from barley leaves infected with BMV (5, 55, 56). This enzyme complex shows a strong preference for BMV RNA templates over other viral RNAs and over nonviral RNAs (reviewed in 11), and it is distinct from the plant-encoded enzyme (18, 49), suggesting the involvement of one or more of the nonstructural proteins in the replication process.

Viral proteins presumed to be involved in this replication process were first identified in experiments suggesting that protein 1a is present in the BMV complex (55). In further experiments, antibodies raised against protein 1a completely blocked (−)-strand synthesis (50, 57), indicating that protein 1a is a component of the RdRp complex. An antiserum specific for protein 2a had no such inhibitory effect on (−)-strand synthesis (50). However, immunoblot analyses using these antisera revealed the presence of both proteins 1a and 2a in the BMV RdRp complex. Thus, at least protein 1a seems to be part of the catalytic subunit of the RdRp. It appears that, for unknown reasons, the anti-2a serum does not react with protein 2a in the RdRp complex. On the other hand, removal of protein 1a, but not protein 2a, strongly reduces RdRp activity. All of these results emphasize the involvement of protein 1a in the BMV replication complex. Direct participation of protein 2a in the replication process has not been demonstrated, even though this protein is always present in the active complex.

2. BMV MUTANTS: INVOLVEMENT OF PROTEINS ENCODED BY RNA 1 AND RNA 2 IN REPLICATION

The conserved sequence comprising the GDD motif related to RdRp's is detected in protein 2a of BMV (reviewed in *30* and *31*). This favors the involvement of protein 2a as one of the core components of the replicating enzyme (*11*). On the other hand, the NTP-binding domain is contained in the amino-acid sequence of protein 1a (*58, 59*). The C-terminal sequence of this protein contains a domain similar to that of several helicases (*58, 59*). It has also been suggested (*11, 60*) that protein 1a could have a function in the capping of the viral RNA; this could explain the requirement for protein 1a in replication, since uncapped mRNAs are known to be very unstable in plant and animal cytoplasm (*61–63*).

A first series of mutation experiments investigating the function of proteins 1a and 2a in BMV RNA replication involved insertion of the TMV sequence corresponding to the coat-protein gene and the encapsidation site into the 3'-noncoding region of BMV RNAs 1 and 2. This inhibits amplification of the modified RNA in *cis* and also inhibits amplification of coinfecting RNA3 in *trans*. Thus, reduced accumulation of RNAs 1 and 2 seems to limit synthesis of their encoded proteins, leading to reduced production of all viral RNAs (*64*). However, further investigations (*65*) revealed that trace amounts of RNA2 are sufficient to support replication of the BMV genome. Indeed, transfection of barley protoplasts with wild-type RNAs 1 and 3 and serial dilutions of RNA2 transcripts possessing an intact coding sequence but bearing mutations that greatly inhibit replication of RNA2 show that protein 2a produced by the RNA2 mutant at a concentration of $< 6 \times 10^3$ molecules per protoplast is sufficient to support replication of RNAs 1 and 3. Therefore, BMV replication seems to be much more sensitive to a decrease in the level of protein 1a than of protein 2a.

Since conserved domains present in the Sindbis virus nonstructural proteins nsP1 and nsP2 (both believed to be involved in RNA replication) are also contained in the N- and C-terminal sequences of BMV protein 1a, a role of the latter protein in viral RNA replication has been proposed (*60*). A series of insertion mutations was performed in these conserved regions to study the effect of such mutations on BMV RNA replication in barley protoplasts. A number of temperature-sensitive (*ts*) mutants were thus obtained. The analysis of the behavior of these *ts* mutants at permissive and nonpermissive temperatures shows that intact protein 1a is necessary for amplification of the BMV RNAs. Moreover, both domains in protein 1a are involved in RNA replication and seem to be dependent on each other. The C-terminal conserved domain, similar to the domain contained in a number of helicases (*58, 59*), seems to be involved in the synthesis of all species and strands of BMV

RNAs. Thus, helicase activities might be required in different steps of RNA replication. On the other hand, the N-terminal domain seems to be involved only in (−)-strand synthesis (60).

The exchange of RNA2 segments between CCMV and BMV has no effect on the replication of RNA3. Thus, a role for RNA1 in virus-specific differential amplification of RNA3 has been proposed (66).

An *in vivo* replication experiment with wild-type RNAs 1 and 3 and an RNA2 transcript devoid of its 3′-terminal 200 nucleotides was performed (65). Such an RNA2 molecule has no template activity. Under these conditions, detectable amounts of RNAs 1, 3, and 4 are obtained. Consequently, protein 2a produced by the defective RNA2 can support amplification of RNAs 1 and 3. However, in the absence of RNA2, no replication of inoculum containing RNAs 1 and 3 occurs. It thus seems that, in the case of protein 2a, amplification of RNA2 is not necessary for viral RNA replication, since very low levels of this protein are capable of mediating replication in *trans* of all BMV RNA species.

Preliminary mapping of virus-specific replication functions in RNA2 and protein 2a has been performed with a number of hybrids obtained by exchanging specific regions of BMV and CCMV RNA2 (66). By testing these hybrids *in vivo*, it has been possible to identify BMV RNA2 regions controlling *trans*-acting replication functions with respect to RNA1, and *cis*-acting functions that influence RNA2 amplification. Indeed, a hybrid containing the region coding for the N-terminal 358 amino acids of BMV protein 2a is sufficient to render RNA2 functional in directing RNA replication with RNA1, whereas the 5′ fragment of RNA2 corresponding to the 281 N-terminal amino acids of protein 2a allows only *cis*-acting competence for RNA2 amplification. Consequently, the 5′ portion of RNA2 encodes a critical determinant required for successful interaction with RNA1 in viral RNA replication *in vivo*.

In conclusion, the results obtained with the RNA2 hybrid show that successful BMV RNA replication requires that protein 2a interact with protein 1a and/or that it contribute to recognition of RNA1 as a replication template. Moreover, the *trans*-acting function and *cis*-acting template activity both map in the 5′-proximal sequence of RNA2. However, these two characteristics are clearly distinguishable.

The central sequence of BMV RNA2 shares similarities with known polymerases (27, 28, 67). It is flanked by less conserved N- and C-terminal extensions that could be involved in virus-specific interactions, complexing the polymerase-like 2a core protein to protein 1a (66). A number of amino-acid substitution mutations within this conserved portion alter the ratio of genomic to subgenomic RNA and of (+)- to (−)-strand RNA (68), suggesting that protein 2a may play a role in template recognition. Moreover, in some of the resulting *ts* mutants harboring substitutions in this most highly conserved domain, (+)-RNA strand synthesis is completely blocked at either temperature, confirming the requirement of protein 2a in RNA replication. Further characterization of these *ts* mutants also reveals that protein 2a probably plays a role in RNA chain elongation. Similar conclusions were drawn for the Sindbis virus 2a-like protein nsP4 (*69, 70*).

A compilation of these results indicates that BMV RNA replication requires both RNA1 and 2 translation products. Furthermore, the level of replication seems to be much more reduced with a decrease in the level of RNA1 than with a decrease in the level of RNA2. However, despite considerable efforts, the specific contribution of each protein in the replication complex remains unclear.

D. Mechanism of BMV RNA Replication

1. (−)-Strand Synthesis

The high template dependence and specificity of the BMV RdRp preparation (*5, 56*) have motivated several investigations on the characteristics and mechanism of (−)-strand synthesis using (+)-strand RNA as template. In addition, due to its 3′ location on all BMV RNAs, a role of the tRNA-like structure and functions in viral RNA replication was envisaged (*71*).

The initial identification of the polymerase recognition site at the 3′ end of BMV RNA was made by observing the template activity of BMV RNAs modified by nuclease cleavage or by hybridization to cloned cDNA fragments (*53*). A purified 3′-terminal BMV RNA fragment of 134 nucleotides is still able to function efficiently as a template, whereas a shorter fragment containing the 3′-terminal 85 nucleotides is inactive (*72*). Furthermore, the RNA template is blocked by hybridization of cDNA fragments as short as 39 nucleotides that base-pair to the 3′ end of the viral genome (*53*).

A large number of mutations within the 3′ region of BMV RNA have been produced (*71, 73–75*), with two aims. The first is to map the regions of the RNA required for RdRp recognition and for tRNA-associated activities and thus to study the relationship between these two functions. The second is to construct mutants that have lost their *in vitro* tyrosylation capacity but have retained RdRp activity *in vitro*. Such mutants are used in the inoculation of barley protoplasts to determine whether aminoacylation is necessary for replication.

A number of mutations within the "anticodon" triplet (Fig. 2, loop III) show that the RdRp, but not the tyrosyl-tRNA synthetase, interacts with this region of the RNA (*71*). The anticodon seems very important in specific recognition of the RNA by the RdRp. In further experiments, small deletions or single (double- or triple-)-base substitutions within stem III (*74, 75*) or

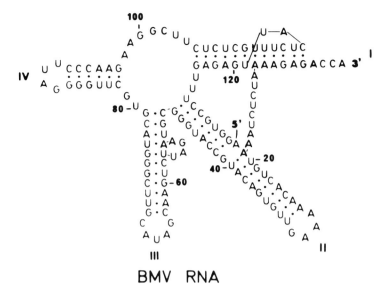

FIG. 2. Possible folding of the 3'-terminal 134 nucleotides conserved among the BMV RNAs. Every 20th nucleotide is numbered. Numbers I–IV correspond to the stems and loops. (Reproduced with permission from 76.)

large deletions within this stem and loop (73) were made, leading to drastic inhibition of RdRp template activity. Thus, it seems that an intact anticodon stem and loop are required for (−)-strand synthesis. These mutations have no such drastic effect on the acylation function. Similarly, mutations within stem II can have a dramatic inhibitory effect on template activity, depending on the position of the deletion (73). Furthermore, substitution of CU by GG (positions 102 and 103) reduces replication to *in vivo* 40% of the wild-type, and substitution of UCU by AGA (positions 113–115) reduces replication to 20% of the wild-type (77). On the other hand, removal of stem and loop IV has no effect on either the acylation or template activities (73).

Mutations of the 3'-terminal −CA drastically reduce RdRp template activity and totally inhibit acylation. However, deletion of the 3'-terminal adenosine residue has little effect on template activity (71). Thus, it seems that the penultimate cytosine residue is necessary for efficient template activity *in vitro*. Moreover, analysis of the (−)-strand products by a chain termination procedure shows that initiation occurs opposite the penultimate nucleotide (72). On the other hand, BMV RNA3 with a hexanucleotide or poly(A) extension beyond the −CCA terminus is an active template *in vitro*. In contrast, extension by 15 bases in the same region leads to an inactive template (72). It is possible that an unstructured region may facilitate initiation of (−)-strand synthesis.

A compilation of these data indicates that sequence alterations (substitutions or small deletions) in most parts of the tRNA-like structure result in decreased (−)-strand synthesis. More importantly, (−)-strand initiation requires the presence of the penultimate nucleotide and integrity of the anticodon stem and loop. It also suggests that acylation and template activities are two independent functions in BMV RNA.

Since the tRNA-like fragment (134 nucleotides) has a high template activity, whereas a shorter 3' fragment (85 nucleotides) is inactive, it has been proposed that the tRNA-like structure alone contains all the signals required for initiation of (−)-strand synthesis *in vitro* (72). The RdRp complex interacts with most of the structure, except stem IV (73; reviewed in 11).

The same series of mutants was also assayed for adenylation capacity. The tests indicate that sequences required for RdRp recognition overlap those directing adenylation (78). Analysis of the behavior of some of these mutants reflects interaction of the nucleotidyltransferase with at least part of the anticodon arm, a region known to be important for recognition by the BMV RdRp. Adenylation is not necessary for (−)-strand synthesis. Further, (−)-strand RNA synthesis is initiated with a pppG residue (72) opposite the 3'-penultimate nucleotide. Adenylation thus has no effect on (−)-strand synthesis, but may be part of the requirement for achieving an acylatable 3' end. In summary, these results indicate that three specific elements are essential for (−)-strand promoter activity *in vitro* (Fig. 2): (1) the pseudo-knot structure in the aminoacyl acceptor stem that, when destabilized, alters the tRNA-like conformation and induces a decrease in template activity; (2) the penultimate C residue, whose substitution or deletion leads to poor initiation of (−)-strand synthesis; and (3) the sequence of stem III in which substitutions or small deletions drastically alter (−)-strand promoter activity. This stem region of the RNA seems to be one of the major features involved in RdRp binding, and particularly nucleotides in loop III appear to be involved in sequence specific interaction with the RdRp. All of these predictions obtained by *in vitro* experiments must be confirmed *in vivo*.

Despite the considerable efforts to understand the mechanism of (−)-RNA synthesis, all attempts to synthesize (+)-RNA *in vitro* on correctly terminated (−)-strand genomic RNA have failed (79). This has been explained by the lack of host organelle or nuclear components that may be required at this step. In addition, (+)-sense genomic RNA3 synthesis from full-length (−)-strand template in cell-free RNA replicating systems has not been achieved. Correctly terminated (−)-RNA3 seems not to be an active template for successful (+)-strand synthesis. A possibility is that additional nucleotides may be required at the 3' end of the (−)-strand template, as is the case for CMV (80). Alternatively, the results obtained may reflect a deficiency in the RdRp preparation, such as the loss of a host factor.

A number of mutants specifically defective in tRNA-like functions and/or promoter activity have been identified. Four of them with low acylation rates *in vitro* were selected, and the corresponding mutations were introduced into the 3' end of full-length RNA3 to test their ability to be replicated *in vivo* (75). The main purpose of these investigations was to determine whether acylation is required for replication, whether it plays a role in modulating progress in infection, or whether it has no detectable role. All RNA3 mutants are replicated at levels between 20% and 70% relative to wild-type, and their accumulation parallels their (−)-strand promoter activity determined *in vitro*. This good agreement between the relative rates of (−)-strand synthesis determined *in vitro* and replication *in vivo* suggests that (−)-strand promoter activity determines the rate of replication *in vivo*.

When inoculated onto barley plants, two of these mutants with mutations upstream from the tRNA-like structure produce wild-type symptoms and wild-type levels of progeny RNAs. However, the two other mutants with substitutions within the tRNA-like structure produce inconspicuous symptoms and variable levels of progeny RNAs. This defect in infectivity in the latter two cases has been attributed to an inefficient spread of these mutants that is prevented by decreased replication of RNA3, presumably required for cell-to-cell movement (11, 81). All four mutations are preserved during replication in protoplasts and plant tissue. No recombination events are observed after two passages. Based on these results, it appears that poor acylation does not prevent efficient replication and RNA accumulation in intact plants. Further investigations are, nonetheless, necessary to totally exclude involvement of acylation in replication.

In a recent report, four BMV RNA3 mutants bearing single- or double-base changes in the 3'-terminal −CCA and known to be deficient in acylation and (−)-strand synthesis *in vitro* were assayed for their ability to replicate in barley protoplasts and plants together with wild-type RNAs 1 and 2 (82). In protoplasts, all mutants are viable with relative levels of (−)- and (+)-strand amplification rates similar to those of wild-type. When inoculated onto barley plants, wild-type phenotypic symptoms appear.

Analysis of the RNA3 progeny indicates that a wild-type 3' terminus is restored in each case. This repairing substitution occurs very early in infection, suggesting that there is a rapid turnover and correction of the 3' termini of BMV RNAs *in vivo*. Sequence correction must be a rapid process, probably finished during translation of viral replication factors from RNAs 1 and 2.

This turnover phenomenon for tRNAs is well known (reviewed in 83). Since BMV RNAs lacking the 3'-terminal nucleotide are efficient substrates for nucleotidyltransferase *in vitro* (76), such correction is attributed to the action of the tRNA nucleotidyltransferase and differs from a recombination event (73).

Taken together, these results provide functional evidence favoring the hypothesis that the tRNA-like structures found in the RNAs of BMV and other viruses function as do telomeres in eukaryotic chromosomes (84). Thus, the function of the nucleotidyltransferase in maintaining an intact 3' end in RNA viruses can be compared to that of the chromosomal telomerase (82), the telomere-specific terminal transferase that preserves intact the extremities of chromosomes.

2. (+)-STRAND SYNTHESIS: RNA3 AMPLIFICATION

In vivo amplification of RNA3 requires *cis*-acting elements located at the 5' and 3' extremities and in a 150-nucleotide intercistronic region of this RNA (85). A 3'-terminal region of 163–200 nucleotides seems to be required for RNA3 amplification *in vivo*. In addition, the entire 5'-end sequence (91 nucleotides) is also essential for RNA3 synthesis. Deletion of either of these domains and/or of part of the 3a- and coat-protein genes drastically decreases RNA3 accumulation *in vivo*. However, RNA3 replication can be restored if the 3a- or coat-protein genes are substituted by heterologous sequences, suggesting that a physical separation between the 5'- and 3'-terminal domains is required for normal RNA3 amplification.

In a recent report, an RNA3 mutant lacking the oligo(A) stretch that is part of the intercistronic region was used together with wild-type RNA1 and RNA2 to inoculate wheat plants. The subsequent analysis of RNA3 progeny revealed that, during replication, the oligo(A) stretch of normal length is restored in the RNA3 replication product (86). Thus, removal of only the oligo(A) stretch, but not the flanking intercistronic region, of RNA3 does not inhibit RNA3 replication in the presence of wild-type RNAs 1 and 2 in infected cells. Furthermore, it seems that, at a certain stage of replication, the wild-type oligo(A) stretch is restored in progeny RNA by a mechanism differing from template copying.

3. SYNTHESIS OF SUBGENOMIC RNA4

Various mechanisms outlined in the introduction of this article (Section I) can be advanced to explain the mechanism of BMV subgenomic RNA4 formation from genomic RNA3. Analyses of double-stranded RNAs corresponding to RFs and RIs purified from BMV-infected tissues have led to differing conclusions. In some cases, the internal initiation mechanism was favored, whereas other data suggested that RNA4 might be synthesized via its own RF (reviewed in *12*).

The definitive mechanism of BMV RNA4 synthesis came from the use of the *in vitro* RdRp system (87), and was the first unequivocal evidence that the subgenomic RNA of a (+)-strand RNA virus is synthesized (at least *in vitro*) by internal initiation of (+)-strand RNA synthesis on a (−)-strand template. *In vitro*, the BMV RdRp binds downstream from the sequence corresponding to RNA4 [the (−)-strand is considered here], and therefore (−)-strand RNA4 cannot serve as template for (+)-RNA4 synthesis.

The internal promoter involved in RNA4 synthesis was identified using altered (−)-RNA3 strands as template (87, 88). Deletions 3′ from the RNA4-corresponding sequence were performed on the (−)-RNA3 strand to identify the core sequence required for initiation of (+)-RNA4 synthesis. This region is delineated by two restriction sites in the cDNA of RNA3 corresponding to *Bgl*II and *Sal*I sites (Fig. 3). They are located, respectively, 20 nucleotides downstream from the RNA4 start site and 17 nucleotides into the RNA4 sequence.

An oligo(U) region 3′ from this (−)-strand core promoter sequence (Fig. 3) seems to function as a spacer, ensuring accessibility of the promoter for the viral RdRp, since its removal leads to an important decrease in RNA4 synthesis (88). Indeed, this region is not involved in secondary folding; thus, it has been postulated that it could facilitate an open RNA structure for the RdRp in the subgenomic promoter region (*11*). However, it is not part of the core promoter (87).

Replacement of the coat-protein gene by the chloramphenicol acetyl-transferase (*CAT*) gene in the RNA3 sequence does not alter subgenomic RNA synthesis *in vivo*, indicating that initiation of subgenomic RNA synthesis occurs at the normal site. These experiments performed in barley protoplasts confirm the involvement of the *Bgl*II–*Sal*I sequence in the core subgenomic promoter (*54*).

Further studies have been performed to investigate the nature and behavior of sequences influencing RNA4 production *in vivo*. The roles of additional downstream sequences and positional effects on promoter functions have also been studied (89, 90). Four regions can be identified as playing a role in RNA4 initiation *in vivo* (Fig. 3). First, as demonstrated *in vitro*, initiation of subgenomic RNA synthesis does not require more than 17 nucleotides of the RNA4 sequence (nucleotides +1 to +17). Second, sequences 3′ from the start site of RNA4 can be divided into three different domains. They correspond to the 20 nucleotides described above (nucleotides −1 to −20); an oligo(U) stretch (nucleotides −20 to −38) downstream from this region; and finally, an (A+U)-rich sequence (nucleotides −38 to −95) adjacent to the oligo(U). The region containing the first two domains acts as the core of the RNA4 promoter, whereas the other two domains contribute in favoring correct initiation of (+)-RNA synthesis. The entire promoter sequence is 112 nucleotides long.

In other studies, several insertions of the RNA4 promoter were made at different positions within the (−)-strand of RNA3. When inoculated onto barley protoplasts in the presence of wild-type RNAs 1 and 2, these modified

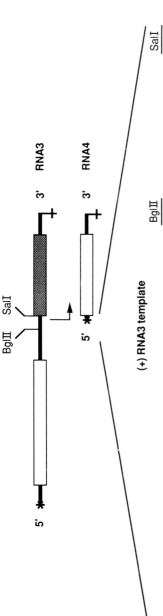

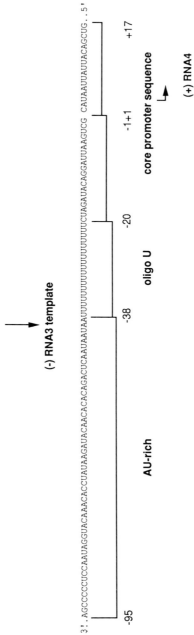

FIG. 3. Internal promoter for BMV RNA4 synthesis. The upper part schematizes the genome organization of RNAs 3 and 4; details are as in Fig. 1. Two restriction enzyme cleavage sites (*Bgl*II and *Sal*I) present on the cDNA of RNA3 are indicated. The remainder of the figure presents the nucleotide sequence within (+)- and (−)-RNA3, corresponding to the internal promoter involved in RNA4 synthesis; the positions of the *Bgl*II and *Sal*I cleavage sites are indicated. Below (−)-RNA3, the domains of the promoter sequence are shown. The arrows pointing to the right correspond to the initiation site for RNA4 synthesis. Numbering on (−)-RNA3 is from the RNA4 initiation site; negative and positive numbers are those 3′ and 5′, respectively, of the RNA4 initiation site. (Adapted from 89, with additional information from 90.)

RNA3 templates lead to two types of subgenomic RNAs: the normal RNA4, and RNAs initiated at the position of the inserted promoters and possessing the predicted sizes. The new species of subgenomic RNAs initiated by promoters inserted within the RNA4 sequence are synthesized more efficiently than those corresponding to promoters inserted within the RNA3 sequence. Their synthesis is even more efficient than that of normal RNA4. These results suggest that the location of the internal promoter has a direct influence on the efficiency of subgenomic RNA synthesis. The normal position of the promoter leads to an equimolar production of (+)-strand RNAs 3 and 4 from the same template (89).

The nucleotide sequence of the core promoter has significant homologies with known internal promoters of alphaviruses and with putative subgenomic promoters of related plant viruses (88, 89). This sequence also reveals significant homologies with internal control region (ICR) 2 and, to a lesser extent, with ICR 1, two regions known to be involved in promoter function and in control of eukaryotic tRNA transcription by RNA polymerase III (79).

In addition, the nucleotide sequence at the 5' end of BMV (+)- and (−)-RNAs also resembles ICR 1 and ICR 2 (91, 92). The presence of such conserved sequences has led to the hypothesis that ICR-like sequences could be the core promoter for (+)-strand RNA synthesis. It was also postulated that RNA polymerase III could be involved in amplification of (+)-strand RNAs. These ICR-like sequences are also detected in the intercistronic region of RNA3 (79), known to be involved in amplification of RNA3 and RNA4. In addition, the absence of an ICR-like domain at the 5' end of RNA4 is a further argument against autonomous replication of RNA4.

E. Plant Protection against BMV Infection: Use of Defective Interfering RNAs

Defective interfering RNAs (DI RNAs) or particles are frequently associated with animal viruses. They harbor nucleotide sequences from the helper virus; they are defective in autonomous replication and thus interfere with the helper virus for the use of the replication machinery. such DI RNAs are very rarely encountered among plant viruses. Artificial DI RNAs have been constructed by large deletions in the central part of the cDNA corresponding to BMV RNA2, and have been tested in protoplasts for their interference behavior with wild-type RNAs 1 and 2 (93). The interference with genomic RNA replication seems to be dependent on the ratio of DI RNAs to wild-type genomic RNAs. At low ratios, DI RNAs interfere specifically with RNA2 amplification, whereas at equal concentrations a decrease of about 37% in amplification of RNAs 1 and 2 is observed. When the concentration of DI RNAs is five times that of RNAs 1 and 2, they completely interfere with genomic RNA amplification. An alternative approach in creating virus-resistant transgenic plants can thus be envisaged using DI RNAs.

III. Replication of Cowpea Chlorotic Mottle Virus RNA

Cowpea chlorotic mottle virus (CCMV) contains a tripartite (+)-sense RNA genome. Its genome organization is analogous to that of BMV (Fig. 1). This bromovirus possesses three genomic RNAs, designated RNA1, RNA2, and RNA3, and a subgenomic RNA designated RNA4. The entire nucleotide sequences of CCMV RNA4 (45), RNAs 2 and 3 (94), and RNA1 (mentioned in 94) have been established. All four RNAs are separately encapsidated in icosahedral capsids formed by multiple copies of the coat protein (20 kDa). As in the case of BMV, the CCMV RNAs are capped at their 5' ends and contain a tRNA-like structure acylatable with tyrosine at their 3' ends. In addition, CCMV possesses very important RNA sequence similarities and antigenic cross-reactivity with BMV. Because of the important similarities between BMV and CCMV, several interviral hybrids (pseudo-recombinants and hybrids) have been constructed with two aims in mind: first, to study recombination events between these two viruses, and second, to investigate virus replication and interaction with the host. The important data gathered on BMV RNA replication have been very profitable in the studies related to CCMV.

Despite its close relationship to BMV, CCMV has a different host spectrum. It infects dicotyledonous plants and, more precisely, legumes (95).

A. Intracellular Location of CCMV RNA Replication

Cytoplasmic disturbances similar to those caused by BMV are detected in CCMV-infected cells. Vesicles generated from the ER and nuclear membranes are present in the infected cytoplasm (47). These vesicles contain electron-dense material identified as nucleic acids. In addition, CCMV infection alters the structure of the chloroplasts (reviewed in 48).

B. Expression of CCMV RNA

Genomic RNAs 1 and 2 are monocistronic; they encode proteins of 104 kDa (protein 1a) and 94 kDa (protein 2a). The 5'-terminal ORF of the dicistronic RNA3 encodes a 32-kDa nonstructural protein, whereas the 3'-proximal ORF encodes the coat-protein gene. The latter ORF remains silent on RNA3 but is translated from RNA4. As with BMV, RNAs 1 and 2 are required for CCMV RNA replication in protoplasts. However, systemic infection in cowpea leaves requires the presence of RNA3 in the inoculum (96). The function of the CCMV nonstructural proteins has not been determined directly. However, amino-acid sequence analyses reveal that the central region of protein 2a contains the conserved sequence, including the GDD motif related to RNA-dependent polymerases. This functional domain is flanked by two less conserved N- and C-terminal regions that are very similar to corresponding sequences in BMV protein 2a (94). RNA3 of CCMV is believed to be involved in host specificity, and protein 3a may have a role in cell-to-cell movement (94, 97, 98).

C. CCMV RdRp

1. ISOLATION AND CHARACTERIZATION

Extracts from CCMV-infected cowpea leaves contain both the membrane-bound CCMV RdRp and a soluble host RNA polymerase (17). More recently, an active template-dependent RdRp has been isolated from CCMV-infected cowpea leaves (99), using the procedure described for the extraction of the BMV RdRp. This enzyme is specific for bromovirus RNAs. It recognizes BMV RNA as well as CCMV RNA, whereas the BMV RdRp does not recognize CCMV RNA. The composition and properties of the CCMV RdRp are still unknown.

2. NONSTRUCTURAL PROTEINS INVOLVED IN CCMV RNA REPLICATION

Full-length cDNA copies and infectious RNA transcripts are available for each CCMV RNA (98). Hybrids have been constructed by exchanging segments between the RNAs 2 of BMV and CCMV. They have led to a primary mapping of virus-specific replication functions specified by CCMV protein 2a (66). Infection of barley protoplasts by these hybrids, together with wild-type CCMV RNAs 1 and 3, have made it possible to identify CCMV RNA 2 regions involved in *trans*-acting functions with RNA1, and *cis*-acting regions influencing RNA2 amplification. These studies with hybrids suggest that the 3′-terminal segment of RNA2 encodes a specific determinant that interacts in *trans* with CCMV RNA1 and/or protein 1a for efficient viral RNA replication. However, for high-level interaction with RNA1, the 5′ region of RNA2 is also required. Indeed, major determinants required for efficient interaction with CCMV RNA1 seem to extend into, or be contained within, the N-terminal third of protein 2a. It thus seems that the 5′ as well as the 3′ segments of CCMV RNA2 are involved in interaction with RNA1 and/or protein 1a for specific viral RNA replication.

In the case of BMV, the 5′ segment of RNA2 is important for successful interaction with RNA1 and/or protein 1a and for efficient replication. In addition, the C-terminal 206 amino acids of protein 2a are also involved in this *trans*-acting function. In summary, it seems that, for bromoviruses, major BMV- and CCMV-specific determinants for successful interaction of protein 2a with protein 1a, RNA1, or both reside in the N-proximal regions of protein 2a (66). This is relatively obvious in the case of interactions with BMV RNA1, but also seems true for interactions with CCMV RNA1.

In bromoviruses, protein 2a contains a highly conserved central region related to RdRp's and flanked by more variable N- and C-terminal domains. These variable domains could be involved in complexing the polymerase-like 2a protein core with the protein 1a.

D. Mechanism of CCMV RNA Replication

Although wild-type CCMV does not infect barley leaves, it does infect barley protoplasts. Consequently, CCMV RNA replication experiments were performed using barley protoplasts. Single-component exchanges between the BMV and CCMV genomes were tested in these protoplasts. Pseudo-recombinant viruses with RNAs 1 and 2 of different origins do not support viral RNA replication, whatever the combination tested. However pseudo-recombinant viruses in which the RNAs 3 have been exchanged do replicate in protoplasts, and RNA3 accumulates (98). While BMV RNAs 2 and 3 are replicated well in CCMV-infected cells, BMV-infected cells replicate CCMV RNA3 very poorly, and CCMV RNA2 not at all (66, 98). The response is thus significantly asymmetrical and may reflect the situation observed in doubly infected cells: BMV multiplication dominates in tobacco protoplasts coinfected with BMV and CCMV, as though BMV could use either replicase for its own benefit (100). This indicates that signals involved in RNA3 synthesis are similar in both viruses. RNA3 exchanges do not allow systemic infection in natural host plants of either virus, suggesting that the RNA3-encoded protein 3a may have a role in host specificity and in cell-to-cell movement, as postulated for BMV.

1. CCMV RNA3 Amplification

cis-Acting signals involved in CCMV RNA3 amplification in vivo have been identified by inoculation of barley protoplasts with wild-type RNAs 1 and 2 and mutant RNAs 3 deleted in different regions (96). The data show that the 5'-terminal 89 nucleotides of the 5'-noncoding region are sufficient and essential for RNA3 amplification. Contrary to what has been reported for BMV RNA3 amplification (85), the intercistronic region is not required for CCMV RNA3 synthesis: Deletion of the entire 200-nucleotide intercistronic sequence or removal of the coat-protein gene does not alter CCMV RNA3 amplification in vivo. An RNA3 mutant containing only the 5'-terminal 93 nucleotides and the 3'-terminal 361 nucleotides is very efficiently replicated. Simultaneous deletion of the coat-protein gene and the intercistronic region has no effect on RNA3 amplification. Larger deletions within this region retaining only the 5'-terminal 57 nucleotides lead to an inefficient RNA3 template mutant. With respect to the 3' terminus, these observations also indicate that more than 125 but less than 220 nucleotides at the 3' terminus are required for RNA3 amplification *in vivo*. This sequence may be involved in (−)-strand promoter function. It includes the tRNA-like structure of about 190 nucleotides.

2. SUBGENOMIC RNA4 SYNTHESIS

Analyses of the double-stranded RNAs found in CCMV-infected leaves reveal the presence of small amounts of RF and RI corresponding to RNA4 (99). Although this result could be in favor of autonomous replication of CCMV RNA4, this model was not retained because of the close relationship between CCMV and BMV and because of unequivocal evidence demonstrating that BMV RNA4 is synthesized by internal initiation of replication on (−)-RNA3 *in vitro* (87, 88). Furthermore, comparisons of the nucleotide sequences between the CCMV intercistronic region in RNA3 and the internal promoter of BMV RNA4 reveal significant homologies (94). Thus, a putative internal promoter core region has been identified in CCMV RNA3. In addition, an oligo(U) stretch of 40 residues is also present in the CCMV (−)-RNA3 sequence 3' from the core promoter sequence. BMV (−)-RNA3 contains an (A + U)-rich sequence harboring partial direct repeats of the core promoter sequence and located immediately 3' from the oligo(U) stretch involved in the internal promoter function (Fig. 3). In CCMV, sequences related to the partial repeats of the BMV core subgenomic promoter are detected 3' from the oligo(U) stretch (94), but no other similarities are discernible.

Experimental confirmation of the internal initiation mechanism came from analyses of the behavior of RNA3 deletion mutants in barley protoplasts (96). *In vivo* replication of these RNA3 mutants showed that the internal promoter of CCMV RNA4 is located within a region containing 160 nucleotides 3' and 30 nucleotides 5' from the RNA4 start site [the (−)-strand is considered here]. An RNA3 mutant with only 20 nucleotides of the intercistronic region (3' from the RNA4 start site) has no promoter activity for RNA4 synthesis *in vivo*.

IV. Replication of Cucumber Mosaic Virus RNA

Cucumber mosaic virus (CMV), the type-member of the cucumoviruses, contains a tripartite RNA genome. Its overall genome organization is similar to that of the bromoviruses (Fig. 1).

The CMV genome consists of three RNAs separately encapsidated in icosahedral capsids. It contains four ORFs (Fig. 1). RNAs 1 and 2 are monocistronic, encoding two nonstructural proteins, protein 1a (111 kDa) and protein 2a (97 kDa) (101), that are involved in CMV RNA replication. RNA3 contains two ORFs: The 5'-proximal gene of RNA3 encodes a nonstructural protein, protein 3a (30 kDa), thought to be involved in cell-to-cell movement (102). During replication, the 3' part of RNA3 generates a subgenomic RNA designated RNA4 (103, 104) that codes for the viral coat protein of about 24 kDa. The 3' terminus of CMV RNA possesses a tRNA-like structure that can be acylated by tyrosine.

CMV infects a wide range of plants, encompassing nearly 800 species in 365 genera and 85 families, including both monocotyledonous and dicotyledonous plants, and is of worldwide economic importance (105, 106).

There are many isolates or strains of this virus that differ in either pathology or host range. On the basis of serology (107) and nucleic acid hybridization (108, 109), CMV strains appear to fall into two subgroups. Of 39 strains examined by nucleic acid hybridization analyses, 30 belong to one subgroup (Subgroup I) and nine belong to a second subgroup (Subgroup II). The two subgroups contain genetically compatible RNAs: They can be reassorted to construct viable pseudo-recombinants (110, 111). The nucleotide sequences of the three genomic RNAs of one strain from Subgroup II, Q-CMV (104, 112, 113), of RNAs 1 and 2 of one strain from Subgroup I, Fny-CMV (114, 115), and of RNA3 of two strains from Subgroup I, Fny-CMV and M-CMV (116), have been determined.

Polyacrylamide gel electrophoresis of CMV RNA resolves four main RNA species (117, 118) in a pattern very similar to the one shown by RNA isolated from BMV, CCMV, and broad been mottle virus (119, 120).

In addition to the encapsidated genomic RNAs and the subgenomic RNA, CMV particles often contain a sat-RNA of 330–386 nucleotides (reviewed in 36 and 37). The CMV sat-RNA is also known as CARNA-5 (for CMV Associated RNA-5; 121). It contains no functional ORF, nor does it contain sequence similarities with the three genomic RNAs, other than short internal regions (11 residues or less) and a U-rich region at its 5' end (113, 122).

The presence of a sat-RNA can result in important modifications of viral symptoms in CMV-infected plants. Some species of sat-RNAs suppress CMV-induced symptoms, some attenuate them, while others trigger new symptoms (123–128). For example, Y sat-RNA induces chlorosis on tobacco, R sat-RNA can attenuate viral symptoms, Q sat-RNA appears to be without effect on symptom development, and $I_{17}N$ sat-RNA induces lethal necrosis exclusively on tomato, attenuating the symptoms on other hosts (reviewed in 37). Ten strains of CMV sat-RNAs capable of inducing necrosis on tomato, as well as 15 non-necrotic strains, have been cloned and sequenced (129–132). The effect produced by a given sat-RNA also depends on the plant species infected (123, 124, 133) and on the strain of helper virus (133, 134).

Most sat-RNAs found associated with various strains of CMV replicate to high levels in solanaceous plants, but poorly in cucurbits, except for the WL_1 sat-RNA, which replicates efficiently in both host families (*134*).

The infectious sat-RNA (+)-strand, its complement, or the double-stranded form of RNA found during replication might be responsible for symptom modulation, and this must be achieved by interacting through an unknown mechanism with the helper virus and/or components within the host cell (reviewed in *37*).

A. Intracellular Location of CMV RNA Replication

Most experiments aimed at defining the site of replication of CMV RNA, as well as of the closely related tomato aspermy virus, have been performed by electron microscopy on thin-sectioned material. In sections of infected cells, CMV particles are difficult to distinguish from cytoplasmic ribosomes, except by their greater resistance to digestion with pancreatic RNase in aldehyde-fixed tissues under appropriate conditions (*135*).

The major change observed in cells infected with CMV is the presence of small vesicles associated with the tonoplast (*136*). Similar structures are not observed in the cells of healthy control plants. The large number of vesicles is therefore correlated with the ability of the virus to reach high concentrations. The content of such vesicles is in contact with the cytoplasm through a "narrow neck" (*136*). These tonoplast-associated vesicles contain double-stranded RNAs that could be viral RFs and/or RIs.

Double-stranded RNAs have been identified in infected cells by their differential susceptibility to RNase in high and low salt conditions (*137*). They appear as electron-dense fibrils, located within vesicles.

B. Expression of CMV RNA

Although RNA1 is clearly required for replication, its specific function is not known. The conserved sequences common to RdRp's, including the GDD motif, are encoded by RNA2 (*67*). The C-terminal one-third of the 111-kDa protein encoded by RNA1 contains the six conserved motifs found in DNA and RNA helicases (*58*), suggesting at least one function for this protein. The most N-terminal domain of similarity between the products of CMV RNA1 and TMV RNA may be similar to that of the capping enzyme.

Pseudo-recombinants were constructed between two strains of CMV (*138*). Strain Fny-CMV shows very severe symptoms in the field and spreads rapidly, whereas strain Sny-CMV exhibits much milder symptoms and spreads slowly throughout the field. Individual purified viral RNAs have been reassorted and inoculated onto zucchini squash. It seems likely that protein 1a is multifunctional. RNA1 probably encodes functions required for interaction with RNA2 and/or its gene product, and with the host. The pathogenic response of zucchini squash to CMV infection, which differs after inoculation with strains containing RNA1 from Fny- or Sny-CMV, does not occur in other cucurbits. This suggests that either RNA1 or its encoded polypeptide plays a direct role in specific host–virus interactions.

Using these pseudo-recombinants (138a), the region involved in replication of WL_1 sat-RNA in zucchini squash has been mapped to RNA1 of CMV. The domain responsible for efficient sat-RNA replication is most likely distinct: Several related strains of CMV either display rapidly appearing severe symptoms or slowly developing mild symptoms, but the inefficiency of WL_1 sat-RNA replication is a property unique to the Sny-CMV strain.

C. CMV Replicase

1. ISOLATION AND CHARACTERIZATION

Several investigations of the replication of CMV RNA have been undertaken (139–141). However, attempts to produce a soluble, template-free CMV RdRp or to demonstrate the presence of proteins 1a and 2a in RNA-containing membrane-bound RdRp preparations remained unsuccessful for long time (101, 142).

Cucumber seedlings infected with CMV contain a virus-induced RdRp in both soluble (143) and particulate (144) fractions of plant extracts; no such activity is found in uninfected plants. Extensive purification and characterization of the soluble and particulate RNA RdRp have been described (143, 144). The membrane-bound RdRp isolated from CMV-infected tobacco protoplasts (145, 146) exclusively elongates (+)-RNA chains initiated in vivo and leads to full-length RNA products.

Recently, a bona fide replicase was prepared from CMV-infected tobacco plants (147). Treatment with a nonionic detergent produces a soluble enzyme, from which endogenous RNA is removed by nuclease digestion. More highly purified preparations are obtained by several chromatographic separations. The specific activity of the purest fraction is 760,000 times that of the membrane-bound enzyme. The replicase depends completely on the addition of CMV RNA as a template, and catalyzes the synthesis of (+)- as well as (−)-RNA strand.

2. NONSTRUCTURAL PROTEINS INVOLVED IN CMV RNA REPLICATION

Proteins 1a and 2a are the only viral requirements for CMV RNA replication. The activity of the viral enzyme was measured in tobacco mesophyll protoplasts by associating in vivo and in vitro steps (148). Protoplasts inoculated with CMV or different combinations of the four different viral RNAs and sat-RNA were harvested at different times after inoculation, and a pellet fraction containing the membrane-bound RNA-polymerizing enzyme associated with the template was used further for in vitro assays. The RNA products elongated *in vitro* were characterized in each case. The enzyme activity from CMV-infected protoplasts increases rapidly 4–6 hours after inoculation. When the inoculum contains RNAs 1, 2, and 3, most of the *in vitro*-elongated products are full-length (+)-strand RNAs that migrate as double-stranded RNAs. Inoculation with RNA1 or RNA2 alone does not yield replicase activity, and no viral RNA is produced. However, inoculation with a mixture of RNAs 1 and 2 produces an enzyme activity leading to the synthesis of full-length (+)-sense RNAs 1 and 2.

These results confirm that the induced enzyme is indeed the CMV RNA enzyme comprising the translation products of RNAs 1 and 2, membrane components of the host, and CMV RNA templates.

The recently purified enzyme (*147*) contains proteins 1a and 2a as well as a host polypeptide of 50 kDa. Evidence that proteins 1a and 2a are both subunits of the replicase and have not just fortuitously copurified with the complex was obtained. Using antibody-linked polymerase assays (*149*), it was demonstrated unequivocally that the two viral proteins are components of the replicase (*147*). The 50-kDa host-encoded protein is apparently bound to the replicase; it cannot be detected in extracts from healthy plants. It is essential for activity, and loss of this polypeptide is always accompanied by a complete loss of replicase activity. This activity is completely dependent on the addition of CMV RNA; No activity is observed in the absence of added template or upon addition of RNAs from viruses belonging to different taxonomic groups.

D. Mechanism of CMV RNA Replication

1. SYNTHESIS OF SUBGENOMIC RNA

In CMV-infected leaves, minor amounts of a double-stranded RNA band corresponding to RNA4 have been detected (*142*). This double-stranded RNA band also appears upon RNase-A digestion of RNA3 under high salt conditions. On the other hand, double-stranded forms corresponding to RNAs 1 and 2, but not to RNA4, were isolated from tobacco protoplasts inoculated with RNAs 1, 2, and 4, suggesting that (+)-RNA4 does not replicate autonomously (*148*).

Moreover, it is not proven that the double-stranded forms of subgenomic RNA are replication forms of RNA4, and it remains unknown in which case the promoter for subgenomic RNA synthesis must lie within the transcribed region on the (−)-strand. Double-stranded RNA4 could be a "dead-end" form, indicative of late stages in the replication cycle. They may reflect aberrant copying of subgenomic RNA and could very likely arise after RNA4 levels have reached a maximum, as observed in protoplasts infected with potato virus X, a potexvirus (D. Baulcombe, personal communication).

2. Model Proposed for CMV RNA Replication

The polarity of the products obtained in CMV-inoculated tobacco protoplasts has been examined (148): The replicase seems to catalyze (+)-strand elongation of in vivo-initiated chains, and the catalytic process terminates when RIs are converted into RFs.

An unpaired G residue on the 3' end of the (−)-strand in the double-stranded forms of both sat-RNA and RNA3 isolated from infected plants has been discovered (80). Such an additional nucleotide could serve as part of a recognition signal for the replicase that would thus initiate nascent (+)-strand synthesis at an internal site. This may also create a 3' overhang for recognition by the helicase, as described for plum pox virus, a potyvirus (150).

The products of the reaction catalyzed by the highly purified enzyme (147) are single- and double-stranded RNA molecules, corresponding in length to RNA's 1–4. Single-stranded RNAs are five times more abundant than double-stranded RNAs. They are predominantly of (+)-sense [seven times more (+)-strands than (−)-strands] and are uniformly labeled. Since an excess of (+)-strand templates is always present, the polymerase must utilize the (−)-strand template preferentially, and each (−)-strand template must be copied more than once. The reaction products obtained using RNA3 as template include subgenomic RNA4, as well as full-length RNA3. This enzyme catalyzes the complete cycle of CMV RNA replication; this constitutes the first report of complete in vitro replication of a eukaryotic virus RNA by a purified, template-dependent replicase. The availability of such a system opens the way for investigations on the mechanism of RNA replication and for studies of the role of the virus- and host-encoded subunits, studies that have, before now, not been possible.

3. Satellite RNA Replication

Very little is known about how sat-RNAs replicate in vivo. Since sat-RNAs require a specific helper virus for their accumulation in infected plants, it is assumed that the virus-encoded replicase is responsible for sat-RNA replication. Terminal nucleotide sequence homology is not the only factor in sat-RNA recognition by viral replicases: The sat-RNA associated with peanut stunt virus (a cucumovirus) and CMV sat-RNA share short conserved sequences and terminal structures at their 3' and 5' ends, but their replication cannot be supported by each other's helper virus (151). Sat-RNAs have also been described that replicate more efficiently in some hosts than in others. Most CMV sat-RNAs do not replicate as well in cucurbit as in solanaceous hosts (134). The terminal 50 residues at the 3' or 5' end are not responsible for differential accumulation of CMV strains in squash. Sat-RNA is synthesized in protoplasts inoculated with RNAs 1 and 2, and sat-RNA. It is therefore replicated by the replicase complex. Sat-RNA suppresses the synthesis of helper CMV RNAs to some extent, especially that of RNAs 1 and 2; it is therefore possible that the sat-RNA competes with viral RNAs for replicase binding (148).

a. Satellite RNAs and Plant Symptoms. A model has been proposed to account for the reduction of symptoms due to CMV sat-RNAs (151). This model proposes that a decrease in the accumulation of CMV observed in infected tobacco leaves is the result of competition between CMV and sat-RNAs for limiting viral or cellular factors that may be necessary for RNA replication (148). The mechanism by which sat-RNA outcompetes the CMV genomic RNAs for replication by the viral replicase is unclear. A short sequence near the 5' end of the sat-RNA is complementary to sequences within the 5' ends of viral RNAs (113). These complementary sequences form hairpin loop structures that might be involved in replicase recognition. Sat-RNAs also bind in vitro to the coding region of the viral coat-protein gene on RNA3 under stringent hybridization conditions (152), and may therefore act as "anti-sense" RNAs to block coat-protein synthesis. No apparent hybridization occurs in vitro between sat-RNA and CMV RNAs 1 and 2, despite the presence of complementary sequences. It is therefore still an open question as to whether anti-sense binding of sat-RNA to RNA3 is directly involved in regulating RNA replication, and whether this interaction plays a role in vivo. Thus, Y sat-RNA is quite effective in reducing the level of helper virus in systemically infected leaves (153), but has very little complementarity with the helper virus due to the presence of additional sequences (relative to other sat-RNAs) in the region of the anti-sense domain.

It is clear that symptom attenuation is not always correlated with low virus levels in systemically infected leaves: Both sat-RNA strain $I_{17}N$ and helper virus, either CMV or TAV, accumulate to high levels in systemically infected tobacco leaves. A slight effect of the sat-RNA on early stages of TAV replication might be sufficient to attenuate symptoms if symptom development is dependent on adequate levels of viral RNA accumulation early in cell development (154).

A sat-RNA need not be replicated and encapsidated in order to attenuate symptom development by a virus (155): The sat-RNA of tobacco ringspot virus (a nepovirus) can inhibit replication of a different nepovirus, cherry leafroll virus, that does not support replication of this satellite.

b. Model Proposed for sat-RNA Replication. The presence of higher-order multimers in sat-RNA-infected tissue has led to the hypothesis that sat-RNAs replicate via a rolling-circle mechanism (156–158). In this model, multimeric (−)-strand RNAs are synthesized from the circular (+)-infectious

RNA strand. Multimeric (+)-strands are then generated from the unit-size (−)-strand template, followed by processing into the final, mature sat-RNAs. Nevertheless, it is not clear that linear sat-RNAs indeed replicate via a rolling-circle mechanism, and some results are difficult to reconcile with this model (159). As with turnip crinkle virus (a carmovirus related to carnation mottle virus), one likely explanation that has been proposed for the multimeric sat-RNAs involves some sort of template switching (D. Baulcombe, personal communication).

The sequence of sat-RNA specifies a variety of functions, among which are viral and/or plant replicase recognition signals. With the development of *in vitro* replication systems and the possibility of synchronizing sat-RNA replication *in vivo* using electroporated protoplasts, specific sequences or structures involved in sat-RNA replication will certainly be identified.

E. Plant Protection against CMV Infection: Use of CMV Sat-RNAs

A potential means by which plants may be protected from the effects of specific viral disease is derived from studies in which the cDNA corresponding to CMV sat-RNA strain $I_{17}N$ has been inserted into the genome of tobacco plants under the transcriptional control of the cauliflower mosaic virus 35-S promoter (154, 160). Initial low levels of sat-RNAs are greatly amplified following inoculation of transformed plants with helper virus, resulting in disease attenuation.

In transgenic tobacco, dimeric copies of the sat-RNA $I_{17}N$ can generate infectious satellites only when the plant is subsequently infected with CMV. The sat-RNA then affects symptoms in the expected way, decreasing the intensity of the disease (160).

Transcripts based on monomeric forms of CMV sat-RNA are also recognized by the CMV replicase when introduced into plants, and produce large quantities of biologically active sat-RNA; tolerance to CMV is thereby conferred (159).

More recently, sat-RNAs were transferred to tobacco and tomato, based either on the necrogenic $I_{17}N$ sat-RNA or on the non-necrogenic R strain. The cDNA corresponding to the sat-RNAs of either group was inserted in both orientations into host plants. Upon infection with sat-RNA-free CMV, transgenic tobacco plants bearing one of four sequences, $I_{17}N(+)$, $I_{17}N(−)$ $R(+)$ and (−), produce large quantities of (+)-sense sat-RNA as expected. These results suggest that the CMV replication complex is equally capable of recognizing (+)- or (−)-sat-RNA in the precursor transcripts (161). If this hypothesis is correct, RIs that are partially double-stranded would be found in preparations of total RNAs from infected plants. This point is currently being investigated; the same approach is also being tested on tomato (162).

The two main advantages of using sat-RNAs to protect plants against diseases are, first, efficiency of protection even at very low levels of sat-RNA expression, and second, absence of novel proteins in the transgenic plants (*163*). Nevertheless, this sat-RNA-based strategy still needs further development to remove the hazards associated with the use of certain strains of sat-RNA of CMV. The strategy presents two major drawbacks: First, few plant viruses harbor sat-RNAs; second, only a few base differences exist between sat-RNAs that attenuate or intensify disease symptoms (*131, 153, 164, 165*). It is therefore necessary to create new sequences, coding for non-necrogenic sat-RNAs incapable of becoming necrogenic and being transmitted to other plants. Indeed, there is a real possibility that, after the transformed plants are infected with CMV, the sat-RNA could spread with the helper virus to other plants and cause severe disease. The aim of future work on sat-RNAs will therefore be to disarm the RNA so as to eliminate this potential hazard.

V. Replication of Alfalfa Mosaic Virus RNA

Alfalfa mosaic virus (AlMV) is a tricornavirus, a member of the ilarviruses (*166*). Its three RNA genome parts, RNAs 1, 2, and 3 (in order of decreasing size), as well as a subgenomic RNA designated RNA4, are separately encapsidated (*167*) into bacilliform nucleocapsid particles, designated B, M, Tb, and Ta, that are more or less elongated, depending on the size of the RNA they contain. The AlMV capsids are composed of multiple copies of a single coat-protein molecule. RNAs 1–4 are single-stranded and of (+)-polarity. RNA4 derives from the 3′ region of RNA3 and is the messenger for the coat protein of 24 kDa (Fig. 1). Each RNA bears a cap structure at its 5′ end and a noncoding stretch [devoid of tRNA-like properties or of a poly(A) tail] at its 3′ end. The complete nucleotide sequences of RNA1 (*168*), RNA2 (*169*), RNA3 (*170–172*), and RNA4 (*173*) have been established. RNA1 (3644 nucleotides) and RNA2 (2593 nucleotides) are monocistronic and code, respectively, for the nonstructural proteins P1 (126 kDa) and P2 (96 kDa) presumably involved in viral RNA replication. RNA3 (2037–2142 nucleotides) is dicistronic: Its 5′-proximal ORF encodes the nonstructural protein P3 (32 kDa) involved in spreading the virus from cell to cell, whereas the 3′-proximal ORF contains the coat-protein gene.

The coat protein of ilarviruses plays a dual role, in RNA encapsidation and as regulator of the infection process (reviewed in *174*). Indeed, inoculation of the three genome RNAs onto leaves or protoplasts does not lead to infection unless either a few coat-protein molecules or RNA4 is included (*167, 175*). Presumably, RNA4 directs the synthesis of coat-protein molecules indispensable for RNA replication. The coat protein acts by binding to homologous stem–loop structures found in the 3′-terminal region (of about 80 nucleotides) of all the genome parts (*176–178*). A few coat-protein molecules must bind to each of the genome segments to trigger infection (*179*). Mild treatment of the coat protein with trypsin removes the 25 N-terminal amino acids from the coat protein, which then becomes inactive (*180*) and no longer binds specifically to the 3' region of the AlMV RNAs (*181*).

A. Intracellular Location of AlMV RNA Replication

Incubation of AlMV-infected leaf cells with radiolabeled uridine followed by electron-microscopic autoradiography demonstrated that the radioactivity incorporated is recovered in the nuclei as well as in the cytoplasm (*182*). These early results suggested that the nucleus as well as the cytoplasm might be involved in AlMV RNA synthesis.

More recently, the location of AlMV RNA replication has been investigated (*183*), using protoplasts isolated from infected tobacco plants, or tobacco protoplasts inoculated *in vitro*. At early times after infection, using immunocytological methods, the coat protein and (−)-RNA strands are detected in the cytoplasm, but not in the nucleus (*184*). Late in infection, coat protein can also be detected in the nucleus. Thus, coat protein and/or virus particles accumulate in the nucleus. Fractionation of infected protoplast extracts demonstrated that newly synthesized (−)-RNA strands are associated with a fraction that contains disrupted chloroplasts and membranous material, but not with the nuclear fraction. AlMV replication therefore does not seem to take place in the nucleus.

B. Expression of AlMV RNA

Polypeptides corresponding to the four ORFs have been detected by *in vitro* translation experiments programmed by the viral RNAs (*185*). They are also detected in AlMV-inoculated protoplasts after suppression of host metabolism by UV-irradiation (*186*), or by the use of specific antibodies in the productive infection of protoplasts (*184, 187*; see next section).

C. AlMV RdRp

1. Isolation and Characterization

Using conditions reminiscent of those that were successful for isolation of the BMV RdRp (*56*), an AlMV-specified RdRp was isolated from *Phaseolus vulgaris* plants 3 days after inoculation with AlMV (*188*). This enzyme preparation is totally dependent on the addition of AlMV RNA and produces full-length transcripts of (−)-sense corresponding to the four AlMV RNAs. It does not use TYMV RNA as template. The crude RdRp preparation contains endogenous coat protein as well as many other proteins, whose identities have not been established. Most of the endogenous coat protein can be removed from the enzyme preparation by mild trypsin treatment. The activity of the resulting RdRp preparation is over 30% greater than the activity of the RdRp prior to trypsin treatment, suggesting an inhibitory effect of the coat protein on $(-)$-strand synthesis. Moreover, if intact or trypsin-treated RdRp complex is incubated with viral RNAs incubated in advance with intact coat protein, the level of RNA synthesis decreases. To explain the differential activity of the coat protein, it has been proposed (189) that the coat protein is a positive regulator of RNA replication at early times after infection, and a negative regulator at late times. This model is discussed below (Section V, D).

2. NONSTRUCTURAL PROTEINS INVOLVED IN RNA REPLICATION

The fate of the viral proteins was investigated in AlMV-infected tobacco leaves (187) and in tobacco and cowpea protoplasts, using antibodies against the C-terminal part of proteins P1, P2, and P3 (184). Maximum levels of proteins P1 and P2 are detected early in infection (70 hours in leaves; 16 hours in protoplasts) and levels decrease thereafter. A good correlation exists between the amount of proteins P1 and P2 (but not of protein P3) and RdRp activity (187), suggesting that proteins P1 and P2 are involved in viral RNA replication. In protoplasts, in which infection is easier to synchronize than in infected leaves and in which infection is comparable to early stages of virus development in plants, proteins P1 and P2 and $(-)$-RNA strands are recovered in the 1000 g pellet (containing nuclei, chloroplasts, and membranes attached to these organelles) rather than in the 30,000 g pellet. In the protoplast system (184), two forms of protein P2 appear, one comigrating with the protein synthesized in vitro, the other migrating more slowly, implying that protein P2 is, in part, post-translationally modified.

3. MUTANTS AFFECTING AlMV RNA REPLICATION

The behavior of certain AlMV ts mutants, obtained originally as spontaneous mutants (190), has been examined in detail in cowpea protoplasts (191). These mutants are fully active at the permissive (nonrestrictive) temperature of 23°C, but one or more of their functions is impaired at the nonpermissive (restrictive) temperature of 30°C.

At the nonpermissive temperature, two mutants of RNA1 (Bts 03 and Bts 04), and two mutants of RNA2 (Mts 03 and Mts 04) are all defective in $(-)$-strand synthesis, whereas $(+)$-strand synthesis is only minimally affected (191). It appears that this 70–90% reduction in $(-)$-strand synthesis at the nonpermissive temperature does not prevent an RNA3-encoded protein from actively favoring the production of $(+)$-strand RNA. With none of the four mutants is the level of RNA4 production reduced at the nonpermissive temperature. Two of the mutants, Bts 03 and Mts 04, lead to interruption of coat-protein synthesis at 30°C, even though RNA4 is produced in normal quantities; consequently, no infectious virus particles are produced. The RNA4 derived from these mutants is efficiently translated *in vitro*. Consequently, the defective translation of RNA4 observed with these mutants at 30°C in infected protoplasts indicates that a factor contained in P1 or P2, or a host factor induced by these proteins, is somehow involved in RNA4 translation.

These results suggest that, in addition to their function in viral (−)-strand synthesis, proteins P1 and P2 are also involved in the regulation of synthesis of the coat protein. The mechanism by which these mutants interfere with coat-protein synthesis is unknown. Thus, the proteins encoded by RNAs 1 and 2 could be involved in the formation of a complex required in viral RNA replication and/or in controlling RNA4 translation (*192*). Indeed, these two proteins are produced in similar molar amounts in UV-irradiated alfalfa protoplast (*186*). It has been proposed that the P1 and P2 proteins produced at the nonpermissive temperature would be unable to assume correct folding to yield a stable productive complex at that temperature (*192*).

Another interesting *ts* mutant, from the point of view of viral RNA replication, is Tbts 7. This mutant was obtained by combining wild-type B and M particles with UV-irradiated Tb particles. It induces necrotic lesions, followed by systemic necrosis on Samsun NN tobacco plants (*190*), as opposed to wild-type AlMV, which induces systemic chlorosis. In tobacco-leaf disks from inoculated plants and in inoculated cowpea protoplasts, Tbts 7 produces infectious virus at 23°C, but not at 30°C. In Tbts 7, the coat protein contains a single amino-acid substitution that results in its altered electrophoretic behavior (*193*). As a consequence, the mutated coat protein is incapable of activating the AlMV genome, at the nonpermissive temperature, and no infectious virus is produced. At 25°C, mutant Tbts 7 is replicated in tobacco-leaf disks, but if wild-type Tb is included, only the latter type of RNA3 is replicated, suggesting a decreased affinity of the replicase for mutant RNA3. It has been proposed that the mutation of RNA3 leads to a temperature-sensitive defect in an early function of virus replication, such as replication of RNA3 (*194*).

In spite of the vast amount of work that has gone into trying to decipher the mechanism of replication using *ts* mutants of AlMV, it is still difficult to correlate a mutation with an impaired function of the corresponding protein involved in AlMV RNA replication. Even when structure–function relationships will have been established for the mutants described above, added complications can be foreseen: (1) certain mutants may present a modification at the nucleotide level that would not affect the corresponding amino-acid sequence; (2) more than one mutation may co-exist in a single mutant; (3) mutations may lie within the noncoding regions of the viral RNAs; and (4) during propagation, additional mutations may arise. The first three complications could be circumvented by the use of site-directed mutagenesis, but to date no method is available to circumvent the fourth complication.

4. EXPRESSION OF THE AlMV RdRp

Transgenic tobacco plants constitutively expressing nearly complete AlMV RNA1 or RNA2 have been obtained (195). The transcripts produced by such plants are of the expected size, but the corresponding translation products cannot be detected using antibodies raised against the C-terminal parts of proteins P1 or P2. Nevertheless, transgenic protoplasts containing the cDNA of RNA1 can complement an infection by AlMV particles M plus Tb, containing RNAs 2 and 3, respectively, since 24 hours after infection, coat protein and RNAs 2–4 appear (the amount of RNA1 produced is below the detection level). Thus, biologically active protein P1 can complement infection by RNAs 2 and 3. However, the transcript produced by the cDNA of RNA1 appears not to be replicated in this system. Likewise, transgenic protoplast containing the cDNA of RNA2 can complement an infection by AlMV particles B plus Tb, indicating here also that biologically active P2 can complement infection by RNAs 1 and 3 (196). In tobacco plants transformed with cDNA copies of RNAs 1 and 2, initiation of infection with RNA 3 requires no coat protein; the results obtained with these transgenic protoplasts suggest that coat protein is required for replication of RNAs 1 and 2 (197).

Full-length cDNA inserts corresponding to RNA2 have been introduced into a yeast expression vector (198). The recombinant yeasts produce high levels of a protein with all the characteristics of protein P2. The purified protein should provide information on the role of protein P2 in viral RNA replication.

D. Mechanism of AlMV RNA Replication

For viral RNA to be synthesized, cowpea protoplasts must be inoculated with B and M particles. Either of these alone fails to induce RNA replication (175). Further analyses (189) using the Northern blot technique, revealed a striking difference in the levels of (−)- and (+)-strands produced, depending on the combination of viral particles used for inoculation. With B and M alone, large amounts of (−)-strands are produced, corresponding to RNAs 1 and 2, whereas the production of (+)-strands is much less abundant. On the other hand, mixtures of B, M, and Tb lead to an asymmetrical production in favor of (+)-strand molecules, reflecting the situation that occurs *in vivo*, where the level of (+)-strands is about 1000-fold higher than that of (−)-strands (199). Consequently, an RNA3-specified product is required to block (−)-strand synthesis, and it has been proposed that the coat protein is responsible for the resulting overproduction of (+)-strands. It is unlikely that the RNA3 product is required for (+)-strand synthesis that could not be accomplished by the replicase produced by B plus M, since the excess of (−)-strands in B plus M-inoculated protoplasts is essentially resistant to RNases, indicating that (+)-strand RNA synthesis has also taken place.

Based on the available data, a model of the replication cycle of AlMV RNA (Fig. 4) has been proposed (189). After inoculation with B, M, and Tb and uncoating, and at early times after inoculation, the level of coat protein is low, and the few coat-protein molecules present would remain bound to the high-affinity stem–loop structures located in the 3′ region of the viral RNAs. The RNAs serve as templates for the production of viral proteins P1, P2, and P3. It is assumed that P1 and P2 (possibly in conjunction with host-protein factors), constitute the viral RdRp. This P1/P2 enzyme complex

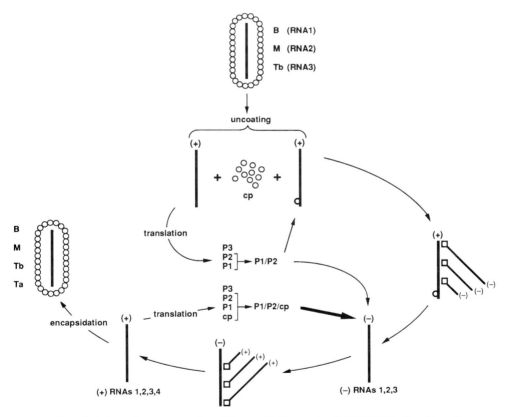

FIG. 4. Schematic representation of the replication cycle of AlMV RNA. The tripartite genome is represented by a single bar. Circles correspond to the viral coat protein. The steps involved in the replication cycle are discussed in the text. (Adapted from 189.)

recognizes the (+)-RNA strands through the coat protein bound to the RNA, and (−)-strands are synthesized. It is believed that coat-protein molecules cannot bind to (−)-RNA strands, since the 3′ regions of these strands lack the homologous sequences present in the 3′ region of the (+)-strands (200). It is proposed that the enzyme complex recognizes the (−)-strands without the help of coat protein, and that RIs are formed. The resulting (+)-strands can serve as template for viral protein synthesis or for the initiation of a new replicative cycle (triggered by the P1/P2/coat-protein complex), or they can be encapsidated (Fig. 4). Thus, at later times after inoculation, the newly synthesized coat-protein molecules would also associate with the P1/P2 enzyme complex, and would thereby prevent the resulting P1/P2/coat-protein complex from interacting with (+)-RNA strands bearing coat-protein molecules; as a result, (−)-RNA synthesis would be inhibited.

1. Synthesis of Subgenomic RNA

Another aspect raised by these experiments is the mode of synthesis of subgenomic RNA4 (189). In infected protoplasts inoculated with B, M, and Ta, or with B, M, and Tb, no (−)-strands corresponding to RNA4 can be detected. Since RNA4 corresponds to the 3′ region of RNA3 and consequently possesses the homologous stem–loop regions to which coat-protein molecules bind, various explanations have been proposed to explain the absence of replication of this subgenomic RNA; these are discussed in the preface of this article.

The data obtained by Northern blot hybridizations as well as results obtained using *ts* mutants of AlMV (201), support the model by which RNA4 is not replicated autonomously, but rather is transcribed from (−)-RNA3 molecules by internal initiation of replication. By deletion analyses, the sequence within (−)-strand RNA3 that serves as promoter for RNA4 synthesis *in vitro* has been located between nucleotides −8 and −55, 3′ from the initiation site for RNA4 synthesis (202).

2. Promoters in AlMV RNA3

The availability of an AlMV-specific RdRp and of cDNA-derived *in vitro* transcripts corresponding to RNA3 has prompted studies on the *cis*-acting elements involved in (−)-RNA strand synthesis (202).

Deletions within the 3′-noncoding region (183 nucleotides) of AlMV RNA3 were effected. This region can adopt seven stem–loop structures, separated by variants of the sequence AUGC (177, 203). Transcripts lacking as many as 133 nucleotides from the 3′ end, thus lacking the five 3′-terminal stem–loop structures, are recognized by RdRp to produce the corresponding (−)-strands. Surprisingly, transcripts lacking only 54 nucleotides (three stem–loop structures) from the 3′ end are more efficient templates than even wild-type RNA3. It has been postulated that the repeated stem–loop structures can perform the function of alternative recognition elements when downstream stem–loop structures are missing. The involvement of the 5' part of the 3'-noncoding region has also been examined by deleting internal stem–loop structures. The results obtained indicate that deletions in the 3'-noncoding region upstream from nucleotide 163 still yield transcripts that have template activity. Larger deletions as far as nucleotide 120 from the 3' end no longer serve as template. Taken together, these results suggest that the sequence between nucleotides 133 and 163 from the 3' end of RNA3 is sufficient to trigger synthesis of the complementary (−)-strand. Consequently, it appears that the high-affinity binding sites for coat protein that are located in the 3' region of AlMV RNA are not required for (−)-strand synthesis *in vitro*.

By deletion analyses similar to those described above, the sequence within (−)-strand RNA3 that serves as promoter for RNA4 synthesis *in vitro* has also been located (202).

VI. Replication of Turnip Yellow Mosaic Virus RNA

Turnip yellow mosaic virus (TYMV), the type-member of the tymoviruses, induces systemic infection in *Cruciferae*. This virus possesses a single-stranded (+)-sense genomic RNA of 6318 nucleotides (204) and a subgenomic RNA of 693 nucleotides (205). Both RNAs have a cap structure at their 5' ends and harbor a tRNA-like structure acylatable with valine at their 3' ends. Both are enclosed in icosahedral capsids comprising 180 copies of coat protein (20 kDa). Other strains of TYMV have been identified in Australia, and the nucleotide sequence of the genomic RNA of the TYMV Club-Lake strain has been determined (206). Full-length cDNA copies and infectious RNA transcripts of the type-member have been obtained (207).

A. Intracellular Location of TYMV RNA Replication

TYMV infection induces significant modifications in chloroplasts and nuclei. In particular, invagination of the double membrane of chloroplasts, leading to the generation of vacuoles, has been reported (reviewed in 12 and 208). Furthermore, electron-microscope studies show that replication occurs within these vesicles (209). *In situ* characterization of RIs also demonstrates the involvement of the chloroplast envelope in TYMV RNA replication (210). TYMV RFs and RIs containing both (+)- and (−)-sense RNAs are present in the outer membrane of chloroplasts. In addition, their differential susceptibility to RNases under high and low salt conditions indicates that, *in vivo*, they are mainly single-stranded, rather than double-stranded, molecules (210).

B. Expression of TYMV RNA

The genomic RNA of TYMV is polycistronic and contains a silent 3'-proximal coat-protein gene (Fig. 5). This gene is translated from a subgenomic RNA generated during virus replication (reviewed in *208*).

Two 5'-proximal genes are translated from the genomic RNA. The longer ORF initiated at the second AUG (nucleotides 95–97) from the 5' end encodes a nonstructural 206-kDa protein that undergoes specific processing, releasing 150- and 78-kDa proteins; the 150-kDa protein appears to be further processed, yielding a 120-kDa and a putative 30-kDa protein (*211–213*). In addition, analysis of the genomic sequence reveals the presence of a second shorter ORF initiated at the first AUG (nucleotides 88–90) and out of phase with respect to the 206-kDa ORF. It codes for a 69-kDa protein detected among the TYMV *in vitro* translation products (*207*). Alteration of the AUG codon at position 88–90 abolishes *in vitro* synthesis of the 69-kDa protein. Both ORFs are conserved among the tymoviruses whose RNA sequence is known (*204, 206, 214–216*).

Except for the coat protein, none of the other RNA-encoded proteins of TYMV has been identified in TYMV-infected tissues. The function of these nonstructural proteins is unknown. However, a search for the conserved functional motifs related to RNA-dependent polymerases in the amino-acid sequence of the TYMV nonstructural proteins revealed the conserved domain comprising the GDD motif (*27, 28, 67*) in the 206-kDa protein (*204*) and after cleavage in the 78-kDa protein. The NTP-binding domain is also located in the 206-kDa sequence (*204*) and in its putative 30-kDa proteolytic maturation product (reviewed in *12*). Inoculation of Chinese cabbage protoplasts with a TYMV RNA transcript mutated in the 206-kDa initiation codon inhibited replication (*207*). These results suggest that at least the 206-kDa protein and/or its cleavage product(s) may be part of the viral replicase.

C. TYMV RdRp

An active TYMV RdRp preparation has been isolated from TYMV-infected Chinese cabbage leaves (*217*). This viral RdRp is chromatographically

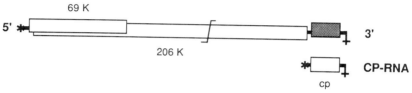

FIG. 5. Genome organization of TYMV. The ORFs corresponding to the 69- and 206-kDa proteins nearly completely overlap. ⌐, Approximate position of the cleavage site of the 206-kDa protein. Other details are as in Fig. 1.

distinct from the host RNA-dependent RNA polymerase as well as in its behavior on sucrose gradients and its template specificities. The viral enzyme is template-dependent; it is highly specific for TYMV RNA and to a lesser extent for eggplant mosaic virus, another tymovirus. On the other hand, the host enzyme only poorly triggers $(-)$-strand synthesis using TYMV RNA as template.

Two proteins of about 115 and 45 kDa have been identified in the RdRp preparation (217). Antibodies against the purified 115-kDa RdRp subunit specifically react with a TYMV nonstructural protein of 120 kDa. These antibodies can partially inhibit synthesis of complementary viral RNA (218), suggesting that the 120-kDa polypeptide resulting from cleavage of the 206-kDa protein is involved in $(-)$-strand synthesis. However, direct immunoprecipitation of the TYMV RNA translation products with the anti-115-kDa protein should be performed to determine whether the 115-kDa protein contained in the RdRp preparation and the 120-kDa protein observed by translation *in vitro* are identical. Surprisingly, none of the functional domains related to RNA-dependent polymerases or to helicase activities is located in the amino-acid sequence of the 120-kDa protein. Thus, it cannot be excluded that other viral-encoded proteins are also involved in replication, particularly the 78-kDa protein containing the GDD motif, the putative 30-kDa protein containing the NTP-binding domain, and even the 206-kDa protein (reviewed in 12). It would be very informative to establish whether the 78-kDa and putative 30-kDa proteins harboring these domains are also part of the active enzyme.

The 45-kDa protein contained in the RdRp preparation is coded by the host, but has not been further characterized. As opposed to what has been reported for the RdRp of bacteriophage Qβ (26), the eukaryotic protein elongation factor EF-1α that can bind to valylated RNA of TYMV is not detected in the RdRp preparation (219). It has not been possible to determine the location and function of this host-encoded subunit in healthy tissues (220).

D. Mechanism of TYMV RNA Replication

1. $(-)$-STRAND RNA SYNTHESIS

It has been proposed that the 3'-terminal 86 nucleotides of TYMV RNA encompassing the tRNA-like structure have a function in viral RNA replication, more precisely, in template recognition for $(-)$-strand RNA amplification. The *in vitro* RdRp system has been used to examine this possibility (221). Toward this aim, RNA transcripts corresponding to the 3'-terminal 100 nucleotides of TYMV RNA were added to an RdRp mixture containing the active enzyme and the viral template. Such short viral RNA fragments compete with the viral RNA for the RdRp *in vitro*, leading to strong inhibition of

(−)-strand synthesis. Moreover, these transcripts serve as templates of the RdRp for complementary RNA strand synthesis. However, an RNA transcript that has lost the major part of the tRNA-like structure (deletion of the 3′-terminal 100 nucleotides) only poorly inhibits (−)-strand synthesis under the same conditions. These results indicate that the 3′-terminal 100 nucleotides of TYMV RNA contain all the information required for recognition by the RdRp and for (−)-strand RNA synthesis *in vitro*.

2. SYNTHESIS OF COAT-PROTEIN SUBGENOMIC RNA

The models envisaged to account for the synthesis of the coat-protein subgenomic RNA *in vivo* have been outlined and are presented in the preface of this article. To distinguish between these models, double-stranded RNAs were isolated from TYMV-infected Chinese cabbage leaves, purified, and characterized (*222*). Only double-stranded RNAs of genomic size can be detected by Northern blot analyses. Neither double-stranded RNAs nor (−)-strand RNAs of subgenomic size appear, thereby excluding the premature termination model. Post-transcriptional processing of (+)-RNA3 can be excluded since the corresponding 5′ RNA fragment resulting from such a processing event is not detected. On the other hand, direct labeling of the nascent (+)-strand RNAs demonstrates the presence of (+)-strand RNAs of both genomic and subgenomic size associated with double-stranded RNAs of genomic size. These results indicate that the subgenomic RNA is synthesized *in vivo* by internal initiation on (−)-RNA strands of genomic length. The internal promoter involved in this mechanism had not been identified. When identified, its sequence could be compared with the sequences of the internal promoters of BMV, AlMV, CCMV, and alphaviruses to search for conserved sequences specific to viruses belonging to the Sindbis virus-like supergroup.

E. Plant Protection against TYMV Infection: The "Sense" RNA Approach

As mentioned above, RNA fragments corresponding to the tRNA-like region (i.e., 100 nucleotides) can inhibit (−)-strand synthesis *in vitro* and are recognized by the RdRp as efficiently as genomic RNA (*221*). Experiments exploiting this sense RNA approach to inhibit viral RNA replication have been pursued *in vivo* with the aim of generating TYMV-resistant transgenic plants. The cDNA corresponding to the tRNA-like region has been introduced into *Brassica napus* plants by *Agrobacterium*-mediated transformation. The resulting transgenic plants are being tested for their ability to overcome TYMV infection (*223*).

VII. Replication of Tobacco Mosaic Virus RNA

Tobacco mosaic was first characterized as an infectious disease in 1886 and the virus responsible for the disease, tobacco mosaic virus (TMV), has been the subject of very intensive investigations ever since. The complete nucleotide sequence of the monopartite genomic RNA of TMV has been determined for the common strain (6395 nucleotides; *224*), for the tomato L strain (6384 nucleotides; *225*), and for tobacco mild green mosaic virus or the TMV-U1 strain (6355 nucleotides; *226*). In the capsid, a rigid rod, the coat protein exists in two forms: 2130 copies of the coat protein per virion (*227*), and approximately one copy of a 26.5-kDa hybrid protein (*228*) that involves ubiquitin coupled to a coat-protein molecule (*229*).

The taxonomic relationships among viral strains are not always clear. TMV-U1 and TMV-OM strains are the American and Japanese isolates of what is referred to as the common, *vulgare*, or type strain of TMV. Their sequences differ by only a few nucleotides (*230*). The TMV-L strain, tomato strain, or tomato mosaic virus (*231*) is a closely related virus approximately 80% similar to TMV-U1 at the nucleotide level (*225*). The cowpea strain of TMV (CcTMV) or sun-hemp mosaic virus (*232*) is the most distantly related virus in this group (*233*); nevertheless it is, by tradition, referred to as a strain of TMV.

TMV RNA carries noncoding regions approximately 70 and 200 nucleotides long at the 5' and 3' termini, respectively (*224–226*). The 3'-terminal noncoding region can be divided into two regions on the basis of structural features (Fig. 6): at the 3' end, a tRNA-like structure (*235, 236*) and three consecutive pseudo-knot structures upstream (*237*).

A cap structure is present at the 5' terminus of the RNA (*238, 239*). In contrast to the highly structured 3'-terminal noncoding region, the 5'-untranslated leader sequence, the Ω fragment (*240*), lacks internal guanosine residues (in the *vulgare* and L strains, but not in tobacco mild green mosaic virus), contains several CAA repeats, and is unlikely to be folded into higher-order structures (*241*). This sequence is well conserved among several common and tomato strains of TMV (*225, 242*).

The genome organization of TMV, the type-member of the tobamoviruses, one of the best studied virus groups, is fairly well understood (Fig. 7). The RNA contains four ORFs. Two proteins, the 126-kDa (*224*) and 183-kDa proteins, previously referred to as the 110-kDa and 165-kDa (*243*) or the 130-kDa (*244, 245*) and 180-kDa (*246*) proteins, are translated from the genomic RNA. Two proteins, the nonstructural 30-kDa protein and the coat protein are encoded by two subgenomic RNAs, respectively, the I_2-RNA (2058 nucleotides; *247, 248*) and the LMC-RNA (698 nucleotides; *249*) or CP-RNA (reviewed in *250* and *251*).

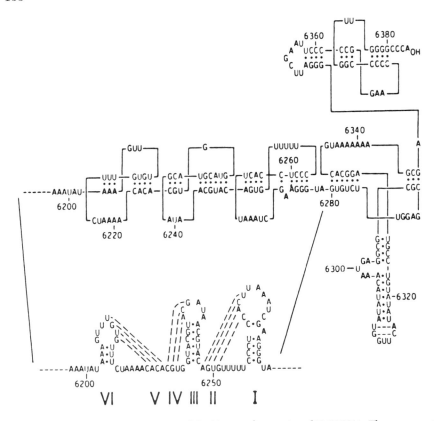

FIG. 6. Schematic representation of the 3′-noncoding region of TMV RNA. The upper part presents the folding between nucleotides 6197 and the 3′ terminus (nucleotide 6384) of the RNA. The lower part depicts a model of the interactions (dashed lines) involved in pseudo-knot formation. I–VI correspond to the six double-helical segments. (Reproduced with permission from 234.)

A third subgenomic RNA, termed I_1-RNA (2991 nucleotides; 252, 253), is found in TMV-infected plants. It contains an ORF for a 54-kDa protein, a putative component of the replicase (43). This ORF corresponds to the read-through portion of the gene encoding the 183-kDa protein (Fig. 7). Of the three subgenomic RNAs, the CP-RNA is not encapsidated, since the assembly origin in the RNA for encapsidation lies upstream from the region corresponding to this RNA, within the 30-kDa protein ORF.

A. Intracellular Location of TMV RNA Replication

Subcellular localization of the TMV RNA replication site has been remarkably difficult to accomplish, and equivocal results have been reported

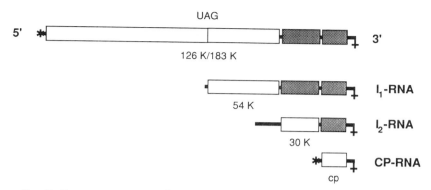

FIG. 7. Genome organization of TMV. Details are as in Fig. 1. The vertical bar interrupting the large ORF in the genomic RNA indicates the position of the suppressible UAG termination codon. Synthesis of the 54-kDa protein from I_1-RNA has been postulated, but not detected.

(254). The major problem is the absence of well-defined cytopathic structures early in infection. It has been postulated that TMV RNA replication takes place at various sites within the cell of its host. One of the earliest events observed after infection is a proliferation of membranes in the cytoplasm (255).

Studies utilizing cell fractionation procedures indicate a nuclear association of virus-synthesized components (256, 257), suggesting that the nucleus might support replication of the RNA. These results contradict earlier findings (254, 258) in which double-stranded TMV RNA was observed to be associated with cytoplasmic membranes. The conflicting evidence presented by such studies may be due to discrepancies in the different methodologies used in subcellular fractionation. Various methods of fractionating tobacco tissue and mesophyll protoplasts were therefore compared to determine which factors are important in subcellular localization of TMV replication (251).

The cellular localization of the putative replicase complex was revealed by the immunogold technique with antisera that specifically react with the 126- and 183-kDa proteins (259). When sections of TMV-infected tobacco leaves are treated with anti 126-kDa protein antiserum and then with protein A/gold complex, most of the gold label is localized on granular inclusion bodies specifically located in the cytoplasm of TMV-infected cells. The very small amounts of label detected in other regions, such as the nucleus, chloroplasts, and mitochondria, are nonspecific.

The 183-kDa protein must be included in the labeled structures observed using the anti-126-kDa protein antiserum, since the 183-kDa protein contains the entire 126-kDa protein sequence. The anti-183-kDa protein antiserum was used to further localize the 183-kDa protein. Most of the gold label is also dispersed over the granular inclusion bodies, as is the case for the anti-126-kDa protein antiserum.

The granular inclusion bodies appear as oval structures of various diameters, ranging from 0.2 to 2.8 μm. TMV particles are usually observed near the granular inclusion bodies as aggregates, but not inside them. Since the 126- and 183-kDa proteins are involved in the replication process, these granular inclusion bodies may be the site of TMV RNA replication.

Results from other experiments making use of the same immunogold technique (260) suggest that replication occurs at the edge of so-called "viroplasms" (261). Viroplasms are non-membrane-bound structures located in the cytoplasm of TMV-infected cells; they contain electron-dense rope-like structures embedded in a ribosome-rich matrix. In cells of infected leaf tissue, immunogold label corresponding to the 126-kDa protein is found almost exclusively in these structures. However, viroplasms are never observed in infected protoplasts (260, 262). Two possible explanations have been put forward to explain this difference between infected cells and infected protoplasts. Either the 126-kDa protein molecules are lost, excreted from the wall-less protoplasts so that they never form viroplasmic tubules, or in leaf tissue the viroplasms represent a metabolically inert form of accumulated 126-kDa protein, and replication takes place elsewhere.

(−)-Strand RNA is also localized in infected protoplasts (263). Radioactive RNA probes were prepared that specifically hybridize to sequences complementary to the 5' and 3' regions of TMV RNA. These probes were used to locate TMV RNA (−)-strands in the subcellular fractions of infected protoplasts. When the protoplasts are lysed, full-length (−)-strands are present in the cytoplasmic, but not the nuclear, fraction; consequently, TMV RNA replicates in association with an extranuclear structure.

B. Expression of TMV RNA

The 5'-proximal region of the genomic RNA encodes two coinitiated nonstructural proteins of 126 and 183 kDa. The larger protein is generated by readthrough of the UAG (amber) termination codon of the smaller one (243). The UAG termination codon is suppressed *in vitro* and *in vivo*. The 30-kDa protein involved in cell-to-cell movement and the coat protein are encoded by two subgenomic RNAs, on which each gene is 5' proximal. The two latter proteins are dispensable for viral RNA replication (264, 265). The third subgenomic RNA encodes the putative 54-kDa protein. The 54-kDa protein has yet to be found in infected cells, but the other four proteins have been observed *in vitro* and *in vivo*.

Both the 126- and 183-kDa proteins are thought to be involved in replication (27, 28, 251). The NTP-binding motif is present in both nonstructural proteins, and the GDD-containing consensus sequence that is part of the polymerase domain is present in the 183-kDa readthrough protein.

With respect to RNA replication, the genome of TMV can be divided into two parts. The 5'-noncoding region and the coding region for the 183-kDa protein comprise one domain, and the 3'-noncoding region comprises a second domain (266).

As is the genomic RNA, the CP-RNA is capped at its 5' end. Indirect evidence suggests that I_2-RNA is not capped (267, 268). Nevertheless, the possibility of the existence of a cap structure at the 5' end of this RNA has been suggested (269). The nature of the 5' end of I_1-RNA has not been determined. The 3' terminus of TMV RNA can be acylated *in vitro* by histidine. Despite the numerous models put forward to explain the function of the tRNA-like structure at the 3' end of TMV RNA, no unambiguous explanation has been provided.

C. TMV RdRp

1. ISOLATION AND CHARACTERIZATION

In spite of an early start in the TMV replication field (270, 271), no real progress has been made so far in solubilizing this enzyme. A host RdRp is present in tobacco, and it has been proposed that TMV uses his enzyme exclusively for replication of its RNA (272, 273). Furthermore, as long as the RdRp remains associated with the sedimentable fraction after homogenization, it will probably be impossible to free the RdRp from its template.

A strategy was adopted to solubilize the complex containing TMV RdRp activity and then to fractionate this preparation by chromatography (251). The first step, solubilization of the RdRp from the pellet fraction, is essential in separating the replication complex from the host-encoded polymerase and other components residing in the same fraction. Of the detergents examined, only CHAPS [3-(3-cholamidopropyl)-dimethylammonio 1-propanesulfonate] (274) solubilizes high levels of TMV RdRp. In the fraction in which the 126- and 183-kDa proteins are eluted, many other proteins—virus- and host-encoded—are also eluted. It is therefore impossible to conclude that these two proteins are responsible for the RdRp activity observed in this fraction. Nevertheless, the prominence of the 126- and 183-kDa proteins in the partially purified RdRp preparation strongly supports the proposal that these proteins are components of the TMV replication complex. This enzyme complex does not depend on added RNA template for its activity; the RdRp only elongates RNA chains, but is incapable of initiating them.

2. NONSTRUCTURAL PROTEIN INVOLVED IN TMV RNA REPLICATION

An approach to studying the components of the replicase has made use of either chimeric RNAs or mutagenized TMV RNAs. Some recent examples of such *in vivo* studies with infected tobacco plants and/or protoplasts are presented.

a. Chimeric TMV. The replication process was analyzed in chimeric TMV-L, carrying heterologous 3'-noncoding regions thought to be important in the specific initiation of viral (−)-strand synthesis (266). Three TMV-derived chimeras were constructed by replacing the 3'-noncoding region of TMV-L RNA with the corresponding sequences of three different tobamoviruses: TMV-OM, cucumber green mottle mosaic virus (CGMMV), and CcTMV. The genomic RNAs of TMV-L, TMV-OM, and CGMMV carry histidine-accepting tRNA-like structures at their 3' termini, while the tRNA-like structure of CcTMV RNA accepts valine (275).

All chimeric viruses are able to multiply in tobacco protoplast and in tobacco plants. Multiplication of the chimeric virus containing a TMV-OM sequence is similar to that of the TMV-L strain, whereas multiplication decreases in the case of the two other chimeras. Sequence analyses of progeny RNAs reveal that viruses with chimeric sequences can propagate. These data suggest that the TMV-L replicase recognizes the 3'-terminal structures and/or sequences of TMV-OM, CGMMV, and CcTMV and can initiate (−)-strand synthesis. The relationships between the virus-encoded component(s) of TMV replicase and the 3'-terminal region therefore may not be so stringent.

b. TMV Mutants. Replication-deficient *ts* mutants were examined (276). One group of mutants is deficient in the synthesis of all viral RNAs when shifted from 25°C to the nonpermissive temperature of 35°C (277). In the other group of mutants, double-stranded RNA synthesis continues, but single-stranded RNA synthesis ceases after the temperature shift (278). The first set of mutants seems to have lost a function required for the synthesis of all RNAs, and it is possible that they have a defect in the GDD motif-containing sequence. The second set of mutants is perhaps defective in a function that regulates (+)/(−)-RNA ratios, or is required to initiate (+)-strands at the 3' terminus of (−)-strands.

An *in vitro* transcription system was established to produce infectious TMV RNA from a cloned cDNA copy (279). Using this system, several TMV mutants were transcribed *in vitro* from cDNA clones mutagenized at or near the leaky UAG termination codon of the 126-kDa protein gene, and their infectivity was assayed on tobacco plants. Two frameshift mutants and one mutant that has a change from a leucine codon (UUA) to a UAA (ochre) termination codon two codons downstream from the UAG termination codon lead to intact 126-kDa protein, but a defective 183-kDa protein. These mutants are not infectious, while two mutants with one triplet insertion in the gene for the 183-kDa protein are still infectious.

When the UAG codon is deleted, infectivity is lost. However, when UAG is replaced by either UAU (tyrosine) or UAA, infectivity is retained. In the latter situation, viral multiplication is greatly impaired compared to that of the wild-type. Since this mutant presumably produces the authentic 183-kDa protein, but no (or little, if any) 126-kDa protein, the 126-kDa protein is thought to be dispensable for replication. However, for normal efficient replication, balanced synthesis of both 126- and 183-kDa proteins seems necessary (279). Analyses reveal that the mutations are retained in progeny viral RNA sequences, except in the progeny of the amber-to-tyrosine mutant, which contains a mixture of the parental mutagenized RNA and a pseudo-revertant with a UAA codon.

Hybrid viruses of two types were constructed by inserting an ORF either between the 30-kDa and coat-protein ORFs, or between the coat-protein gene and the 3'-noncoding region (280).

Three different mutants of the first type were generated by inserting the ORFs for the CAT protein (281), the coat protein (282), or the 30-kDa protein (280). These insertional mutants were used to evaluate the effects of modified viral genome organization on replication and gene expression. Using RNase-protection assays, they were also evaluated for their stability upon systemic infection of tobacco plants and subsequent host passage. Except for the choice of the ORF inserted, these hybrid RNAs are almost identical. However, their stability during replication is remarkably different. The mutants with an additional coat-protein ORF inserted between the 30-kDa and coat-protein ORFs are the most unstable (282). Both the 30-kDa and CAT gene mutants replicate efficiently in inoculated leaves. Of these three similar hybrids, the one with the largest insert—the 30-kDa ORF—is the most stable, for reasons that are unclear.

In mutants of the second type, the 30-kDa protein ORF was inserted between the coat-protein gene and the 3'-noncoding region. Such mutants replicate poorly and are particularly unstable; none of them produces wild-type-like progeny. These results suggest that hybrid mutants of TMV with an insertion in this region replicate less efficiently than do mutants with an ORF inserted between the 30-kDa and coat-protein ORFs.

Deletion mutants were constructed to elucidate the biological functions of the pseudo-knot region (234; Fig. 6). The ability of these mutants to multiply was tested in tobacco plants and in tobacco protoplasts. *Nicotiana tabacum* L. cv. Xanthi and *N. tabacum* L. cv. Samsun were used as local lesion and systemic hosts. Deletion mutants in the five double-helical 5'-proximal segments (II–VI) develop efficiently, suggesting that the pseudo-knot structures are dispensable for multiplication. When the deletion concerns the central pseudo-knot region (segments III and IV in Fig. 6), virus multiplication is reduced, with loss of development of mosaic symptoms on the systemic host. Multiplication is totally abolished when the sequence involved in formation of the double-helical segment I (Fig. 6) just upstream from the tRNA-like structure is deleted. This segment is therefore essential for viral RNA multiplication.

To define the regions within the 5' leader sequence essential for viral multiplication, mutants of TMV-L were constructed that carry several deletions in this 71-nucleotide sequence (241). Virus multiplication was assayed by introducing the mutated RNA into tobacco protoplasts. Large deletions abolish multiplication. When short deletions are introduced throughout this 5' sequence, only the deletion from residues 2–8 abolishes virus multiplication. Thus, this 5'-proximal portion is probably essential for RNA replication. Nevertheless, the same mutant can direct synthesis of the 126-kDa protein *in vitro*.

To understand the replication mechanism of TMV RNA and also the function of the 126- and 183-kDa proteins in replication, the time course of the accumulations of viral (+)- and (−)-strand RNAs was examined (283).

Tobacco protoplasts were infected with wild-type TMV, as well as with two kinds of mutants, one lacking the 30-kDa and coat-protein genes and the other with the UAG-to-tyrosine (UAU) mutation (279), resulting in a deficiency of 126-kDa protein synthesis. In protoplasts inoculated with wild-type RNA, (+)- and (−)-strands accumulate differently, not only in quantity, but also in the kinetics of their appearance. The time course of accumulation of the genomic and coat-protein mRNAs is similar. In contrast, the accumulation of (−)-strand RNA stops earlier, when the level of (+)-strands exceeds that of the (−)-strands by about 100 times and when (+)-strand synthesis still continues vigorously. The cause of this specific halt of (−)-strand accumulation is not exclusively attributed to the encapsidation of the genomic RNA, since a similar halt is also observed upon infection with a deletion mutant lacking the 30-kDa and coat-protein genes. Upon infection with a mutant that cannot produce the 126-kDa protein, accumulation of both (+)- and (−)-strands decreases compared to the parental wild-type virus.

D. Mechanism of TMV RNA Replication

1. Synthesis of Subgenomic RNA

Recent work with Sindbis virus suggests that one or two domains of the 126- or 183-kDa protein in TMV might be involved in the production of the subgenomic I_2-RNA (284). An attenuated strain of TMV-L was isolated that induces only mild symptoms and is produced in reduced amounts in tomato plants, but replicates as efficiently as the wild-type TMV-L strain in protoplasts (285). Sequencing has demonstrated that the attenuated strain differs from the TMV-L strain by 10 nucleotides within the 126-kDa protein ORF, three of which result in amino-acid substitutions in these two domains.

2. ANALYSIS OF TMV REPLICATIVE STRUCTURES

It is known that the membranous fraction of cell-free extracts of TMV-infected tobacco leaves can synthesize structures resembling TMV RFs and RIs (271). This system can synthesize viral-specific products and is template-independent; only the synthesis of partially completed replicative structures is achieved.

When pulsed for short periods with radiolabeled uridine, cell suspensions prepared from infected leaves incorporate the isotope preferentially into RIs and RFs (249). Free (−)-strands have not been detected. Genomic RNAs are quickly assembled into virions, and the concentration of free (+)-strands is never more than a small percentage of the final amount of viral RNA produced (286).

Several double-stranded RNA species have been detected in infected leaves (252, 287–289). Most of them are of genomic length, but the size of one that appears in low amounts corresponds to the expected size of the RF of coat-protein RNA. It has been suggested that the presence of double-stranded RNAs of subgenomic size could result from artifacts (252). Nevertheless, a pellet fraction isolated from TMV-infected protoplasts and containing the RdRp/template complex can synthesize not only genomic RNA, but also subgenomic coat-protein RNA (257).

The kinetics of appearance of radioactivity in double- and single-stranded RNAs has been studied after exposure of infected tobacco-leaf tissue to labeled uridine for various periods. These experiments demonstrate that double-stranded RNAs are preferentially labeled after short labeling periods (290). Longer labeling periods lead to accumulation of radioactivity predominantly into stable forms of RNAs—transfer RNA, ribosomal RNA, and single-stranded TMV RNA (258). Hybridization results indicate that while both (+)- and (−)-strand syntheses occur in the enriched RF fraction, only (+)-strands are synthesized in the enriched RI fraction. Thus, (−)-strand synthesis seems to occur predominantly in structures containing only one nascent strand, leading to the production of RFs labeled in the (−)-strand. By contrast, (+)-strand synthesis apparently occurs in structures in which one or more nascent (+)-strands are present on the same template RNA.

To date, it has not been possible to isolate an active RdRp complex able to initiate RNA synthesis in vitro from TMV-infected leaves. Limitations in the study of in vitro replication have been pointed out (291). RdRp activity is short-lived in vitro, reaching a plateau in less than 20 minutes, and little, if any, free progeny TMV RNA is produced.

3. POSSIBLE MECHANISM OF TMV RNA REPLICATION

The 183-kDa protein contains the consensus sequence harboring the GDD motif characteristic of a number of virus-coded proteins shown or suspected to be RNA-dependent polymerases (27). Furthermore, the 126- and 183-kDa proteins have considerable amino-acid sequence similarities (including the NTP motif) with nonstructural proteins produced by several (+)-strand RNA viruses, such as BMV and Sindbis virus, thought to be involved in RNA replication (28, 29).

Since no infection is detected in tobacco plants or tobacco protoplasts inoculated with mutants that cannot produce the 183-kDa protein (279), this protein is essential for the viability of the virus. In contrast, mutants in which the UAG codon ending the gene for the 126-kDa protein is replaced by UAU yield progeny virus containing the parental sequence and producing local lesions. Thus, the 126-kDa protein may not be essential for replication.

With respect to a possible role of the 126-kDa protein in RNA replication, it is worth recalling experiments performed using the radioactive photoaffinity analogs 8-azidoguanosine 5′-triphosphate or 8-azidoadenosine 5′-triphosphate (292). When either analog was incubated in the presence of homogenates from TMV-infected tobacco protoplasts, a 120-kDa protein was specifically labeled. Labeling of this protein was prevented by the presence of various NTPs. These results favor the participation of a virus-induced 120-kDa protein in replication; this protein may correspond to the viral nonstructural 126-kDa protein that harbors the NTP motif. The possibility that the 183-kDa readthrough protein also binds the analogs has not been considered.

Using the RNase-protection method, the mode of accumulation of the genomic RNA, of its (−)-strand, and of the coat-protein RNA in TMV-infected protoplasts was examined (283). The time courses of accumulation of genomic RNA and of the coat-protein RNA are quite similar, whereas the time course of (−)-RNA accumulation is distinct. Such results imply that the replication machinery for (+)- and (−)-strand syntheses may involve different kinds of factors or different modes of molecular interactions.

For (+)-strand synthesis, it is unlikely that the rate-limiting factor is the amount of 183-kDa protein. In infected tobacco protoplasts, the two nonstructural proteins are synthesized and accumulate even after 24 hours following infection (293). Host factors involved in (+)-strand synthesis and/or in the amount of (+)-strand might constitute the limiting factor(s).

Shut-off of (−)-strand synthesis has been reported for animal alphaviruses, such as Semliki Forest virus or Sindbis virus (294, 295). It has been suggested that cessation of (−)-strand synthesis is not due to the failure of continuous synthesis of viral nonstructural proteins (296).

Mechanisms for cross-protection that do not involve the coat protein probably also exist (reviewed in 40 and 297). The observation of the cessation of (−)-strand accumulation at early stages of infection (293) may imply another possible mechanism of viral cross-protection. In cells infected by a given TMV strain and in which RNA replication has reached a stage at which further accumulation of (−)-strand RNAs does not occur, *de novo* (−)-strand synthesis of a challenge virus may be strongly repressed. New approaches for plant protection against viral infections therefore exist.

E. Plant Protection against TMV Infection: Plants Transformed with the TMV 54-kDa ORF That Are Resistant to TMV

Transgenic tobacco plants were obtained containing the 54-kDa protein gene sequence that encodes a putative component of the replicase complex. These plants are resistant to infection when challenged with either the virus or the viral RNA (43).

The presence of the 54-kDa protein gene sequence prevents the development of local chlorosis and any systemic development of symptoms. Viral RNAs cannot be detected in either the inoculated leaves or in the systemic leaves of host plants that demonstrate resistance; therefore, resistance does not merely result in suppression of symptom development. The 54-kDa protein-induced resistance is absolute and is not simply a delay in symptom development: Complete resistance is observed in plants challenged with concentrations as high as 500 or 300 μg/ml of virus or viral RNA, respectively. It is therefore not as "fragile" as coat-protein-induced resistance, which may break down when challenged with high concentrations of inoculum or when viral RNA is used (298).

The transformed plants accumulate a 54-kDa protein-specific RNA transcript of the expected size, but no protein product is detected. Possibly the 54-kDa protein is very labile and rapidly turned over in the cell or it is made at levels below the limit of detection. On the other hand, transgenic plants containing the complete 126-kDa protein gene sequence are as susceptible to infection as untransformed plants.

Constitutive synthesis of either the 54-kDa transcript, or possibly the 54-kDa protein that includes the polymerase domain, probably interferes with TMV RNA replication. The 54-kDa protein could induce resistance by competing with the 183-kDa protein, a likely constituent of the replication complex.

VIII. Replication of Cowpea Mosaic Virus RNA

Cowpea mosaic virus (CPMV) is the type-member of the comoviruses. Viruses of this group have a bipartite RNA genome—B-RNA and M-RNA— that are separately encapsidated within icosahedral B and M particles, respectively. The capsids of both B and M components are composed of 60 copies of each of two distinct coat proteins, designated VP37 and VP23. The 5′ end of both RNAs is covalently linked by a phosphodiester linkage with the N-terminal serine of a small virus-coded protein VPg (Viral Protein, genome-linked), whereas the 3' end bears a poly(A) tail (reviewed in *10, 299* and *300*). The total nucleotide sequence of the two CPMV RNAs has been established (*301, 302*). M-RNA and B-RNA contain 3481 and 5889 nucleotides, respectively, excluding the poly(A) tails.

A. Intracellular Location of CPMV RNA Replication

Early after infection with CMPV, characteristic cytopathic structures, consisting of electron-dense material and membranous vesicles, are formed within the cytoplasm of infected cowpea-leaf cells or cowpea protoplasts (*303–307*). The electron-dense material of undefined structure contains the B-RNA-derived nonstructural proteins, as demonstrated by immunocytochemical techniques using colloidal gold-labeled protein A (*307*). Whether this represents a reservoir for the deposit of inactive nonstructural proteins or whether the electron-dense material also participates in viral replication is not established. The vesicular constituent contains fibrils resembling nucleic acid and appears to be the site of viral RNA replication, as demonstrated by autoradiography of sections of isolated cytopathic structures incubated with radiolabeled uridine (*304*). When cowpea protoplasts are inoculated with B-RNA alone, similar cytopathic structures appear, suggesting that a B-RNA-encoded function is responsible for the development of these structures (*306, 307*). Virus particles accumulate in large amounts (up to 1 mg per gram of leaves), primarily in the cytoplasm.

B. Expression of CPMV RNA

The expression of the virus-coded proteins was originally examined by translation *in vitro* (reviewed in *10* and *308*) and *in vivo* in cowpea mesophyll protoplasts (reviewed in *10, 309* and *310*). The results established that each RNA codes for a polyprotein that undergoes specific proteolytic cleavages to yield the final viral products (Fig. 8). These studies have been confirmed by RNA sequence data, since both RNAs contain one large ORF; the size of the

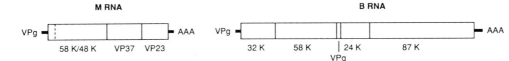

FIG. 8. Genome organization of CPMV. Vertical bars indicate the cleavage sites within the polyprotein; the dashed bar corresponds to the beginning of the alternative protein initiation site. The designations of the proteins resulting from post-translational cleavage of the polyproteins are provided below the open boxes. VPg, Viral protein, genome-linked; AAA, poly(A) tail. Other details are as in Fig. 1.

proteins encoded by these two ORFs agrees with the size of the largest translation products synthesized by the viral RNAs *in vitro*. This strategy as well as other characteristics of CPMV have placed comoviruses in the supergroup of picornaviruses (*30, 311*).

M-RNA codes for the two viral coat proteins, VP37 and VP23, and for two overlapping nonstructural proteins of 58 and 48 kDa that are involved in cell-to-cell movement of CPMV (*312*). B-RNA codes for viral nonstructural proteins; the role of some of these final gene products has been established. The 24-kDa protein is the proteinase responsible for the specific cleavages occurring in the M- and B-RNA-encoded polyproteins. The 32-kDa protein is a proteinase cofactor that participates in *trans* cleavage by the 24-kDa protein of the M polyproteins at the Q/M sites (*308*). VPg (28 amino-acid residues long) is believed to function as primer for the initiation of viral RNA synthesis. The 87-kDa protein represents the "core" of the viral replicase (discussed in *10*). Both RNAs are required for infectivity in plants, but B-RNA can replicate in cowpea protoplasts in the absence of M-RNA. Thus, B-RNA codes for all of the viral proteins necessary for RNA replication. The NTP-binding domain (*59*) and the polymerase domain containing the GDD sequence (*27*) are located in the 58- and 87-kDa polypeptides, respectively, which derive from the 200-kDa polyprotein programmed by B-RNA. The presence of the polymerase domain in the 87-kDa polypeptide and in its precursors make this polypeptide and/or one of its precursors a likely candidate in CPMV RNA replication.

C. CPMV RdRp

1. ISOLATION AND CHARACTERIZATION

Experiments aimed at determining the nature of the enzyme involved in RNA replication have led to the isolation of an RdRp complex from CPMV-infected cowpea leaves (*23, 313*). This complex, prepared 3–4 days after inoculation, is devoid of host RdRp, and is solubilized from the membrane fraction by the nonionic detergent Triton X-100. It contains polymerase molecules still bound to endogenous template strands, and can resume *in vitro* elongation of RNA strands initiated *in vivo*. Primarily (+)-strand molecules are produced that appear as RFs; no single-stranded progeny RNA molecules are produced. This overproduction of (+)-strands with respect to (−)-strands may be related to the time after virus inoculation when the extract was prepared; it is conceivable that the synthesis of (−)-strands prevails at earlier times after inoculation.

Comparisons have been made between CPMV RNA replication using crude membrane fractions from infected cowpea or *Chenopodium amaranticolor* (*314*). The *C. amaranticolor* extract also elongates nascent RNA chains, yielding, at early times of incubation, RIs that are "chased" to RF molecules; in addition, it also produces full-length progeny RNA molecules. RI is thus a functional intermediate: It appears early during incubation and is chased into RF and single-stranded RNA. It has been proposed that the RF is a dead-end molecule, since it appears after longer incubation times and requires previous denaturation to infect cowpea leaves (315).

Although the C. amaranticolor RdRp complex contains much lower levels of CPMV nonstructural proteins than does the cowpea RdRp complex, the RdRp activities of the two complexes are comparable. This suggests that only a small fraction of the cowpea RdRp is active in cowpea plants (313), and, more pertinently, that the RdRp functions only once (316). This may explain why attempts to prepare a template-dependent CPMV RdRp complex have failed; indeed, such a complex containing "used" polymerase molecules would no longer be active (discussed in 10).

2. NONSTRUCTURAL PROTEINS INVOLVED IN CPMV RNA REPLICATION

The protein composition of the CPMV RdRp complex was analyzed after the final purification step (313). It contains predominantly three proteins, of 110, 68, and 57 kDa. The 110-kDa protein is the only viral polypeptide consistently associated with RdRp activity. The other two major polypeptides are presumably of host origin; their function in viral RNA synthesis or within the cell is unknown. Other results support the notion that a host factor participates in CPMV RNA replication: A mutant of CPMV has been isolated that no longer replicates in cowpea plants, but is still able to grow in bean plants (317).

Thus, the 110-kDa protein constitutes the central element of the viral RdRp. It is worth recalling that its C-terminal region contains the polymerase domain, and that it also presents over 20% sequence homology with the C-terminal part of the poliovirus replicase (protein 3D) that also harbors the polymerase domain (27; discussed in 10).

A few ts mutants of CPMV have been obtained by nitrous acid mutagenesis. One of these, N168, affects the symptom pattern in the infected hosts (318). Both the M- and B-RNAs of N168 carry mutations. It has so far not been established whether the ts defect in M-RNA affects the replicase itself or another function such as proteolytic cleavage or encapsidation. The two ts mutants 8-10 and 8-14 (319) produce only low amounts of M- and B-RNAs at the restrictive temperature in the inoculated leaves, and the RNAs are not encapsidated into infectious virus particles. Mutations are contained within both RNAs for 8-10, and only in B-RNA for 8-14. Here again, the exact nature of the mutations has not been established, and it is not known whether one of the mutations of 8-10 affects replication itself or another step in virus development.

3. EXPRESSION OF THE CPMV RdRp

To gain some insight into the role of the 100-kDa polypeptide in RNA replication, the genes of this protein and of its C-terminal cleavage product, the 87-kDa polypeptide, were introduced into an *Escherichia coli* expression system (*320*), or into a baculovirus system (*321, 322*). Both systems produce the expected products, but lack RdRp activity. In contrast, the poliovirus RdRp similarly produced in *E. coli* (*320*) or in the baculovirus system (*322*), and the foot-and-mouth disease virus RdRp (protein 3D) similarly produced in the baculovirus system (*322, 323*), are active in a poly(A)/oligo(U)-polymerase assay. Lack of activity of the CPMV RdRp may reflect the need for additional viral proteins, such as the B-RNA-encoded 32-kDa protein whose gene was not contained within any of the constructs introduced into the expression vectors, or it may again reflect the need for a host factor(s).

D. Mechanism of CPMV RNA Replication

The availability of full-length cDNA clones from which infectious transcripts can be obtained (*324, 325*) has led to studies concerning the regions within the viral RNAs that may be required for RNA replication (*326;* discussed in *300*). Since replication of both CPMV RNAs depends on the viral nonstructural proteins produced by B-RNA, it is conceivable that the two RNAs share certain common structural features recognized by these proteins. Indeed, both the B- and M-RNAs contain the sequence UUUUAUU immediately upstream from the poly(A) tail. This heptanucleotide, together with the nucleotides just preceding it (5'—GU—3' in B-RNA), and at least the first four A residues of the poly(A) tail can be folded into a stem–loop structure. The potential folding of this region of the viral RNAs is supported by the fact that a homologous counterpart of this sequence is present in the 5' leader of both viral RNAs; furthermore, a similar folding pattern can be constructed from the nucleotide sequence of M-RNA of another comovirus, red clover mottle virus (*327*).

To investigate whether this stretch of 11 nucleotides (UUUUAUUAAAA) located on the 5' side of the remainder of the poly(A) tail constitutes a signal in replication, mutants of CPMV B-RNA were engineered in which the heptanucleotide was gradually deleted, nucleotides within this sequence were substituted by others, or additional nucleotides were introduced within this sequence. The ability of the various mutants to be replicated was investigated by transfection into cowpea protoplasts. Infectivity was determined by immunofluorescent staining (*326*). Progressive removal of one to three nucleotides from the 3' end of the heptanucleotide still allows stem–loop formation, due to the remaining four U residues in this region that can base-pair to the poly(A) tail. Such mutations moderately interfere with infectivity.

When such constructs are used to inoculate cowpea plants, symptom expression is observed; analysis of progeny RNA isolated from systematically infected leaves reveals that the mutated sequence reverts to the wild-type sequence. Further removal of U residues interferes with stem–loop formation and also dramatically reduces infectivity. Other mutations that would interfere with stem–loop formation, such as insertions, or shortening of the poly(A) tail to four residues or less, also abolish infectivity. Consequently, the heptanucleotide together with the first four A residues of the poly(A) tail are required for infectivity and probably have a function in viral RNA replication.

Because no *in vitro* template-dependent system of CPMV RNA replication exists, the mechanism governing initiation of viral RNA synthesis remains obscure. No free VPg-pU has been detected, nor has uridylation of VPg or its 60-kDa precursor; such precursors have been observed in poliovirus RNA replication (328). The involvement of VPg in early stages of CPMV RNA replication is suggested by the fact that the RFs contain VPg at the 5′ ends of both the (−)- and (+)-RNA strands (329). A model for CPMV RNA replication has been proposed (10) in which replication is closely linked to protein processing. In this model, the 110- and 60-kDa proteins (or even the 170-kDa protein), tightly bound to membranes of the cytopathic structures together with a host factor, would bind to template RNA to allow initiation of RNA replication. The 60-kDa protein in such a complex would supply the VPg and the 58-kDa protein that might be involved in membrane attachment. The 110-kDa protein would provide the 24-kDa protein needed to release the VPg and the 87-kDa protein that would initiate RNA replication. This attractive model still needs to be substantiated by experimental evidence.

IX. Replication of Velvet Tobacco Mottle Virus RNA

Velvet tobacco mottle virus (VTMoV), a relative of the sobemoviruses (reviewed in 330), is composed of isometric particles 30 nm in diameter. The capsid of these particles contains one major protein of 33 kDa and two minor ones of 36 and 31 kDa (331); the relationship between these polypeptides has not been established. These particles contain a monopartite (+)-sense single-stranded RNA genome designated RNA1 (331, 332). In addition, most isolates also encapsidate a viroid-like RNA, often referred to as a virusoid, that occurs either as a closed circular molecule (RNA2) or as a linear molecular (RNA3). The viroid-like RNA presents no detectable sequence homologies with RNA1, as established by hybridization assays. It is not essential for VTMoV infection, but depends on VTMoV for its propagation (333), and is therefore considered a sat-RNA. The nucleotide sequence of RNA1

(1.5 × 10⁶ Da, or about 4500 nucleotides) has not been established; the sat-RNA is composed of 366 or 367 nucleotides and has no coding capacity (*334*, *335*). Because of the structural similarities that exist between the sat-RNA and viroids (reviewed in *36*), the question of the replication of the former is particularly interesting, since it differs from viroids that depend entirely on host enzymes for there replication.

A. Intracellular Location of VTMoV Replication

VTMoV was first isolated from *Nicotiana velutina*, a species from Central Australia. The leaves of the infected plants present characteristic yellow mosaics with prominent blistering (*331*). The virus can be mechanically transmitted to other *Nicotiana* species. Thin sections of infected leaf tissue show electron-dense particles predominantly in the cytoplasm. The infected leaves also present vesicles containing electron-dense material; these vesicles are located inside the ER and the nuclear envelope.

B. Expression of VTMoV RNA

Upon *in vitro* translation of total VTMoV RNA, a 115-kDa protein appears that is thought to be the readthrough product of the 60-, 30- and 19-kDa polypeptides (*336*). A 37-kDa protein is also synthesized that may be the coat protein, and that might be coded by a subgenomic RNA of 0.63×10^6 Da (*332*).

C. VTMoV RdRp

An RdRp complex has been isolated from VTMoV-infected tobacco leaves (*337*); its activity is detectable 4 days after inoculation and increases until 8 days after inoculation. Most of the enzyme is recovered in the 17,000 g supernatant, suggesting that it is not associated with membranous material such as nuclei, chloroplasts, or mitochondria. The enzyme preparation does not initiate RNA strand synthesis. It only elongates (+)-strand RNAs 1 and 3 that have been initiated *in vivo* on their (−)-strand templates; it does not release the completed (+)-strands.

It has been proposed that VTMoV sat-RNA replicates by a rolling-circle mechanism (*338*, *339*). This would entail the production from RNA2 of a (−)-strand concatemer RNA that would act as template for the production of (+)-strand concatemer RNAs; these would be specifically processed to yield unit-length linear RNA3 molecules. Ligation of RNA3 would then produce RNA2. According to this model, RNA3 is a precursor of RNA2. Pulse–chase experiments performed with strips of leaf tissue excised from VTMoV-infected tobacco plants have shown that this is indeed the case (*340*), even though not all newly synthesized RNA3 is ultimately recovered as RNA2. Sat-RNA is produced in large amounts, of which only a small proportion is encapsidated. Thus, it appears that the sat-RNA has a greater affinity for the replicase than does RNA1.

Other features distinguish replication of the VTMoV sat-RNA from viroids. Viroids are located and replicate within the nucleus of their hosts (341, 342). Both DNA-dependent DNA polymerases II and III from the host appear to be involved in viroid replication (342, 343) and viroid replication is inhibited by α-amanitin (343–345). On the other hand, α-amanitin does not affect the syntheses of VTMoV RNAs 1 and 3, nor does it influence accumulation of virus coat protein in tobacco-infected protoplasts (346); it does not affect the syntheses of VTMoV RNAs 1 and 3 *in vitro* (337).

X. Discussion

Following this overview of plant viral RNA replication, a few additional comments should be made. These center on the following aspects: the replicase complex itself; the mechanism of RNA replication related to capping of the RNA and to the importance of generating a faithful 5′ end on the viral RNA for efficient replication; and the significance of tRNA-like structures.

A major concern in preparing the RdRp is related to the solubilization of the enzyme complex. The "attachment" of the RdRp complex to membranes accounts for its appearance in most cases in the "particulate" fraction of crude extracts. Except for the situation recently reported on the isolation of the CMV replicase in which Nonidet P-40 served as detergent (147), the different procedures used to release the RdRp from membranes have been only partially effective. Non-ionic detergents such as Nonidet P-40 or Tween-80 for BMV (5), Lubrol W for TYMV (217), CHAPS for TMV (251), and Triton X-100 for CPMV (23, 313) have been used. Such treatments ultimately solubilize the RdRp activity, but they consistently result in a decrease in template specificity. An alternative detergent, dodecyl β-D-maltoside was used more recently to isolate the BMV RdRp (55), since it might be functionally similar to membrane components, and since it enhances both activity and stability of the enzyme.

The isolation of the RdRp probably requires the establishment of strong and synchronous infection, non-ionic extraction conditions, and meticulous attention to the quality and concentration of the reaction components. The quality of the enzyme preparation is determinant to guarantee reliable and reproducible results *in vitro*, and a complete description of the preparation is therefore important.

In the cases of BMV (52), CMV (148), and AlMV (175, 189), RNAs 1 and 2 can replicate independently of RNA3. These observations suggest that probably RNAs 1 and 2 of most viruses with a tripartite genome encode essential information for viral RNA replication.

A very poorly studied aspect of viral RNA replication is whether a host-coded subunit is an intrinsic component of all viral replicases. The CMV (147), TYMV (217), and CPMV (313) enzyme preparations clearly contain at least one host polypeptide of about 50 kDa that remains unidentified and whose role in the RNA replication process is unknown. Thus, the best-defined systems all show involvement of a host factor. It will be particularly interesting to determine whether a relationship exists among the host poly-peptides of the CMV, TYMV, and CPMV RNA enzymes, and what function these polypeptides fulfill in uninfected cells.

With the exception of the recently isolated CMV replicase (147), the RdRp's isolated to date only produce (−)-strands from (+)-strand templates, but cannot synthesize full-length (+)-strands from the (−)-strand. Two hypotheses have been put forward to explain this "deficiency" of the RdRp's. (1) The proteins involved in viral RNA replication might be used only once, as suggested for the CPMV RdRp, perhaps due to a stringent coupling of polyprotein processing and replication (10); thus, having produced a (−)-strand, the RdRp would be inactivated. (2) The failure to synthesize progeny (+)-RNA strands might be attributed to a defect in the post-transcriptional modification of the (−)-strands produced in vitro, due to a defect in the RdRp complex itself. Interestingly, an unpaired G residue is located at the 3′ ends of the (−)-RNAs contained in the double-stranded RNAs of CMV and of sat-RNA isolated from plants infected with the virus and its satellite (80), as observed with the RFs of alphaviruses (347, 348) and the bacteriophage Qβ (349). The enzyme responsible for this addition remains unknown, as does the possible function of this "nonviral" residue. The recently purified CMV replicase (147) should permit elucidation of the nature of the 3′-terminal nucleotide of the in vitro-synthesized (−)-RNAs.

Except for CPMV (reviewed in 10, 299 and 300) and possibly VTMoV (reviewed in 330), the RNAs of all the viruses examined here possess a cap structure at the 5′ end. Capping of eukaryotic mRNAs is believed to occur inside the nucleus. Since most viral RNAs, such as those of CMV, CCMV, AlMV, TYMV, and TMV (reviewed in 6 and 8), are synthesized outside the nucleus, the question arises as to how the cap is bound during RNA synthesis. The nature of the enzyme responsible for capping of viral RNAs in the cytoplasm has not been determined. It has been proposed that protein 1a of BMV might be involved in capping of the RNA (11). On the other hand, the level of infectivity of uncapped TMV RNA is very low (350), implying that the cap structure is not essential for TMV infection, although it dramatically increases infectivity.

There is some evidence that the enzyme responsible for capping might be virus-coded. It was proposed that the methyltransferase activity of Sindbis virus is associated with the nsP1 protein (351). Since significant homologies exist between nsP1 and nonstructural proteins coded by BMV, AlMV, and TMV (29), these proteins could perform similar functions.

Recently, a guanylytransferase-like activity has been described associated with the 126-kDa protein of TMV, which is probably a component of the TMV RNA replicase (352). On the basis of RNA sequence comparisons, it has been postulated that other members of the Sindbis virus-like supergroup might have a virus-coded guanylytransferase, presumably associated with one of the nonstructural proteins.

The importance for efficient infectivity of avoiding, or at least reducing, the number of additional nonviral nucleotides at the 5′ end of *in vitro*-derived transcripts of (+)-polarity has been stressed by several investigators (353, 354). Indeed, whereas additional residues are usually without effect when present at the 3′ ends of such transcripts, nonviral nucleotides at the 5′ ends interfere with infectivity of RNAs from plant viruses more than they do of RNAs from animal viruses (discussed in 355).

The RNA polymerase of bacteriophage T7 is generally used for *in vitro* transcription, and it is known that the activity of this enzyme is dramatically reduced when transcription begins with one or two G residues instead of the more favorable three G residues. One or two G residues are therefore often present as nonviral nucleotides in the resulting viral transcripts. *In vitro* transcripts of BMV RNA3 with one additional G residue at the 5′ end are only one-third as infectious as are transcripts without the additional nucleotide, but the presence of more than one nonviral G residue dramatically suppresses biological activity (354). *In vitro* transcripts of CMV corresponding to RNAs 1, 2, and 3 with one additional G residue at the 5′ end are still infectious, but much less than the natural CMV RNAs (356); the infectivity is reduced by addition of one G residue at the 5′ end, compared to infectivity of transcripts without nonviral nucleotides and is very low when two additional G residues are present (357).

An inoculum containing AlMV transcripts of cDNAs 1, 2, and 3 and the viral coat protein is not infectious on bean leaves, probably because of the presence of 21–23 nonviral nucleotides at the 5′ termini of these transcripts (358). So far, infectious transcripts have only been obtained for RNA3 of AlMV (355). In this RNA, one additional G residue at the 5′ end does not abolish infectivity, whereas two G residues do suppress infectivity. In early studies, TMV transcripts were obtained using *E. coli* polymerase (359). Transcripts lacking non-viral nucleotides at the 5′ end were infectious, whereas the infectivity was very low when six additional nucleotides were present at the 5′ end. A strong effect of nonviral nucleotides at the 5′ end of RNAs is also clear with CPMV: B- and M-RNA transcripts with two nonviral G residues at their 5′ ends present low levels of infectivity, compared to virion

RNA (324). The infectivity of the transcripts greatly increases when only one additional G residue is present at the 5' ends of both RNAs (325).

A striking feature of many plant RNA viruses is the presence of a tRNA-like structure at the 3' end of the viral RNA recognized by many enzymes normally thought to be specific for tRNAs. Its conservation presumably indicates the effect of a strong positive selection pressure for replication. This structure plays a critical role in the replication of BMV RNA (79), although the relationship that might exist between tRNA functions (e.g., adenylation by the nucleotidyltransferase or acylation by an aminoacyl-tRNA synthestase) and RNA replication is not understood.

The hypothesis has been put forward that such tRNA-like structures could be molecular fossils of an original "RNA world" (84), where they tagged genomic RNA molecules (82) for replication and also functioned as primitive telomeres (the terminal regions of eukaryotic chromosomes that are essential for stability and replication of linear DNA molecules). It has been speculated (84, 360) that an evolutionary relationship exists between telomerase and nucleotidyltransferase. To ensure that 3'-terminal nucleotides are not lost during replication, the tRNA-like structure found in the BMV RNAs would function as a telomere (82). Early RNA replicases would have been catalytic RNAs, whereas proteins would have assumed this function later in evolution, the tRNA-like structures being specifically acylated by an aberrant activity of the replicase.

Such a point of view implies that current forms of RNA polymerases, both RNA- and DNA-dependent, may have evolved from a common ancestor and therefore may have the common ability to recognize RNA as template for replication. In general, DNA-dependent RNA polymerase also recognize RNA templates *in vitro*, although this can be a very inefficient reaction (361). An example is the DNA-dependent RNA polymerase of bacteriophage T7, which replicates defined RNA sequences that can adopt a clover-leaf structure (362, 363). An extension of the hypothesis concerning the original fossil tRNA-like structure (84) has therefore been proposed, suggesting that RNA polymerases, both cellular and viral, have the capacity to replicate tRNA-like molecules (363).

ICR-like sequences are frequent in the RNA genome of plant viruses (91). Such sequences could function as promoters of viral (+)-strand synthesis. Among the viruses studied here, BMV RNA1, CMV RNAs 1, 2, and 3, TMV RNA, and TYMV RNA contain ICR-like sequences (reviewed in 91). Their importance in viral RNA replication is implied by their conservation and location. They are always located within known or putative promoter sequences involved in viral RNA replication and they could therefore be considered proof of the existence of related replication strategies for these viruses. Thus, a role of RNA polymerase III involved in tRNA synthesis can be envisaged in viral RNA replication. Indeed, RNA polymerase III of cauliflower and wheat contains a subunit of, respectively, 50 and 55 kDa (364). It can be hoped that further investigations will elucidate the role—if any—of RNA polymerase III in viral RNA application and, more precisely, that they will determine whether a subunit of this complex enzyme could be a component of the viral replicase.

ACKNOWLEDGMENTS

We are grateful to François Chapeville for his continued interest in our work and for his encouragement. We are indebted to numerous colleagues who kindly provided us with manuscripts prior to publication, and to P. Ahlquist, D. Baulcombe, J. Bol, T. C. Hall, Y. Okada, M. Tepfer, and J. Wellink, who carefully read various parts of this manuscript and offered helpful suggestions. R.G.-B. is grateful to the Ministère des Affaires Etrangères, France, for a fellowship. This study was partly supported by the Action Concertée: Biologie Végétale (MRT Grant 89 C 0868) and by a grant from the Ligue Nationale Française Contre le Cancer. The Institut Jacques Monod is an Institut Mixte, CNRS–Université Paris VII.

REFERENCES

1. R. Hull and J. W. Davies, *Adv. Virus Res.* **28**, 1 (1983).
2. T. M. A. Wilson, *Virology* **137**, 255 (1984).
3. T. M. A. Wilson, *Virology* **138**, 353 (1984).
4. J. G. Shaw, K. A. Plaskitt and T. M. A. Wilson, *Virology* **148**, 326 (1986).
5. S. F. Hardy, T. L. German, L. S. Loesch-Fries and T. C. Hall, *PNAS* **76**, 4956 (1979).
6. G. P. Martelli and M. Russo, *Methods Virol.* **8**, 143 (1984).
7. A. Van Kammen, *Microbiol. Sci.* **2**, 170 (1985).
8. R. I. B. Francki, in "Positive Strand RNA Viruses" (M. A. Brinton and R. R. Rueckert, eds.), UCLA Symp. Ser. 54, p. 423. Liss, New York, 1987.
9. M. Zaitlin and R. Hull, *Annu. Rev. Plant Physiol.* **38**, 291 (1987).
10. R. Eggen and A. Van Kammen, in "RNA Genetics" (E. Domingo, J. J. Holland and P. Ahlquist, eds.), Vol. 1, p. 49. CRC Press, Boca Raton, Florida, 1988.
11. T. W. Dreher and T. C. Hall, in "RNA Genetics" (E. Domingo, J. J. Holland and P. Ahlquist, eds.), Vol. 1, p. 91. CRC Press, Boca Raton, Florida, 1988.
12. R. Gargouri and A. L. Haenni, *NATO Adv. Study Inst. Ser., Ser. H* **41**, 163 (1990).
13. P. M. Grimley, J. G. Levin, I. K. Berezesky and R. M. Friedman, *J. Virol.* **10**, 492 (1972).
14. R. M. Friedman, J. G. Levin, P. M. Grimley and I. K. Berezesky, *J. Virol.* **10**, 504 (1972).
15. M. Garnier, R. Mamoun and J. M. Bové, *Virology* **104**, 357 (1980).
16. S. Astier-Manifacier and P. Cornuet, *BBA* **232**, 484 (1971).
17. J. L. White and W. O. Dawson, *Virology* **88**, 33 (1978).
18. Z. A. Khan, K. T. Hiriyanna, F. Chavez and H. Fraenkel-Conrat, *PNAS* **83**, 2383 (1986).
19. C. Le Roy, C. Stussi-Garaud and L. Hirth, *Virology* **82**, 48 (1977).
20. C. T. Duda, M. Zaitlin and A. Siegel, *BBA* **319**, 62 (1973).
21. M. Ikegami and H. Fraenkel-Conrat, *PNAS* **75**, 2122 (1978).
22. L. Dorssers, P. Zabel, J. Van Der Meer and A. Van Kammen, *Virology* **116**, 236 (1982).
23. L. Dorssers, J. Van Der Meer, A. Van Kammen and P. Zabel, *Virology* **125**, 155 (1983).
24. H. Fraenkel-Conrat, *PNAS* **80**, 422 (1983).
25. D. I. Jackson, R. J. Hayes and K. W. Buck, *Abstr., Int. Congr. Virol., 8th* 460 (1990).

26. T. Blumenthal and G. G. Carmichael, *ARB* **48**, 525 (1979).
27. G. Kamer and P. Argos *NARes* **12**, 7269 (1984).
28. J. Haseloff, P. Goelet, D. Zimmern, P. Ahlquist, R. Dasgupta and P. Kaesberg, *PNAS* **81**, 4358 (1984).
29. P. Ahlquist, E. G. Strauss, C. M. Rice, J. H. Strauss, J. Haseloff and D. Zimmern, *J. Virol.* **53**, 536 (1985).
30. R. Goldbach and J. Wellink, *Intervirology* **29**, 260 (1988).
31. A. E. Gorbalenya, V. M. Blinov, A. P. Donchenko and E. V. Koonin, *J. Mol. Evol.* **28**, 256 (1989).
32. R. W. Goldbach, *Annu. Rev. Phytopathol.* **24**, 289 (1986).
33. R. W. Goldbach, *Microbiol. Sci.* **4**, 197 (1987).
34. D. Zimmern, in "RNA Genetics" (E. Domingo, J. J. Holland and P. Ahlquist, eds.), Vol. 2, p. 211. CRC Press, Boca Raton, Florida, 1988.
35. J. H. Strauss and E. G. Strauss, *Annu. Rev. Microbiol.* **42**, 657 (1988).
36. R. I. B. Francki, *Annu. Rev. Microbiol.* **39**, 151 (1985).
37. A. E. Simon, *Plant Mol. Biol. Rep.* **6**, 240 (1988).
38. L. Sequeira, *Trends Biotechnol.* **2**, 25 (1984).
39. R. P. C. Valle, J. Skrzeczkowski, M. D. Morch, R. L. Joshi, R. Gargouri, G. Drugeon, J. C. Boyer, F. Chapeville and A. L. Haenni, *Biochimie* **70**, 695 (1988).
40. R. N. Beachy, *In* "Plant Gene Research: Temporal and Spatial Regulation of Plant Genes" (D. P. S. Verma and R. B. Goldberg, eds.), p. 313. Springer-Verlag, New York, 1988.
41. R. N. Beachy, L. S. Loesch-Fries and N. E. Tumer, *Annu. Rev. Phytopathol.* **28**, 451 (1990).
42. P. Palukaitis and M. Zaitlin, in "Plant–Microbe Interactions: Molecular and Genetic Perspectives" (T. Kosuge and E. W. Nester, eds.), Vol. 1, p. 420. Macmillan, New York, 1984.
43. D. B. Golemboski, G. P. Lomonossoff and M. Zaitlin, *PNAS* **87**, 6311 (1990).
44. P. Ahlquist, V. Luckow and P. Kaesberg, *JMB* **153**, 23 (1981).
45. R. Dasgupta and P. Kaesberg, *NARes* **10**, 703 (1982).
46. P. Ahlquist, R. Dasgupta and P. Kaesberg, *JMB* **172**, 369 (1984).
47. J. Burgess, F. Motoyoshi and E. N. Fleming, *Planta* **117**, 133 (1974).
48. G. P. Martelli and M. Russo, in "The Plant Viruses: Polyhedral Virions with Tripartite Genomes" (R. I. B. Francki, ed.), Vol. 1, p. 163. Plenum, New York, 1985.
49. T. C. Hall, W. A. Miller and J. J. Bujarski, in "Advances in Plant Pathology" (D. S. Ingram and P. H. Williams, eds.), p. 179. Academic Press, New York, 1982.
50. M. Horikoshi, K. Mise, I. Furusawa and J. Shishiyama, *J. Gen. Virol.* **69**, 3081 (1988).
51. L. S. Loesch-Fries and T. C. Hall, *J. Gen. Virol.* **47**, 323 (1980).
52. P. Kibertis, L. S. Loesch-Fries and T. C. Hall, *Virology* **112**, 804 (1981).
53. P. Ahlquist, J. J. Bujarski, P. Kaesberg and T. C. Hall, *Plant Mol. Biol.* **3**, 37 (1984).
54. R. French, M. Janda and P. Ahlquist, *Science* **231**, 1294 (1986).
55. J. J. Bujarski, S. F. Hardy, W. A. Miller and T. C. Hall, *Virology* **119**, 465 (1982).
56. W. A. Miller and T. C. Hall, *Virology* **125**, 236 (1983).
57. R. Quadt, H. J. M. Verbeeck and E. M. J. Jaspars, *Virology* **165**, 256 (1988).
58. T. C. Hodgman, *Nature* **333**, 22 (1988).
59. A. E. Gorbalenya and E. V. Koonin, *NARes* **17**, 8413 (1989).
60. P. A. Kroner, B. M. Young and P. Ahlquist, *J. Virol.* **64**, 6110 (1990).
61. M. R. Green, T. Maniatis and D. A. Melton, *Cell* **32**, 681 (1983).
62. P. Ahlquist, R. French, M. Janda and L. S. Loesch-Fries, *PNAS* **81**, 7066 (1984).
63. L. S. Loesch-Fries, N. P. Jarvis, K. J. Krahn, S. E. Nelson and T. C. Hall, *Virology* **146**, 177 (1985).
64. R. Sacher, R. French and P. Ahlquist, *Virology* **167**, 15 (1988).

65. A. L. N. Rao and T. C. Hall, *J. Virol.* **64**, 2437 (1990).
66. P. Traynor and P. Ahlquist, *J. Virol.* **64**, 69 (1990).
67. P. Argos, *NARes* **16**, 9909 (1988).
68. P. A. Kroner, D. Richards, P. Traynor and P. Ahlquist, *J. Virol.* **63**, 5302 (1990).
69. D. J. Barton, S. G. Sawicki and D. L. Sawicki, *J. Virol.* **62**, 3597 (1988).
70. D. L. Sawicki, D. B. Barkhimer, S. G. Sawicki, C. M. Rice and S. Schlesinger, *Virology* **174**, 43 (1990).
71. T. W. Dreher, J. J. Bujarski and T. C. Hall, *Nature* **311**, 171 (1984).
72. W. A. Miller, J. J. Bujarski, T. W. Dreher and T. C. Hall, *JMB* **187**, 537 (1986).
73. J. J. Bujarski, T. W. Dreher and T. C. Hall, *PNAS* **82**, 5636 (1985).
74. T. W. Dreher and T. C. Hall, in "Positive Strand RNA Viruses" (M. A. Brinton and R. R. Rueckert, eds.), UCLA Symp. Ser. 54, p. 317. Liss, New York, 1987.
75. T. W. Dreher and T. C. Hall, *JMB* **201**, 31 (1988).
76. R. L. Joshi, S. Joshi, F. Chapeville and A. L. Haenni, *EMBO J.* **2**, 1123 (1983).
77. T. W. Dreher, A. L. N. Rao and T. C. Hall, *JMB* **206**, 425 (1989).
78. J. J. Bujarski, P. Ahlquist, T. C. Hall, T. W. Dreher and P. Kaesberg, *EMBO J.* **5**, 1769 (1986).
79. L. E. Marsh and T. C. Hall, *CSHSQB* **52**, 331 (1987).
80. C. W. Collmer and J. M. Kaper, *Virology* **145**, 249 (1985).
81. P. Ahlquist, R. French and J. J. Bujarski, *Adv. Virus Res.* **32**, 215 (1987).
82. A. L. N. Rao, T. W. Dreher, L. E. Marsh and T. C. Hall, *PNAS* **86**, 5335 (1989).
83. M. P. Deutscher, *in* "The Enzymes" (P. D. Boyer, ed.), Vol. 15, p. 183. Academic Press, New York, 1982.
84. A. M. Weiner and N. Maizels, *PNAS* **84**, 7383 (1987).
85. R. French and P. Ahlquist, *J. Virol.* **61**, 1457 (1987).
86. O. V. Karpova, L. G. Tyulkina, K. J. Atabekov, N. P. Rodionova and J. G. Atabekov, *J. Gen. Virol.* **70**, 2287 (1989).
87. W. A. Miller, T. W. Dreher and T. C. Hall, *Nature* **313**, 68 (1985).
88. L. E. Marsh, T. W. Dreher and T. C. Hall, *in* "Positive-Strand RNA Viruses" (M. A. Brinton and R. R. Rueckert, eds.), UCLA Symp. Ser. 54, p. 327. Liss, New York, 1987.
89. R. French and P. Ahlquist, *J. Virol.* **62**, 2411 (1988).
90. L. E. Marsh, T. W. Dreher and T. C. Hall, *NARes* **16**, 981 (1988).
91. L. E. Marsh, G. P. Pogue and T. C. Hall, *Virology* **172**, 415 (1989).
92. T. C. Hall, A. L. N. Rao, G. P. Pogue, C. C. Huntley and L. E. Marsh, *in* "New Aspects of Positive-Strand RNA Viruses" (M. A. Brinton and F. X. Heinz, eds.), p. 47. ASM Press, Washington, D.C., 1990.
93. L. E. Marsh, G. P. Pogue and T. C. Hall, *Abstr., Int. Congr. Virol. 8th* 123 (1990).
94. R. F. Allison, M. Janda and P. Ahlquist, *Virology* **172**, 321 (1989).
95. L. Lane, *in* "Handbook of Plant Virus Infection and Comparative Diagnosis" (E. Kurstak, ed.), p. 333. Elsevier/North-Holland Biomedical Press, Amsterdam, 1981.
96. R. F. Pacha, R. F. Allison and P. Ahlquist, *Virology* **174**, 436 (1990).
97. J. B. Bancroft, *J. Gen. Virol.* **14**, 223 (1972).
98. R. F. Allison, M. Janda and P. Ahlquist, *J. Virol.* **62**, 3581 (1988).
99. W. A. Miller and T. C. Hall, *Virology* **132**, 53 (1984).
100. J. W. Watts and J. R. O. Dawson, *Virology* **105**, 501 (1980).
101. K. H. J. Gordon, D. S. Gill and R. H. Symons, *Virology* **123**, 284 (1982).
102. C. Stussi-Garaud, J. C. Garaud, A. Berna and T. Godefroy-Colburn, *J. Gen. Virol.* **68**, 1779 (1987).
103. M. H. Schwinghamer and R. H. Symons, *Virology* **79**, 88 (1977).
104. A. R. Gould and R. H. Symons, *EJB* **126**, 217 (1982).

105. L. Douine, J. B. Quiot, G. Marchoux and P. Archange, *Ann. Phytopathol.* **11**, 439 (1979).
106. J. M. Kaper and H. E. Waterworth, *in* "Handbook of Plant Virus Infection and Comparative Diagnosis" (E. Kurstak, ed.), p. 257. Elsevier/North-Holland Biomedical Press, Amsterdam, 1981.
107. J. C. Devergne and L. Cardin, *Ann. Phytopathol.* **7**, 255 (1975).
108. T. J. Gonda and R. H. Symons, *Virology* **88**, 361 (1978).
109. P. Piazzolla, J. R. Diaz-Ruiz and J. M. Kaper, *J. Gen. Virol.* **45**, 361 (1979).
110. A. L. N. Rao and R. I. B. Francki, *J. Gen. Virol.* **61**, 197 (1982).
111. M. C. Edwards, D. Gonsalves and R. Provvidenti, *Phytopathology* **73**, 269 (1983).
112. M. A. Rezaian, R. H. V. Williams, K. H. J. Gordon, A. R. Gould and R. H. Symons, *EJB* **143**, 277 (1984).
113. M. A. Rezaian, R. H. V. Williams and R. H. Symons, *EJB* **150**, 331 (1985).
114. T. M. Rizzo and P. Palukaitis, *J. Gen. Virol.* **69**, 1777 (1988).
115. T. M. Rizzo and P. Palukaitis, *J. Gen. Virol.* **70**, 1 (1989).
116. J. Owen, M. Shintaku, P. Aeschleman, S. Ben Tahar and P. Palukaitis, *J. Gen. Virol.* **71**, 2243 (1990).
117. P. B. Nelson, B.Sc. thesis. University of Adelaide, Adelaide, South Australia, 1970.
118. J. M. Kaper and C. K. West, *Prep. Biochem.* **2**, 251 (1972).
119. L. C. Lane and P. Kaesberg, *Nature NB* **232**, 40 (1971).
120. R. Hull, *J. Gen. Virol.* **17**, 111 (1972).
121. N. Habili and J. M. Kaper, *Virology* **112**, 250 (1981).
122. K. H. J. Gordon and R. H. Symons, *NARes* **11**, 947 (1983).
123. D. W. Mossop and R. I. B. Francki, *Virology* **95**, 395 (1979).
124. H. E. Waterworth, J. M. Kaper and M. E. Toussignant, *Science* **204**, 845 (1979).
125. M. Jacquemond and H. Lot, *Agronomie* **1**, 927 (1981).
126. Y. Takanami, *Virology* **109**, 120 (1981).
127. D. Gonsalves, R. Provvidenti and M. C. Edwards, *Phytopathology* **72**, 1533 (1982).
128. J. M. Kaper and C. W. Collmer, *in* "RNA Genetics" (E. Domingo, J. J. Holland and P. Ahlquist, eds.), Vol. 3, p. 171. CRC Press, Boca Raton, Florida, 1988.
129. S. Hidaka, K. Hanada, K. Ishikawa and K. I. Miura, *Virology* **164**, 326 (1988).
130. J. M. Kaper, M. E. Tousignant and M. T. Steen, *Virology* **163**, 284 (1988).
131. M. Jacquemond and G. J. M. Lauquin, *BBRC* **151**, 388 (1988).
132. D. E. Sleat, *NARes* **18**, 3416 (1990).
133. C. Masuta, S. Kutwata and Y. Takanami, *Ann. Phytopathol. Soc. Jpn.* **54**, 332 (1988).
134. P. Palukaitis, *Mol. Plant–Microbe Interact.* **1**, 175 (1988).
135. T. Hatta and R. I. B. Francki, *Virology* **93**, 265 (1979).
136. T. Hatta and R. I. B. Francki, *J. Gen. Virol.* **53**, 343 (1981).
137. T. Hatta and R. I. B. Francki, *Virology* **88**, 105 (1978).
138. M. J. Roossinck and P. Palukaitis, *Mol. Plant–Microbe Interact.* **3**, 188 (1990).
138a. M. J. Roossinck and P. Palukaitis, *Virology* **181**, 371 (1991).
139. J. T. May, J. M. Gilliland and R. H. Symons, *Virology* **39**, 54 (1969).
140. J. T. May, J. M. Gilliland and R. H. Symons, *Virology* **41**, 653 (1970).
141. J. T. May and R. H. Symons, *Virology* **44**, 517 (1971).
142. E. M. J. Jaspars, D. S. Gill and R. H. Symons, *Virology* **144**, 410 (1985).
143. R. Kumarasamy and R. H. Symons, *Virology* **96**, 622 (1979).
144. D. S. Gill, R. Kumarasamy and R. H. Symons, *Virology* **113**, 1 (1981).
145. Y. Takanami and H. Fraenkel-Conrat, *Bchem* **21**, 3161 (1982).
146. Y. Takanami, N. Nitta and S. Kubo, *Abstr., Int. Congr. Virol. 6th* 222 (1984).
147. R. J. Hayes and K. W. Buck, *Cell* **63**, 363 (1990).
148. N. Nitta, Y. Takanami, S. Kuwata and S. Kubo, *J. Gen. Virol.* **69**, 2695 (1988).

149. J. Van Der Meer, L. Dorssers and P. Zabel, *EMBO J.* **2**, 233 (1983).

150. S. Lain, J. L. Reichmann and J. A. Garcia, *NARes* **18**, 7003 (1990).

151. J. M. Kaper and M. E. Tousignant, *Endeavour* **8**, 194 (1984).

152. M. A. Rezaian and R. H. Symons, *NARes* **14**, 3229 (1986).

153. M. Jaegle, M. Devic, M. Longstaff and D. Baulcombe, *J. Gen. Virol.* **71**, 1905 (1990).

154. B. D. Harrison, M. A. Mayo and D. C. Baulcombe, *Nature* **328**, 799 (1987).

155. F. Ponz, A. Rowhani, S. M. Mircetich and G. Bruening, *Virology* **160**, 183 (1987).

156. A. D. Branch and H. D. Robertson, *Science* **223**, 450 (1984).

157. M. Ishikawa, T. Meshi, T. Ohno, Y. Okada, T. Sano, I. Ueda and E. Shikata, *MGG* **196**, 421 (1984).

158. C. J. Hutchins, P. Keese, J. E. Visvader, P. D. Rathjen, J. L. Meinnes and R. H. Symons, *Plant Mol. Biol.* **4**, 293 (1985).

159. M. Jacquemond, J. Anselem and M. Tepfer, *Mol. Plant–Microbe Interact.* **1**, 311 (1988).

160. D. C. Baulcombe, G. R. Saunders, M. W. Bevan, M. A. Mayo and B. D. Harrison, *Nature* **321**, 446 (1986).

161. D. Tousch, M. Tepfer and M. Jacquemond, *Abstr., Int. Congr. Virol. 8th* 483 (1990).

162. D. Tousch, M. Jacquemond and M. Tepfer, *Abstr., Int. Congr. Virol. 8th* 483 (1990).

163. D. Baulcombe, M. Devic, M. Jaegle and B. Harrison, *UCLA Symp. Mol. Cell. Biol. New Ser.* **101**, 257 (1989).

164. D. E. Sleat and P. Palukaitis, *PNAS* **87**, 2946 (1990).

165. M. Devic, M. Jaegle and D. Baulcombe, *J. Gen. Virol.* **71**, 1443 (1990).

166. L. Van Vloten-Doting, R. I. B. Francki, R. W. Fulton, J. M. Kaper and L. C. Lane, *Intervirology* **15**, 198 (1981).

167. J. F. Bol, L. Van Vloten-Doting and E. M. J. Jaspars, *Virology* **46**, 73 (1971).

168. B. J. C. Cornelissen, F. T. Brederode, R. J. M. Moormann and J. F. Bol, *NARes* **11**, 1253 (1983).

169. B. J. C. Cornelissen, F. T. Brederode, G. H. Veeneman, J. H. Van Boom and J. F. Bol, *NARes* **11**, 3019 (1983).

170. R. F. Barker, N. P. Jarvis, D. V. Thompson, L. S. Loesch-Fries and T. C. Hall, *NARes* **11**, 2881 (1983).

171. M. Ravelonandro, M. Pinck and L. Pinck, *Biochimie* **66**, 395 (1984).

172. K. Langereis, M. A. Mugnier, B. J. C. Cornelissen, L. Pinck and J. F. Bol, *Virology* **154**, 409 (1986).

173. F. T. Brederode, E. C. Koper-Zwarthoff and J. F. Bol, *NARes* **8**, 2213 (1980).

174. E. M. J. Jaspars, *in* "Molecular Plant Virology" (J. W. Davies, ed.), Vol. 1, p. 155. CRC Press, Boca Raton, Florida, 1985.

175. A. Nassuth, F. Alblas and J. F. Bol, *J. Gen. Virol.* **53**, 207 (1981).

176. C. J. Houwing and E. M. J. Jaspars, *Bchem* **17**, 2927 (1978).

177. C. J. Houwing and E. M. J. Jaspars, *Bchem* **21**, 3408 (1982).

178. D. Zuidema and E. M. J. Jaspars, *Virology* **135**, 43 (1984).

179. C. H. Smit, J. Roosien, L. Van Vloten-Doting and E. M. J. Jaspars, *Virology* **112**, 169 (1981).

180. J. F. Bol, B. Kraal and F. T. Brederode, *Virology* **58**, 101 (1974).

181. D. Zuidema, M. F. A. Bierhuizen and E. M. J. Jaspars, *Virology* **129**, 255 (1983).

182. M. Bassi, M. A. Favali, G. G. Conti and F. Betto, *Phytopathol. Z.* **69**, 247 (1970).

183. H. Van Pelt-Heerschap, H. Verbeek, J. W. Slot and L. Van Vloten-Doting, *Virology* **160**, 297 (1987).

184. H. Van Pelt-Heerschap, H. Verbeek, M. J. Huisman, L. S. Loesch-Fries and L. Van Vloten-Doting, *Virology* **161**, 190 (1987).

185. L. Van Vloten-Doting and E. M. J. Jaspars, *Compr. Virol.* **11**, 1 (1977).

186. D. A. Samac, S. E. Nelson and L. S. Loesch-Fries, *Virology* **131**, 455 (1983).
187. A. Berna, J. P. Briand, C. Stussi-Garaud and T. Godefroy-Colburn, *J. Gen. Virol.* **67**, 1135 (1986).
188. C. J. Houwing and E. M. J. Jaspars, *FEBS Lett.* **209**, 284 (1986).
189. A. Nassuth and J. F. Bol, *Virology* **124**, 75 (1983).
190. L. Van Vloten-Doting, J. A. Hasrat, E. Oosterwijk, P. Van't Sant, M. A. Schoen and J. Roosien, *J. Gen. Virol.* **46**, 415 (1980).
191. A. N. Sarachu, M. J. Huisman, L. Van Vloten-Doting and J. F. Bol. *Virology* **141**, 14 (1985).
192. M. J. Huisman, A. N. Sarachu, F. Alblas and J. F. Bol, *Virology* **141**, 23 (1985).
193. M. J. Huisman, B. J. C. Cornelissen, C. F. M. Groenendijk, J. F. Bol and L. Van Vloten-Doting, *Virology* **171**, 409 (1989).
194. M. J. Huisman, F. C. Lanfermeyer, L. S. Loesch-Fries, L. Van Vloten-Doting and J. F. Bol, *Virology* **160**, 143 (1987).
195. C. M. P. Van Dun, L. Van Vloten-Doting and J. F. Bol, *Virology* **163**, 572 (1988).
196. J. F. Bol and P. E. M. Taschner, *Abstr., Int. Congr. Virol.*, *8th* 457 (1990).
197. P. E. M. Taschner, A. C. Van Der Kuyl, L. Neeleman and J. F. Bol, *Virology* **181**, 445. (1991).
198. C. Erny, T. Van Der Kuyl, J. F. Bol, C. Stussi-Garaud and T. Godefroy-Colburn, *Abstr., Int. Congr. Virol.*, *8th* 476 (1990).
199. F. Bol, F. T. Brederode, G. C. Janze and D. K. Rauh, *Virology* **65**, 1 (1975).
200. E. C. Koper-Zwarthoff, F. T. Brederode, G. Veeneman, J. H. Van Boom and J. F. Bol, *NARes* **8**, 5635 (1980).
201. C. H. Smit and E. M. J. Jaspars, *Virology* **117**, 271 (1982).
202. A. C. Van Der Kuyl, K. Langereis, C. J. Houwing, E. M. J. Jaspars and J. F. Bol, *Virology* **176**, 346 (1990).
203. E. C. Koper-Zwarthoff and J. F. Bol, *NARes* **8**, 3307 (1980).
204. M. D. Morch, J. C. Boyer and A. L. Haenni, *NARes* **16**, 6157 (1988).
205. H. Guilley and J. P. Briand, *Cell* **15**, 113 (1978).
206. P. Keese, A. Mackenzie and A. Gibbs, *Virology* **172**, 536 (1989).
207. J. J. Weiland and T. W. Dreher, *NARes* **17**, 4657 (1989).
208. L. Hirth and L. Givord, *in* "The Plant Viruses" (R. Koening, ed.), p. 163. Plenum, New York, 1988.
209. D. Laflèche and J. M. Bové, *Physiol Veg.* **9**, 487 (1971).
210. M. Garnier, R. Mamoun and J. M. Bové, *Virology* **104**, 354 (1980).
211. M. D. Morch and C. Bénicourt, *J. Virol.* **34**, 85 (1980).
212. M. D. Morch, W. Zagorski and A. L. Haenni, *EJB* **127**, 259 (1982).
213. M. D. Morch, G. Drugeon, P. Szafranski and A. L. Haenni, *J. Virol.* **63**, 5153 (1989).
214. M. E. Osorio-Keese, P. Keese and A. Gibbs, *Virology* **172**, 547 (1989).
215. S. W. Ding, P. Keese and A. Gibbs, *Virology* **172**, 555 (1989).
216. S. Ding, P. Keese and A. Gibbs, *J. Gen. Virol.* **71**, 925 (1990).
217. C. Mouchès, T. Candresse and J. M. Bové, *Virology* **134**, 78 (1984).
218. T. Candresse, C. Mouchès and J. M. Bové, *Virology* **152**, 322 (1986).
219. R. L. Joshi, J. M. Ravel and A. L. Haenni, *EMBO J.* **5**, 1143 (1986).
220. M. Garnier, T. Candresse and J. M. Bové, *Virology* **151**, 100 (1986).
221. M. D. Morch, R. L. Joshi, T. M. Denial and A. L. Haenni, *NARes* **15**, 4123 (1987).
222. R. Gargouri, R. L. Joshi, J. F. Bol, S. Astier-Manifacier and A. L. Haenni, *Virology* **171**, 386 (1989).
223. F. Cellier, B. Zaccomer, M. D. Morch, A. L. Haenni and M. Tepfer, *Abstr., Int. Congr. Virol.* *8th* 123 (1990).

224. P. Goelet, G. P. Lomonossoff, P. J. G. Butler, M. E. Akam, M. J. Gait and J. Karn, *PNAS* **79**, 5818 (1982).

225. T. Ohno, M. Aoyagi, Y. Yamanashi, H. Saito, S. Ikawa, T. Meshi and Y. Okada, *J. Biochem.* **96**, 1915 (1984).

226. I. Solis and F. Garcia-Arenal, *Virology* **177**, 553 (1990).

227. D. L. D. Caspar, *Adv. Protein Chem.* **18**, 37 (1963).

228. A. Asselin and M. Zaitlin, *Virology* **91**, 173 (1978).

229. D. D. Dunigan, R. G. Dietzgen, J. E. Schoelz and M. Zaitlin, *Virology* **165**, 310 (1988).

230. T. Meshi, T. Ohno and Y. Okada, *J. Biochem.* **91**, 1441 (1982).

231. A. A. Brunt, *in* "The Plant Viruses: The Rod-Shaped Plant Viruses" (M. H. V. Van Regenmortel and H. Fraenkel-Conrat, eds.), Vol. 2, p. 181. Plenum, New York, 1986.

232. A. Varma, *in* "The Plant Viruses: The Rod-Shaped Plant Viruses" (M. H. V. Van Regenmortel and H. Fraenkel-Conrat, eds.), Vol. 2, p. 249. Plenum, New York, 1986.

233. A. J. Gibbs, *in* "The Plant Viruses: The Rod-Shaped Plant Viruses" (M. H. V. Van Regenmortel and H. Fraenkel-Conrat, eds.), Vol. 2, p. 168. Plenum, New York, 1986.

234. N. Takamatsu, Y. Watanabe, T. Meshi and Y. Okada, *J. Virol.* **64**, 3686 (1990).

235. K. Rietveld, K. Linschooten, C. W. A. Pleij and L. Bosch, *EMBO J.* **3**, 2613 (1984).

236. R. L. Joshi, F. Chapeville and A. L. Haenni, *NARes* **13**, 347 (1985).

237. A. Van Belkum, J. P. Abrahams, C. W. A. Pleij and L. Bosch, *NARes* **13**, 7673 (1985).

238. D. Zimmern, *NARes* **2**, 1189 (1975).

239. J. Keith and H. Fraenkel-Conrat, *FEBS Lett.* **57**, 31 (1975).

240. S. J. Mandeles, *JBC* **243**, 3671 (1968).

241. N. Takamatsu, Y. Watanabe, T. Iwasaki, T. Shiba, T. Meshi and Y. Okada, *J. Virol.* **65**, 1619 (1991).

242. T. Meshi, M. Ishikawa, N. Takamatsu, T. Ohno and Y. Okada, *FEBS Lett.* **162**, 282 (1983).

243. H. R. B. Pelham, *Nature* **272**, 469 (1978).

244. M. Zaitlin, C. T. Duda and M. A. Petti, *Virology* **53**, 300 (1973).

245. R. Scalla, P. Romaine, A. Asselin, J. Rigaud and M. Zaitlin, *Virology* **91**, 182 (1978).

246. N. Takamatsu, T. Ohno, T. Meshi and Y. Okada, *NARes* **11**, 3767 (1983).

247. G. Bruening, R. Beachy, R. Scalla and M. Zaitlin, *Virology* **71**, 498 (1976).

248. R. N. Beachy and M. Zaitlin, *Virology* **81**, 160 (1977).

249. A. O. Jackson, M. Zaitlin, A. Siegel and R. I. B. Francki, *Virology* **48**, 655 (1972).

250. P. Palukaitis and M. Zaitlin, *in* "The Plant Viruses: The Rod-Shaped Plant Viruses" (M. H. V. Van Regenmortel and H. Fraenkel-Conrat, eds.), Vol. 2, p. 105. Plenum, New York, 1986.

251. N. Young, J. Forney and M. Zaitlin, *J. Cell Sci., Suppl.* **7**, 277 (1987).

252. P. Palukaitis, F. Garcia-Arenal, M. A. Sulzinski and M. Zaitlin, *Virology* **131**, 533 (1983).

253. M. A. Sulzinski, K. A. Gabard, P. Palukaitis and M. Zaitlin *Virology* **145**, 132 (1985).

254. R. K. Ralph, S. Bullivant and S. J. Wojcik, *Virology* **43**, 713 (1971).

255. T. Nilsson-Tillgren, L. Kohenmainen-Seveus and D. van Wettstein, *Virology* **104**, 124 (1969).

256. H. J. Van Telgen, R. W. Goldbach and L. C. Van Loon, *Virology* **143**, 612 (1985).

257. Y. Watanabe and Y. Okada, *Virology* **149**, 64 (1986).

258. T. Nilsson-Tillgren, M. C. Kielland-Brandt and B. Bekke, *MGG* **128**, 157 (1974).

259. T. Saito, D. Hosokawa, T. Meshi and Y. Okada, *Virology* **160**, 477 (1987).

260. G. J. Hills, K. A. Plaskitt, N. D. Young, D. D. Dunigan, J. W. Watts, T. M. A. Wilson and M. Zaitlin, *Virology* **161**, 488 (1987).

261. R. E. F. Matthews, "Plant Virology." Academic Press, New York, 1981.

262. Y. Otsuki, I. Takebe, Y. Honda and C. Matsui, *Virology* **49**, 188 (1972).

263. S. Okamoto, Y. Machida and I. Takebe, *Virology* **167**, 194 (1988).

264. T. Meshi, Y. Watanabe, T. Saito, A. Sugimoto, T. Maeda and Y. Okada, *EMBO J.* **6,** 2557 (1987).
265. N. Takamatsu, M. Ishikawa, T. Meshi and Y. Okada, *EMBO J.* **6,** 307 (1987).
266. M. Ishikawa, T. Meshi, Y. Watanabe and Y. Okada, *Virology* **164,** 290 (1988).
267. T. Hunter, R. Jackon and D. Zimmern, *NARes* **11,** 801 (1983).
268. S. Joshi, C. W. A. Pleij, A. L. Haenni, F. Chapeville and L. Bosch, *Virology* **127,** 100 (1983).
269. Y. Watanabe, T. Meshi and Y. Okada, *FEBS Lett.* **173,** 247 (1984).
270. R. K. Ralph and S. Wojcik, *Virology* **37,** 276 (1969).
271. D. W. Bradley and M. Zaitlin, *Virology* **45,** 192 (1971).
272. H. Fraenkel-Conrat, *TIBS* **4,** 184 (1979).
273. M. Ikegami and H. Fraenkel-Conrat, *Virology* **100,** 185 (1980).
274. L. H. Hjelmeland, *PNAS* **77,** 6368 (1980).
275. R. N. Beachy, M. Zaitlin, G. Bruening and H. Israel, *Virology* **73,** 498 (1976).
276. W. O. Dawson and G. E. Jones, *MGG* **145,** 308 (1976).
277. W. O. Dawson and J. L. White, *Virology* **90,** 209 (1978).
278. W. O. Dawson and J. L. White, *Virology* **93,** 104 (1979).
279. M. Ishikawa, T. Meshi, F. Motoyoshi, N. Takamatsu and Y. Okada, *NARes* **14,** 8291 (1986).
280. K. Lehto and W. O. Dawson, *Virology* **175,** 30 (1990).
281. W. O. Dawson, D. J. Lewandowski, M. E. Hilf, P. Bubrick, A. J. Raffo, J. J. Shaw, G. L. Grantham and P. R. Desjardins, *Virology* **172,** 285 (1989).
282. D. L. Beck, Ph.D. thesis. University of California, Riverside, California, 1988.
283. M. Ishikawa, T. Meshi, T. Ohno and Y. Okada, *J. Virol.* **65,** 861 (1991).
284. Y. S. Hahn, E. G. Strauss and J. H. Strauss, *J. Virol.* **63,** 3142 (1989).
285. M. Nishigushi, S. Kikuchi, Y. Kiho, T. Ohno, T. Meshi and Y. Okada, *NARes* **13,** 5585 (1985).
286. W. O. Dawson and D. E. Schlegel, *Phytopathology* **66,** 437 (1976).
287. A. Zelcer, K. F. Weaber, E. Balazs and M. Zaitlin, *Virology* **113,** 417 (1981).
288. M. Bar-Joseph, A. Rosner, M. Moscovitz and R. Hull, *J. Virol. Methods* **6,** 1 (1983).
289. R. L. Jordan and J. A. Dodds, *Acta Horticult.* **164,** 101 (1985).
290. T. Nilsson-Tillgren, *MGG* **109,** 246 (1970).
291. N. D. Young and M. Zaitlin, *Plant Mol. Biol.* **6,** 455 (1986).
292. R. K. Evans, B. E. Haley and D. A. Roth, *JBC* **260,** 7800 (1985).
293. Y. Watanabe, Y. Emori, I. Ooshika, T. Meshi, T. Ohno and Y. Okada, *Virology* **133,** 18 (1984).
294. D. L. Sawicki and S. G. Sawicki, *J. Virol.* **34,** 108 (1980).
295. D. L. Sawicki, S. G. Sawicki, S. Keränen and L. Kääriäinen, *J. Virol.* **39,** 348 (1981).
296. S. G. Sawicki and D. L. Sawicki, *Virology* **152,** 507 (1986).
297. M. Zaitlin, *Phytopathology* **66,** 382 (1976).
298. P. Powell-Abel, R. S. Nelson, B. De, N. Hoffmann, S. G. Rogers, R. T. Fraley and R. N. Beachy, *Science* **232,** 738 (1986).
299. R. Goldbach and A. Van Kammen, *in* "Molecular Plant Virology" (J. W. Davies, ed.), Vol. 2, p. 83. CRC Press, Boca Raton, Florida, 1985.
300. J. Wellink, R. Eggen, J. Verver, R. Goldbach and A. Van Kammen, *in* "New Aspects of Positive-Strand RNA Viruses" (M. A. Brinton and F. X. Heinz, eds.), p. 116. ASM Press, Washington, D.C., 1990.
301. P. Van Wezenbeek, J. Verver, J. Harmsen, P. Vos and A. Van Kammen, *EMBO J.* **2,** 941 (1983).
302. G. P. Lomonossoff and M. Shanks, *EMBO J.* **2,** 2253 (1983).
303. A. M. Assink, H. Swaans and A. Van Kammen, *Virology* **53,** 384 (1973).

304. G. A. De Zoeten, A. M. Assink and A. Van Kammen, *Virology* **59**, 341 (1974).
305. T. Hibi, G. Rezelman and A. Van Kammen, *Virology* **64**, 308 (1975).
306. G. Rezelman, H. J. Franssen, R. W. Goldbach, T. S. Ie and A. Van Kammen, *J. Gen. Virol.* **60**, 335 (1982).
307. J. Wellink, J. Van Lent and R. Goldbach, *J. Gen. Virol.* **69**, 751 (1988).
308. P. Vos, J. Verver, M. Jaegle, J. Wellink, A. Van Kammen and R. Goldbach, *NARes* **16**, 1967 (1988).
309. G. Rezelman, R. Goldbach and A. Van Kammen, *J. Virol.* **36**, 366 (1980).
310. G. Rezelman, A. Van Kammen and J. Wellink, *J. Gen. Virol.* **70**, 3043 (1989).
311. H. Franssen, J. Leunissen, R. Goldbach, G. Lomonossoff and D. Zimmern, *EMBO J.* **3**, 855 (1984).
312. J. Wellink and A. Van Kammen, *J. Gen. Virol.* **70**, 2279 (1989).
313. L. Dorssers, S. Van Der Krol, J. Van Der Meer, A. Van Kammen and P. Zabel, *PNAS* **81**, 1951 (1984).
314. R. Eggen, A. Kaan, R. Goldbach and A. Van Kammen, *J. Gen. Virol.* **69**, 2711 (1988).
315. M. Shanks, G. P. Lomonossoff and D. Evans, *J. Gen. Virol.* **66**, 925 (1985).
316. A. Van Kammen and H. I. L. Eggen, *BioEssays* **5**, 261 (1986).
317. D. Evans, *J. Gen. Virol.* **66**, 339 (1985).
318. C. P. De Jager, P. Zabel, C. P. Van Der Beek and A. Van Kammen, *Virology* **76**, 164 (1977).
319. D. Evans, *Virology* **141**, 275 (1985).
320. O. C. Richards, R. Eggen, R. Goldbach and A. Van Kammen, *Gene* **78**, 135 (1989).
321. H. Van Bokhoven, J. Wellink, M. Usmany, J. M. Vlak, R. Goldbach and A. Van Kammen, *J. Gen. Virol.* **71**, 2509 (1990).
322. H. Van Bokhoven, M. Mulders, J. Wellink, J. M. Vlak, R. Goldbach and A. Van Kammen, *J. Gen. Virol.* **72**, 567 (1991).
323. J. Roosien, G. J. Belsham, M. D. Ryan, A. M. Q. King and J. M. Vlak, *J. Gen. Virol.* **71**, 1703 (1990).
324. P. Vos, M. Jaegle, J. Wellink, J. Verver, R. Eggen, A. Van Kammen and R. Goldbach, *Virology* **165**, 33 (1988).
325. R. Eggen, J. Verver, J. Wellink, A. De Jong, R. Goldbach and A. Van Kammen, *Virology* **173**, 447 (1989).
326. R. Eggen, J. Verver, J. Wellink, K. Pleij, A. Van Kammen and R. Goldbach, *Virology* **173**, 456 (1989).
327. M. Shanks, J. Stanley and G. P. Lomonossoff, *Virology* **155**, 697 (1986).
328. N. Takeda, R. J. Kuhn, C. F. Yang, T. Takegami and E. Wimmer, *J. Virol.* **60**, 43 (1986).
329. G. P. Lomonossoff, M. Shanks and D. Evans, *Virology* **144**, 351 (1985).
330. R. Hull, *in* "The Plant Viruses: Polyhedral Virions and Monopartite RNA Genomes" (R. Koenig, ed.), Vol. 3, p. 113. Plenum, New York, 1988.
331. J. W. Randles, C. Davies, T. Hatta, A. R. Gould and R. I. B. Francki, *Virology* **108**, 111 (1981).
332. A. R. Gould, *Virology* **108**, 123 (1981).
333. R. I. B. Francki, C. J. Grivell and K. S. Gibb, *Virology* **148**, 381 (1986).
334. J. Haseloff and R. H. Symons, *NARes* **10**, 3681 (1982).
335. P. A. Kibertis, J. Haseloff and D. Zimmern, *EMBO J.* **4**, 817 (1985).
336. R. I. B. Francki, J. W. Randles, P. W. G. Chu, J. Rohozinski and T. Hatta, *in* "Subviral Pathogens of Plants and Animals: Viroids and Prions" (K. Maramorosch and J. J. McKelvey, eds.), p. 265. Academic Press, New York, 1985.
337. J. Rohozinski, R. I. B. Francki and P. W. G. Chu, *Virology* **155**, 27 (1986).
338. P. W. G. Chu, R. I. B. Francki and J. W. Randles, *Virology* **126**, 480 (1983).

339. C. J. Hutchins, P. Keese, J. E. Visvader, P. D. Rathjen, J. L. McInnes and R. H. Symons, *Plant Mol. Biol.* **4**, 293 (1985).
340. K. Hanada and R. I. B. Francki, *Virology* **170**, 48 (1989).
341. J. Schumacher, H. L. Sänger and D. Riesner, *EMBO J.* **2**, 1549 (1983).
342. J. S. Semancik and K. L. Harper, *PNAS* **81**, 4429 (1984).
343. H. R. Rackwitz, W. Rohde and H. Sänger, *Nature* **291**, 297 (1981).
344. H. P. Mühlbach and H. L. Sänger, *Nature* **278**, 185 (1979).
345. R. Flores and J. S. Semancik, *PNAS* **79**, 6285 (1982).
346. J. G. Wu, W. J. Lu and P. Tien, *J. Gen. Virol.* **67**, 2757 (1986).
347. G. Wengler, G. Wengler and H. J. Gross, *Nature* **282**, 754 (1979).
348. G. Wengler, G. Wengler and H. J. Gross, *Virology* **123**, 273 (1982).
349. H. Weber and C. Weissman, *JMB* **51**, 215 (1970).
350. T. Meshi, M. Ishikama, F. Motoyoshi, K. Semba and Y. Okada, *PNAS* **83**, 5043 (1986).
351. S. Mi, R. Durbin, H. V. Huang, C. M. Rice and V. Stollar, *Virology* **170**, 385 (1989).
352. D. D. Dunigan and M. Zaitlin, *JBC* **265**, 7779 (1990).
353. S. Van der Werf, J. Bradley, E. Wimmer, F. W. Studier and J. J. Dunn, *PNAS* **83**, 2330 (1986).
354. M. Janda, R. French and P. Ahlquist, *Virology* **158**, 259 (1987).
355. J. M. Dore, Ph.D. thesis. University of Strasbourg, France, 1988.
356. T. M. Rizzo and P. Palukaitis, *MGG* **222**, 249 (1990).
357. R. J. Hayes and K. W. Buck, *J. Gen. Virol.* **71**, 2503 (1990).
358. K. Langereis, Ph.D. thesis. University of Leiden, The Netherlands, 1987.
359. W. O. Dawson, D. L. Beck, D. A. Knorr and G. L. Grantham, *PNAS* **83**, 1832 (1986).
360. T. R. Cech, *Nature* **332**, 777 (1988).
361. M. J. Chamberlin, *ARB* **43**, 721 (1974).
362. M. M. Konarska and P. Sharp, *Cell* **57**, 423 (1989).
363. M. M. Konarska and P. Sharp, *Cell* **63**, 609 (1990).
364. T. J. Guifoyle, G. Hagen and S. Malcom, *JBC* **259**, 640 (1984).

Intron Splicing and Intron-mediated Enhanced Expression in Monocots

RALPH M. SINIBALDI
AND IRVIN J. METTLER

Sandoz Agro, Inc.
Plant Biotechnology Department
Palo Alto, California 94304

I. Introns and Perspective

The discovery in 1977 that eukaryotic genes are interrupted by introns (intervening sequences, IVSs) catalyzed a new era of study in the control of gene expression. After this discovery, it became clear that eukaryotic systems are far more complex than had been expected, and offer the possibility of combining coding regions (exons) in an almost endless array of combinations. Since this breakthrough, a wealth of information has been uncovered by many investigators. Most of this information has come from studies of mammalian and yeast systems, which were instrumental in uncovering many of the intricate nuances of how introns are processed.

It is not intent of this essay to expound a comprehensive view of the latest mechanistic details of RNA splicing; several recent reviews on RNA splicing meet this charge (1–5). Here we focus on plant introns and how the splicing of pre-mRNA may result in the enhanced expression of genes lacking introns in a monocot system, maize. We also discuss how plant introns may differ from introns of other systems, and focus on differences between introns of monocotyledonous and dicotyledonous plants. After a brief review of the general features of introns and the various mechanisms by which they can be processed, we delve into the subject of plant introns.

Progress in Nucleic Acid Research
and Molecular Biology, Vol. 42

A. Splicing Mechanisms and General Features of Pre-mRNA Introns

Mechanistically, there are four or five ways by which introns are removed and exon sequences are ligated (for reviews, see 3 and 4). Four of these mechanisms operate in a *cis* manner (splicing within the RNA molecule) and one in *trans* (between different RNA molecules). The first two, Group-I and Group-II introns, involve self-splicing, utilizing RNA structures contained within the intron. Group-I introns catalyze a series of transesterification reactions that result in their excision from the precursor RNA and concomitant ligation of the flanking exon sequences. This splicing mechanism is Mg^{2+}- (or Mn^{2+}-) and guanosine- (or guanylate-) dependent, and the structure of the RNA is important for processing. An example of Group-I intron splicing is the rRNA processing observed in *Tetrahymena* (6) and in the RNAs of mitochondria and chloroplasts. Group-II introns undergo a self-splicing process similar to that of nuclear pre-mRNA, forming an intermediate "lariat" structure utilizing a branchpoint, but without involving external factors or ATP. Here again, RNA structure is important for the splicing. Group-II intron processing is observed in RNAs of mitochondria and chloroplasts of many organisms. The processing of nuclear pre-mRNA into mature cytoplasmic mRNA is a two-step process using the association of a group of small nuclear ribonucleoproteins (snRNPs) and RNA helicases into a spliceosomal complex in a stepwise fashion (see 1 for a review). Several of the spliceosomal snRNAs bind sequentially to the intron in a sequence-specific manner. Five prominent *trans*-acting factors (U1, U2, U4, U5, and U6, which exist as ribonucleoprotein complexes) are involved in the splicing of pre-mRNA (7, 8) as well as ATP. In nuclear pre-mRNA, splicing RNA structure is thought to be less important. The splicing of the nuclear pre-mRNA into cytoplasmic mRNA can occur within minutes or, depending on the number of introns and efficiency of splicing, can take up to 20 minutes before the mature product reaches the cytoplasm.

Introns can be positioned within the actual coding region or in either the 5' or 3' untranslated leaders of the pre-mRNA. Of interest is a recent report of an intron located within an intron (referred to as a "twintron") in chloroplasts (9). Introns range in size from 36 bp to greater than 100,000 bp (10). Pre-mRNAs containing introns have three short sequences that are essential, though not sufficient, for the intron to be accurately spliced. These sequences are the 5' splice-site, the 3' splice-site, and the branchpoint, and are similar in yeast, animal, and plant introns (with a few differences). The 5' splice-site (or donor-site) can be generalized to consist of the consensus sequence AG:GTAAGT and the 3' splice-site (or acceptor-site) as $(T/Y)_{11}$ G/N CAG:G. The 5' proximal portion of the 3' splice-site has a tract of pyrimidines that plays an important role in splice-site recognition in verte-brate genes. Introns from plants generally lack this pronounced poly-pyrimidine stretch (*11, 12*), although they do have a similar poly(T) region adjacent to the 3′ splice-site. The branchpoint sequence is usually located 15–40 nucleotides upstream from the 3′ splice-site and is most invariant in yeast, consisting of TACTAAC. Plant and animal introns exhibit more se-quence deviation in the branchpoint, the consensus being CTRAY or YNYTRAY.

The 5′ splice-site and branchpoint sequence bind to U1 and U2 snRNPs, respectively, by base-pairing and other associations (*7, 13–20*). The recogni-tion sequences on U1 and U2 are highly conserved in eukaryotes (*7*). The base-pairing of U1 with the 5′ end of the intron is important for recognition, but apparently not sufficient for cleavage-site selection (*13–17*). The 3′ splice-site is identified in the second step of the splicing reaction as the first CAG:G downstream from the branchpoint. The 3′ splicing reaction probably occurs after the 5′ splice-site reaction and formation of the lariat structure with the branchpoint. The snRNPs U4, U5, and U6 do not bind to the pre-mRNA in an obvious base-pairing manner, but are intimately associated in the splicing lariat complex. Additional components, such as RNA helicases and other proteins, are also involved the splicing process (*1*). After the formation of a large splicing complex with U4, U5, U6, and additional com-ponents, the lariat intron is released and the two exons are joined, complet-ing the splicing process.

The splicing of pre-tRNAs is the final example of a *cis*-splicing event. A single intron is usually found and it is commonly located within or near the anticodon. There are two steps involved in the splicing of pre-tRNA; these steps differ from those utilized in the processing of pre-mRNA. The primary transcript is cut twice to remove the intron, and the ends are sealed to-gether. This occurs through a simple enzymatic process that involves a 3′-cyclic-phosphate intermediate. The structure of the RNA molecule is impor-tant in this type of splicing, as it is in Group-I and Group-II splicing.

The fifth way introns can be processed is by the *trans*-splicing pathway utilized in certain trypanosomes and *C. elegans*. In this mechanism, nuclear mRNAs acquire the same capped nucleotide sequence at their 5′ end as a consequence of *trans*-splicing. The mechanistic details of the *trans*-splicing pathway are not as clearly defined as those in the *cis* pathways. *C. elegans*, in which both *cis*- and *trans*-splicing of nuclear RNAs occurs, is believed to utilize the same components for *trans*-splicing as for *cis*-splicing with one additional novel snRNP (*21*). Plant chloroplasts can also utilize a *trans*-splic-ing mechanism very similar to a Group-I process (*22*). There are indications that plants utilize most, if not all, of the previously mentioned mechanisms to process RNA.

Introns and splicing mechanisms are not limited to eukaryotic systems, for they have been found in prokaryotes. There is evidence that introns may have existed before the divergence of prokaryotes and eukaryotes (23). Therefore, a wide array of living systems utilize the basic splicing mechanisms and have evolved variations. To further complicate matters, many organisms can utilize alternative splicing for splicing mRNA, in which noncontiguous exons are joined together, resulting in different combinations of exon–exon ligation products from a single pre-mRNA. (For a review of alternative splicing, see 24 and 25).

B. Intron Recognition by Monocots and Dicots

The remarkable precision with which the splicing reactions remove different intron regions from pre-mRNA has encouraged efforts to define the conserved sequences responsible for the accuracy of intron-splicing reactions. As exon–intron sequences became known, it became obvious that the limited absolute conservation of the GT dinucleotide at the 5' end and AG at the 3' end of introns would not be sufficient. Rather, current evidence indicates that splicing accuracy is achieved by the presence of general sequence elements to which the various snRNP particles and other proteins bind to form the active splicesome complex. The specific interactions of the various regions with snRNPs and mechanistic details are not discussed here, but only the generally acknowledged parameters important for the recognition of intron sequences are dealt with.

As stated earlier, the specific requirements for intron recognition have been best studied in yeast and vertebrate genes. The sequences at the 5' and 3' splice-sites and the branchpoint are highly conserved in yeast and are thought to be the major determinants of the 5' and 3' site-specificity. In vertebrate genes, four sequence elements are thought to be involved in the recognition of introns: the 5' splice-site, the 3' splice-site, the branch-site region, and a polypyrimidine region next to the 3' acceptor-site.

The requirements for intron recognition in plants have not been as well studied experimentally. Based on comparisons of potential consensus sequences, plant recognition sites are more similar to vertebrates than to yeast. The 5' consensus is very similar to the vertebrate sequence (Table I). More significant differences are found at the 3' end of plant introns. Perhaps the most obvious difference between plant and vertebrate introns is the lack of a distinct polypyrimidine tract. Although some plant introns do contain a high frequency of pyrimidines at their 3' ends, a more general characterization of plant genes would be a tendency for high T content, with reduced G, C, and A residues (Table II). Sequences similar to the branch-site consensus of vertebrate introns, CTRAY, can be found in plant introns (Table III)

TABLE I

NUCLEOTIDE FREQUENCIES AT THE 5' SPLICE JUNCTIONS OF MONOCOT
AND DICOT INTRONS

Monocot introns (% composition from 218 introns)

Position[a]	-4	-3	-2	-1	:	1	2	3	4	5	6	7	8
G	25	22	9	79	100	0	14	5	60	10	18	11
A	23	41	64	7	0	0	72	40	19	17	33	24
C	28	29	14	8	0	0	7	27	11	23	17	26
T	24	8	12	6	0	100	7	29	10	50	32	38
Consensus[b]		A	A	G	:	G	T	A	A	G	T	a

Dicot introns (% composition from 505 introns)

Position[a]	-4	-3	-2	-1	:	1	2	3	4	5	6	7	8
G	23	19	9	82	100	0	8	3	48	10	9	7
A	28	37	61	7	0	0.2	71	53	24	22	39	32
C	22	34	10	3	0	0.4	6	16	9	15	17	19
T	27	10	20	8	0	99	16	28	18	53	35	42
Consensus[b]		C/a	A	G	:	G	T	A	A	G	T	a

[a]Positions are numbered from the splice-site.
[b]Lower-case letters in the splice consensus indicate a base frequency of 5–15% above the overall gene frequency (see Table IV). Upper-case letters indicate >15% above the mean frequency.

upstream from the 3' end, but the importance of such a sequence is unknown, as no plant branch-site has been determined experimentally.

Plant introns display a unique characteristic: They have a reduced frequency of G and C and are enriched in T, compared to exon regions. This relative increase in A and T occurs throughout the entire intron region. The use of synthetic introns with different A+T content provided experimental evidence for the importance of A+T-rich regions in plant introns (12) for intron recognition and efficient splicing.

The absence of a polypyrimidine tract in plant introns and the requirements for A+T richness may explain the observations that plant cells often fail to process vertebrate introns despite the general structural similarities

TABLE II
NUCLEOTIDE FREQUENCIES AT THE 3' SPLICE JUNCTIONS OF MONOCOT AND DICOT INTRONS

Monocot introns (% composition from 218 introns)

Pos[a]	-15	-14	-13	-12	-11	-10	-9	-8	-7	-6	-5	-4	-3	-2	-1	:	1	2	3
G	20	18	20	20	18	19	15	22	20	19	9	49	1	0	100		62	24	25
A	19	21	15	18	14	23	16	18	18	18	9	17	5	100	0		14	18	21
C	22	16	22	20	21	22	25	15	21	17	17	11	82	0	0		15	18	24
T	40	45	43	41	47	35	44	44	41	46	65	23	12	0	0		9	39	30
Cons[b]	t	T	t	t	T	t	T	T	t	T	T	G	C	A	G	:	G	t	

Dicot introns (% composition from 504 introns)

Pos[a]	-15	-14	-13	-12	-11	-10	-9	-8	-7	-6	-5	-4	-3	-2	-1	:	1	2	3
G	17	14	16	14	15	17	14	16	17	17	11	45	0.4	0	100		57	17	26
A	26	22	20	24	23	22	24	30	21	26	15	29	5	100	0		18	21	31
C	13	11	10	8	10	13	11	11	14	10	6	7	62	0	0		14	15	15
T	45	54	54	54	52	48	52	43	47	48	69	19	33	0.2	0		11	46	28
Cons[b]	t	T	T	T	T	t	T	t	t	t	T	G	C	A	G	:	G	t	

[a] Positions are numbered from the splice-site.
[b] Lower-case letters in the splice consensus indicate a base frequency 5–15% above the overall gene frequency (see Table IV). Upper-case letters indicate >15% above the mean frequency.

and close match to preferred consensus sequences (26, 27). We have been interested in a related problem: failure of splicing monocot or dicot introns by the heterologous system (28, 29). Previous surveys of plant intron consensus sequences (11, 27) combined monocot and dicot introns into a simple "plant" category. With the addition of new gene sequences to data bank libraries, enough sequences have been reported to enable us to separate monocot and dicot introns for analysis. Genes with the intron splice-sites specified were obtained from Genebank (Release 66, December 1990) and EMBL (January 1991) data bases. The data were compiled from 218 monocot intron sequences and 505 dicot introns. Multiple copies of essentially the same gene were removed to decrease any specific bias. Several annotation errors were detected in the data base. Some were obvious typographical errors and were simply corrected before calculation. Other annotation sites that did not correspond to the minimum intron splice consensus

TABLE III
NUCLEOTIDE FREQUENCIES AT PUTATIVE BRANCHPOINTS OF MONOCOT AND DICOT INTRONS

Monocot putative branchpoint[a] (% composition from 218 introns)

Position[b]	-5	-4	-3	-2	-1	0	1	2	3	4
G	19	22	4	0	50	0	4	29	18	22
A	26	35	4	1	33	100	22	16	32	24
C	18	17	56	2	8	0	26	16	20	21
T	37	27	36	97	8	0	48	38	30	32
Consensus[c]		a	C/Y	T	G/R	A	t/y	g	a	

Dicot putative branchpoint[a] (% composition from 505 introns)

Position[b]	-5	-4	-3	-2	-1	0	1	2	3	4
G	13	20	2	0	25	0	1	21	13	19
A	28	32	2	0	58	100	17	27	30	25
C	13	12	32	0	7	0	10	13	11	13
T	46	36	64	100	11	0	71	40	47	43
Consensus[c]		g	T/Y	T	A/R	A	T	g	t	

[a] The 3' region of introns (from -15 to -50) were scanned for the sequence that best matched the vertebrate consensus sequence CTRAY.

[b] Positions are numbered from the putative attachment site (A).

[c] Lower-case letters in the consensus indicate a base frequency 5–15% above the mean base frequency within introns (see Table IV). Upper-case letters indicate >15% above the mean frequency.

(/GT . . . AG/) could often be aligned by shifting one to three nucleotides and so were assumed also to have been a simple error in the data base. Three dicot introns did not conform to the 5'/GT rule and may be legitimate exceptions to an absolute requirement for a GT dinucleotide in the 5' splice consensus.

As shown in Table I, the 5' splice consensus sequences for monocots and dicots do not differ greatly. The eight most highly conserved nucleotides of the derived 5' splice consensus (5'—AG/GTAAGT—3') are hypothesized to base-pair with the 5' end of U1 snRNA. The great variability within the proposed consensus sequence for the 5' splice-site has prompted some (30) to subclassify the "eukaryotic" intron consensus into separate motifs, such as AG/GTA, /GTAAGT, RG/GTGAG, and AG/GTXXGT, in an attempt to define patterns necessary and sufficient for recognition of the 5′ splice-site. Although most monocot and dicot introns can be separated into such categories, enough variability remains to question the usefulness of such a process.

A more useful concept may involve base-pairing with the U1 snRNA and the concept of "variable geometry" (31). Any one region or individual base of the consensus sequence [except the invariant G(1)] can be substituted, providing that other positions are retained. Most 5′ splice-sites of plant introns will only match 5 or 6 bp with the U1 snRNA sequence (Fig. 1). In fact, the number of introns containing an exact match was significantly reduced from the expected frequency computed from the base probabilities of the 5′ splice consensus data (for monocots, 10 exact matches would be expected, but none were found; and for dicots, 24 were expected, with only two found).

By sorting intron splice-sites based on actual nucleotides present, a simple pattern emerges. Substitutions at the A(−2) or G(−1) sites are associated with a higher consensus frequency at remaining sites. If both A(−2) and G(−1) are substituted, the consensus increase further. Conversely, sequences containing both A(−2) and G(−1) show a reduced consensus match in the remaining sequence. A similar pattern is displayed by substitutions at A(3) through G(5). The fact that most plant 5′ splice-sites only match five or six nucleotides of the major eight-nucleotide consensus sequence suggests that the splicing process is optimal for recognition of a variable sequence but

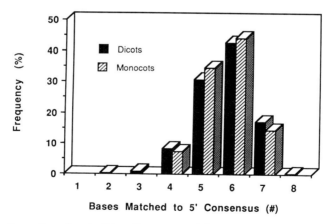

Fig. 1. Proportion of nucleotides of monocot and dicot intron sequences that match the major 5′ splice-site consensus sequence of plant introns. The 218 monocot and 505 dicot introns were compared to the common plant consensus 5′—AG/GTAAGT—3′. The number of nucleotides that matched for each intron was computed and the overall percentage was calculated for monocot and dicot introns.

not for a maximum match to the 5′ consensus sequence. The first consensus base(−3) and final T(6) respond less to changes in consensus sequence and so may not contribute significantly to the optimization of base-pairing with U1 snRNA.

While the absence of a polypyrimidine stretch at the 3′ end of most plant introns and the requirement for an increased A+T content within plant introns may explain differential heterologous splicing efficiency between vertebrate and plant systems, our analysis of the consensus sequences did not provide any obvious reasons for the splicing problems observed between monocots and dicots. However, analysis of the base composition of monocot and dicot genes may indicate the cause of a lack of efficient splicing. As is readily apparent in Fig. 2, the average A+T and G+C composition of monocots and dicots is quite different. Goodall and Filipowicz demonstrated that A+T-rich sequences are required for efficient intron splicing to occur in a dicot test system (12). The significantly lower A+T content of monocot introns (mean of 60%, with a range of 31–78%) compared to dicots (mean of

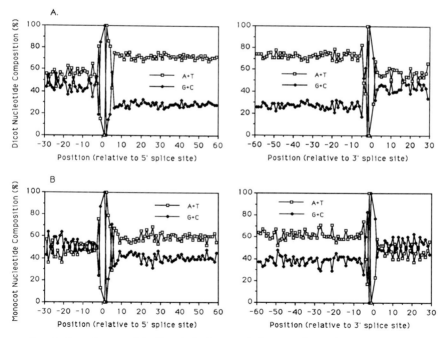

FIG. 2. Distribution of A+T and G+C around the 5′ and 3′ splice sites of dicot and monocot introns. Data were compiled from (A) 505 dicot and (B) 218 monocot intron sequences. The initial 5′ G of the IVS is at position 1 for plots of the 5′ splice-site; the terminal 3′ G is at position −1 for the plots of the 3′ splice-site.

71%, with a range of 55–91%) may reduce heterologous splicing of certain introns. Closer examination of intron and exon base composition indicates that the greatest changes occur in the mean percentage of T, G, and C bases, and that the percentage of A is only slightly increased (Table IV). Although monocot and dicot genes differ in overall nucleotide composition, the respective differences between intron and exon regions are similar and suggest that any mechanism that may recognize the high U + A and low G + C content of RNA for recognition and splicing of intron sequences may be similar in both classes, but optimized for different levels of mean base composition.

The larger number of introns available in expanded data bases (218 monocot and 505 dicot) have enabled us to catalog more accurately the splice junctions of monocots and dicots than was previously reported for combined plant sequences (Ref. 11; 177 total introns). The 5' splice consensus we identified is almost identical to the previous cataloged values (Table V). We identified differences in the 3' splice-site and in the putative branchpoint. In both monocots and dicots, the 3' splice-site is preceded by a poly(T) region with a distinct reduction in the mean frequency of G, C, and A. With a lack of direct experimental confirmation of the role of branchpoints in plant introns and a report that a synthetic intron without a branchpoint sequence was spliced (12), we are hesitant to suggest that the distinct differences between monocot and dicot putative branchpoint sequences may contribute to inefficient heterologous splicing.

Even with a thorough analysis of intron consensus sequences and nucleotide compositions, it is still unclear exactly how plant cells can accurately recognize the correct intron–exon borders. There is much variability among different introns, even within the same gene. Examples of authentic introns that appear to conflict with the general consensus rules we have just discussed can be found, and a search of gene sequences will find potential

TABLE IV
MEAN NUCLEOTIDE BASE COMPOSITION OF MONOCOT AND DICOT GENES

Base	Monocots[a]			Dicots[a]		
	Intron	Exon	Δ	Intron	Exon	Δ
G	19	29	−10	15	24	−9
A	25	24	1	30	29	1
C	21	25	−4	14	20	−6
T	35	21	14	41	26	15

[a]The mean precentage of nucleotide base composition was computed for the 218 monocot and 505 dicot introns and their internal exons.

TABLE V
COMPARISON OF MONOCOT, DICOT, PREVIOUS CATALOG OF COMBINED PLANT, AND VERTEBRATE INTRON CONSENSUS SEQUENCES.

5' Splice-site[a]

	-3	-2	-1	:	1	2	3	4	5	6	7
Monocot	A_{41}	A_{64}	G_{79}	:	G_{100}	T_{100}	A_{72}	A_{40}	G_{60}	T_{50}	a_{33}
Dicot	C_{34}	A_{61}	G_{82}	:	G_{100}	T_{99}	A_{71}	A_{53}	G_{48}	T_{53}	a_{32}
	a_{37}										
Plant[b]	C_{33}	A_{55}	G_{72}	:	G_{100}	T_{99}	A_{70}	A_{55}	G_{65}	T_{49}	
	A_{33}										
Vertebrate[c]	C_{38}	A_{62}	G_{77}	:	G_{100}	T_{100}	A_{60}	A_{74}	G_{84}	T_{50}	
	A_{39}										

3' Splice-site[a]

	-15	-14	-13	-12	-11	-10	-9	-8	-7	-6	-5	-4	-3	-2	-1	:	1	2
Monocot	t_{40}	T_{45}	t_{43}	t_{41}	T_{47}	t_{35}	T_{44}	T_{44}	t_{41}	T_{46}	T_{65}	G_{49}	C_{82}	A_{100}	G_{100}	:	G_{62}	t_{39}
Dicot	t_{45}	T_{54}	T_{54}	T_{54}	T_{52}	t_{48}	T_{52}	t_{43}	t_{47}	t_{48}	T_{69}	G_{45}	C_{62}	A_{100}	G_{100}	:	G_{57}	t_{46}
Plant[b]	T_{47}	T_{53}	T_{51}	T_{44}	T_{53}	T_{47}	T_{42}	T_{38}	T_{41}	T_{44}	T_{68}	G_{50}	C_{67}	A_{100}	G_{100}	:	G_{60}	
				R_{44}			R_{39}	R_{47}	R_{44}	R_{43}								
Vertebrate[d]	T_{51}	T_{44}	T_{50}	T_{53}	T_{60}	T_{49}	T_{49}	T_{45}	T_{45}	T_{57}	T_{58}	n	C_{65}	A_{100}	G_{100}	:	G_{52}	
	Y_{70}	Y_{69}	Y_{71}	Y_{74}	Y_{84}	Y_{79}	Y_{82}	Y_{72}	Y_{81}	Y_{93}	Y_{85}							

Branchpoint[a]

	-5	-4	-3	-2	-1	0	1	2	3
Monocot	n	a_{35}	C_{56}	T_{97}	G_{50}	A_{100}	t_{48}	g_{29}	a_{32}
			Y_{92}		R_{83}		y_{74}		
Dicot	n	g_{20}	T_{64}	T_{100}	A_{58}	A_{100}	T_{71}	g_{21}	t_{47}
			Y_{96}		R_{83}				

(*cont.*)

TABLE V (*Cont.*)

Plant[b]	T_{40}	T_{33}	C_{69}	T_{100} R_{74}	A_{100}	Y_{71}
	R_{45}	R_{54}	T_{24}			
Vertebrate[e]			C_{76}	T_{95} G_{51}	A_{98}	C_{51}
			Y_{97}	R_{80}		Y_{80}

[a]These are the reported and proposed consensus sequences for intron recognition. Numbers in subscripts indicate the percentages of sequences with the indicated nucleotides.
[b]Previous catalog of plant consensus values is from Ref. *11*.
[c]Vertebrate 5′ splice consensus are from Ref. *5*.
[d]Vertebrate 3′ splice consensus values are from Ref. *64*.
[e]Vertebrate branchpoint values were compiled from data in Ref. *65*.

splice-sites that are not utilized. More experimental work is required to support and test various hypotheses regarding intron splicing in plants.

We now turn to descriptions of some of our work to test the ability of various introns to affect gene expression in monocots.

II. Intron-mediated Enhanced Expression: Historical Perspective

Introns are essential for normal expression levels of several mammalian genes. Examples include β-globin (*32–34*), SV40 "late" mRNA (*32, 33–37*), and dihydrofolate reductase (*38*). Other genes, such as the polyoma virus middle-T gene (*39*) and the thymidine kinase gene from Herpes simplex (*32*), are expressed at similar levels regardless of the presence or absence of an intron. An initial observation in plants indicated that introns are not required in order to achieve normal expression levels. The seed storage protein phaseolin is expressed at similar levels with or without its native introns (*40*). However, there is a dependence on introns for adequate expression of the maize alcohol dehydrogenase gene or a reporter gene, chloramphenicol acetyltransferase (*CAT*) (*41*). We and others (*42–51*) subsequently confirmed the previously cited observations (*41*) using an additional reporter gene, β-glucuronidase (*GUS*), and various introns. However, we have determined that not all introns can enhance the expression in maize protoplasts of genes lacking introns (*43*).

A. Intron-mediated Enhanced Expression in Maize Protoplasts

We have developed a transient assay system utilizing a plasmid (Fig. 3) containing the 35-S promoter from cauliflower mosaic virus, a multiple clon-

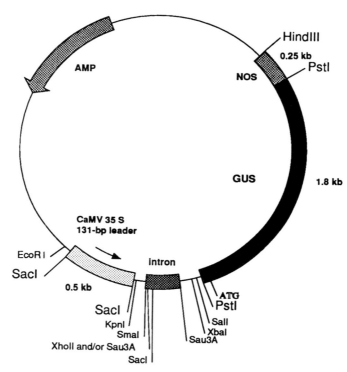

FIG. 3. Diagram of the basic β-glucuronidase expression plasmid. This plasmid is composed of the 35-S promoter from the cauliflower mosaic virus, the β-glucuronidase gene, (GUS) and the poly-(A) region from the nopaline synthetase gene (NOS). It also has several unique restriction sites into which introns can be cloned. The base plasmid without an intron is referred to as pZO 36.

ing-site for the insertion of introns to be tested, a GUS reporter gene, and a poly(A) addition region from the nopaline synthetase gene (NOS). The various plasmid constructs are electroporated into protoplasts and the protoplasts are allowed to recover for 24 hours before protein extracts are prepared from the cells. RNA can also be extracted from a portion of the electroporated protoplasts. The GUS assays and RNA isolations are performed according to methods previously described (52, 53). Utilizing these procedures, we find that we can quickly and easily test individual introns and various lengths of flanking exon sequence for their effect on the transient expression of our reporter gene. The results obtained in these transient assays are usually presented in comparison to the levels of expression obtained with the base plasmid construct (a no-intron control, arbitrarily set to a value of 1.0).

Previously published experiments have established that the addition of an intron to the 5' untranslated region of a reporter gene construct can increase gene expression from 10-fold to as much as 1000-fold (*44*, *50*). Enhanced activity was not found if the intron was placed before the promoter or in the 3' untranslated region of the gene (*44*). Tests with a number of introns have shown that simply the addition of an intron is not sufficient to produce enhanced gene expression (Table VI). Certain introns supported higher rates of enhanced expression. Insertion of multiple introns did not enhance the activity. Instead, irrespective of the order of the introns, the overall enhancement was equivalent to the level produced by the least active intron (*44*).

B. Effect of 5' Exon Length on Enhanced Expression Levels

The level of enhancement produced by introns can also be influenced by the length of the authentic 5' exon included with the construct (Fig. 4). This result has been duplicated with several different introns and suggests that a 5' exon length of 60–90 nucleotides is optimal for intron enhancement (in our test vector). Experiments to determine an optimal 3' exon length did not produce a consistent pattern for optimization. Very short 3' exon sequences

TABLE VI

ENHANCEMENT OF *GUS* AND *CAT* GENE EXPRESSION BY VARIOUS INTRONS
IN ELECTROPORATED MAIZE PROTOPLASTS

Intron construct	Construct activity[a] (relative to no intron)	
	GUS	*CAT*
No intron control	1.0	1.0
maize *Hsp82*, IVS1	3.0	7.0
maize *Hsp81*, IVS1	0.9	1.3
maize *Adh1*, IVS2	--	12.1
maize *Adh1*, IVS6	6.0	20.9
maize *Adh1*, IVS9	--	0.9
maize *Sh1*, IVS1	2.8	--
brassica *Hsp80*, IVS1	2.7	1.9

[a]Black Mexican Sweet protoplasts were electroporated with plasmids containing the *GUS* or *CAT* gene and various introns inserted in the 5' untranslated region following the 35-S promoter from the cauliflower mosaic virus. Samples were removed 1 day after electroporation and tested for levels of transient gene expression.

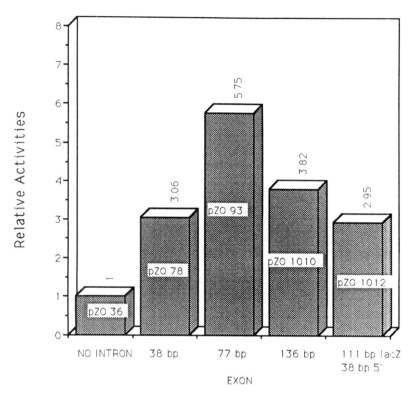

GUS Constructs
5' Exon Lengths

FIG. 4. A graph of the relative β-glucuronidase activities transiently expressed maize protoplasts electroporated with intron expression cassettes containing variable-length 5' exons. All
plasmids utilize the 35-S promoter from the cauliflower mosaic virus, the β-glucuronidase gene,
and the poly(A) region from the nopaline synthetase gene. The lengths of *Hsp82* IVS1-flanking
5' exon are shown on the X axis. With the exception pZO 1012, which contains 111 bp of the
lacZ region of the cloning plasmid in addition to 38 bp of authentic exon, all contain native 5'
exon from the *Hsp82* gene. Each bar represents the mean of the three independent electroporations. The no-intron control (pZO 36) is set to an arbitrary value of 1.00 for comparative
purposes.

(i.e., less than five nucleotides) did appear to eliminate the intron enhancement of expression.

The degree of intron-mediated enhancement in dicot protoplasts is not as
pronounced as it is in monocots. In fact, most introns we have surveyed in
dicot protoplasts significantly reduced expression, compared to expression of

the no-intron control. One intron that yields a slight enhancement (1.05–2.00-fold) is the IVS6 from the *Adh1* gene of maize.

C. Requirement of Splicing for Enhanced Expression

In this section, we present experimental data indicating that (1) splicing is required to achieve enhanced expression of reporter genes in protoplasts, and (2) the various introns are spliced with differing efficiencies. Furthermore, these data demonstrate that the degree of enhanced expression is directly correlated with the efficiency of intron splicing and/or RNA transport.

There are three observations consistent with the requirement of RNA splicing for enhanced expression. The first of these is that, if the intron is cloned into the *GUS* expression vector leader in the opposite, or 3′- to 5′, orientation, there is no *GUS* activity in the electroporated protoplasts. The second involves the specific mutation of the 5′ or 3′ splice-site, which also results in little or no *GUS* expression. In these plasmids, the 5′ donor-site is mutagenized from gat:**GTAAG** to gat:**ATCAG** and the 3′ acceptor-site is changed from TTGCAG:gc to TTGCGC:gc. Electroporations of protoplasts with these plasmids and subsequent *GUS* assays resulted in 0.085 and 0.15 activity relative to the no-intron control (Fig. 5). This is 1/80 and 1/45 of the *GUS* activity, respectively, of the native intron construct. In similar experiments, the constructs containing the 3′ splice mutation consistently yielded twice the activity of the 5′ mutant. Examination of the RNA isolated from protoplasts electroporated with the 3′ splice mutant plasmid revealed a *GUS* RNA shorter than predicted, which could be the result of an alternative 3′ splice-site utilization within the *GUS* gene. The RNA from the protoplasts treated with the splice mutant plasmids was analyzed for evidence of processing by a polymerase-chain-reaction (PCR) procedure and is discussed in the next section.

The third observation consistent with requisite RNA splicing for enhanced expression comes from experiments utilizing temperature shocks. A heat shock of 10–15°C above normal culture temperatures can inhibit intron processing (54–57). Electron-microscopic examination of chromatin from *Drosophila* cells exposed to a heat treatment of 36–37°C reveals that the snRNPs are not effectively deposited on nascent transcripts (unpublished observations, cited in 58). In HeLa cells, the U4–U5–U6 complex is disrupted at 43°C and 46°C, whereas the U1 and U2 snRNPs remain unaffected at 43°C and become somewhat disrupted at 46°C (59). With these observations in mind, we decided to investigate the effect of heat shock on intron-mediated enhanced *GUS* expression in electroporated maize protoplasts. We first investigated the effect on transient gene expression driven off the constitutive 35-S promoter by a 2- to 3-hour heat shock of 40–41°C and found no

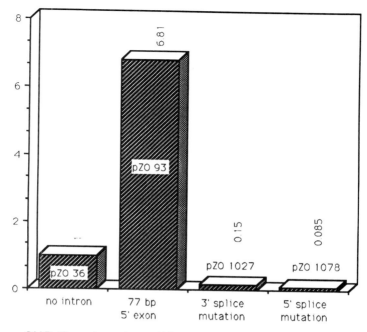

5' Splice Mutagenesis

3' Splice Mutagenesis

initial sequence   GAT:GTAAG
after mutagenesis GAT:ATCAG

initial sequence   TTGCAG:GC
after mutagenesis TTGCGC:GC

FIG. 5. A graph of the relative β-glucuronidase activities transiently expressed in maize protoplasts electroporated with intron splice mutant expression cassettes. All plasmids utilize the 35-S promoter from the cauliflower mosaic virus, the β-glucuronidase gene, and the poly(A) region from the nopaline synthetase gene. The changes in the 5' and 3' splice-sites of the *Hsp82* intron are illustrated below the graph. Each bar represents the mean of three independent electroporations. The no-intron control (pZO 36) is set to an arbitrary value of 1.00 for comparative purposes.

difference from the protoplasts treated at 25°C. This was not too surprising, considering the timing of our standard *GUS* assays. The protoplasts are usually electroporated and allowed to "recover" for 24 hours before cellular extracts are prepared for the *GUS* assays. During this 24-hour recovery period, the 35-S promoter has been producing its gene product, and a 3-hour heat shock at the end of this interval has little effect on overall *GUS* levels. Therefore, we turned to using the heat-shock promoter from a maize

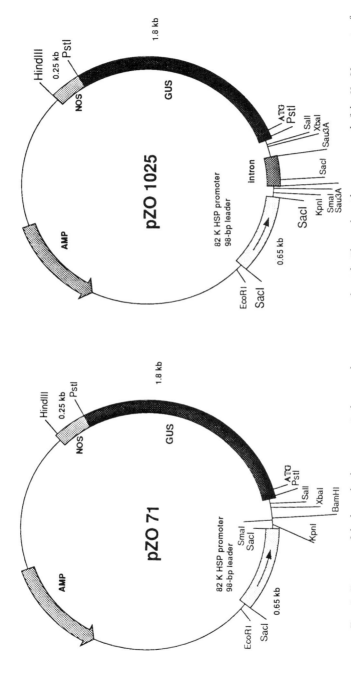

Fig. 6. Diagrams of the heat-shock promoter β-glucuronidase expression plasmids. These plasmids are composed of the *Hsp82* promoter from maize, the β-glucuronidase gene (*GUS*), and the poly(A) region from the nopaline synthetase (*NOS*). The base plasmid without an intron is referred to as pZO 71 and the *Hsp82* IVS1-containing plasmid is pZO 1025.

Hsp82 gene, which exhibits mostly heat-shock-triggered induction of expression (60).

Expression constructs were made with this promoter, 5′ untranslated leader, with and without an intron, the *GUS* gene, and a *NOS* terminator (Fig. 6). The plasmids were electroporated into maize protoplasts and the cells were allowed to recover for 24 hours, at which time a 3-hour heat shock was performed on a portion of the electroporated protoplasts. Protein extracts were prepared from control (25°C) and experimental (40°C) incubated cells and *GUS* assays were performed. The results of these assays are shown in Fig. 7. The *Hsp82* promoter does not support the synthesis of measurable (above background) amounts of *GUS* at the control temperature of 25°C, whereas at 40°C the *Hsp82* promoter drives the synthesis of *GUS* to a level

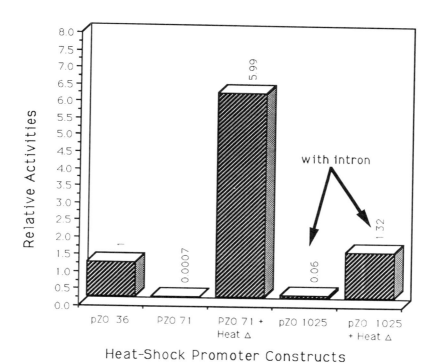

FIG. 7. A graph of the relative β-glucuronidase activities found in maize protoplasts electroporated with expression cassettes utilizing the *Hsp82* heat-shock promoter. The protoplasts were electroporated and allowed to recover for 24 hours before the heat shock and subsequent assays. For comparison, the no-intron 35-S promoter results are shown and set to a value of 1.00. The *Hsp82* promoter constructs were assayed from protoplasts that had been incubated at 40°C for 3 hours. The control protoplasts were left at 25°C for the same period and then assayed.

six times that of the level observed with the 35-S promoter (in protoplasts that have recovered from electroporation for 24 hours). The presence of the intron in the 5' untranslated leader region of the *Hsp82* promoter construct appears to raise basal *GUS* levels at 25°C to a measurable level, and at 40°C (for 3 hours) the intron-containing plasmid yields *GUS* expression levels 1/4.5 that of the no-intron control at the same temperature. This latter observation is consistent with the likelihood that the heat treatment is inhibiting RNA splicing, as reported for other biological systems.

D. Polymerase-chain-reaction Analysis of Splicing

In order to conclusively demonstrate that splicing occurs during intron-mediated enhanced expression in maize protoplasts, we determined, by a PCR amplification of RNA, that a portion of the precursor RNA was spliced. This was done by utilizing a reverse transcriptase cDNA step and subsequent DNA amplification with primers flanking the intron. The resultant PCR-amplified product should display a slower migrating fragment if intron processing has not occurred, and a faster migrating band of 140 bp shorter in the case of the *Hsp82* intron or one that is 345 bp shorter in the case of the *Adh1* IVS6 if proper intron splicing has transpired. Figure 8 shows the results from the PCR amplification of RNA extracted and purified from protoplasts electroporated with assorted plasmids containing the *Hsp82* intron and the *Hsp81* intron. In this particular set of experiments, most samples appear to display a precursor and a processed band (except the splice mutants) of appropriate sizes. The samples from the protoplasts electroporated with the splice mutant plasmids exhibit an unprocessed precursor band only.

It is very common in other systems that alternative splice-sites will be utilized if the primary site is altered via mutation; however, our PCR-based assay will not detect spliced products outside the boundaries of the oligomeric primers. If such a gel (Fig. 9) is blotted and hybridized to a probe containing both intron and flanking exon, the precursor and processed bands strongly hybridize to it. Several minor bands can sometimes be detected by such a probe, and these can be either alternatively processed minor products that occur within the boundaries of the primers or PCR artifacts. In the case of the *Adh1* IVS6 (due to three 100-bp direct repeats within the intron and spanning through the authentic 3' splice-site), at least two alternative 3' splice-sites are found within the intron.

Another phenomenon worth mentioning is the fluctuation of enhanced *GUS* expression observed from experiment to experiment in protoplasts electroporated with the same intron-containing expression plasmid. The day-to-day variation in the maize cell physiology can result in a 6- to 12-fold enhancement of *GUS* expression with the *Adh1* IVS6 in one experiment,

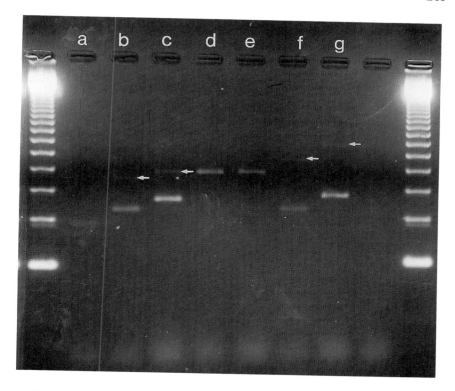

Fig. 8. PCR analysis. Amplified products have been electrophoresed in a 4% NuSieve agarose gel and stained with ethidium bromide. PCR primers were designed for the 3′ end of the 35-S cauliflower mosaic virus promoter and the 5′ end of the β-glucuronidase gene, flanking the intron. The positions of unspliced precursor RNA products are indicated by arrows in all lanes, except lanes a, d, and e. The precursor products are more easily visualized in a Southern blot of the gel (see Fig. 9). PCR analysis of RNA from the various constructs is expected to yield the following size bands:

	Construct	Spiced	Unspliced	Intron
(a)	pZO 36	210 bp (no intron)		
(b)	pZO 78	270 bp	410 bp	IVS1 from *Hsp82*
(c)	pZO 93	309 bp	449 bp	IVS1 from *Hsp82*
(d)	pZO 1027	309 bp	449 bp	IVS1 from *Hsp82*[a]
(e)	pZO 1078	309 bp	449 bp	IVS1 from *Hsp82*[a]
(f)	pZO 95	270 bp	530 bp	ISV1 from *Hsp81*
(g)	pZO 1016	324 bp	666 bp	IVS6 from *Adh1*

[a]Mutated splice-site.

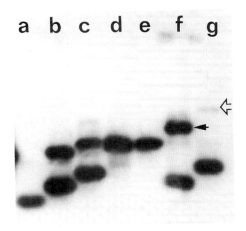

FIG. 9. Southern blot analysis of PCR-amplified products. An agarose gel very similar to that depicted in Fig. 8 was blotted to nitrocellulose using standard Southern blotting techniques and was hybridized to a mixed probe. The probe consists of random priming reactions done with the listed introns and their flanking exon sequences. The samples analyzed are as follows: (a) pZO 36, (b) pZO 78, (c) pZO 93, (d) pZO 1027, (e) pZO 1078, (f) pZO 95, and (g) pZO 1016. Lane f is from an intron (*Hsp81* IVS1) that does not result in enhanced *GUS* expression, and lane g is from an intron (*Adh1* IVS6) that resulted in a high level of enhanced *GUS* expression. The solid arrow in lane f indicates the unspliced pre-mRNA, and the open arrow in lane g depicts the position of the unprocessed RNA.

whereas another experiment can yield a 12- to 20-fold increase in *GUS* expression. When RNA samples from these electroporations are examined, we observed that the degree of intron splicing correlates with the levels of *GUS* expression observed.

E. Mechanism of Intron-mediated Enhanced Expression

This last observation leads us to a discussion of the mechanism by which introns enhance expression in maize protoplasts. If the RNA from experiments described in the previous section is electrophoresed into denaturing formaldehyde gels, blotted to nitrocellulose, and hybridized to a probe encompassing the entire coding region of the *GUS* gene (Fig. 10), the following observations can be made. The degree by which any intron enhances *GUS* expression is correlated with the amounts of steady-state *GUS* mRNA. Protoplasts electroporated with splice mutant constructs produce substantially (particularly the 5′ splice mutant) lower levels of steady-state *GUS* mRNA. The 3′ splice mutant electroporations exhibits several sizes of RNA that hybridize to the *GUS* coding region probe. This could be indicative of alter-

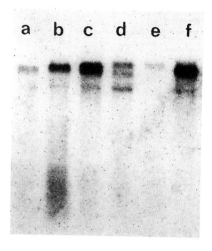

FIG. 10. Northern blot analysis. RNA from post-electroporated protoplasts was electrophoresed on a formaldehyde agarose gel and blotted onto Zetaprobe. Blot was probed with random priming reaction off a β-glucuronidase gene fragment. The lanes contain RNA isolated from protoplasts electroporated with the following plasmids: (a) pZO 36, no intron; (b) pZO 78, 38-bp 5′ exon, *Hsp82* IVS1; (c) pZO 93, 77-bp 5′ exon, *Hsp82* IVS1; (d) pZO 1027, 77-bp 5′ exon, *Hsp82* IVS1, 3′ splice-site mutant; (e) pZO 1078 77-bp 5′ exon, *Hsp82* IVS1, 5′ splice-site mutant; (f) pZO 1016 76-bp 5′ exon, *Adh1* IVS6.

native 3′ splice-site recognition and processing. One observation that leads us to propose an explanation for intron-mediated enhancement is the ratio of unspliced RNA to spliced RNA. Figure 9 shows RNA isolated from protoplasts electroporated with an intron construct that does not result in enhanced *GUS* expression (*Hsp81* IVS1 intron, lane f) and an intron plasmid construct that does enhance *GUS* activity (*Adh1* IVS6, lane g). In the RNA from protoplasts electroporated with the *Hsp81* intron plasmid, there are greater quantities of the unspliced product; whereas in the RNA from protoplasts electroporated with an *Adh1* IVS6-containing plasmid, the spliced *GUS* RNA product is more prevalent than the unspliced form. Therefore, these observations indicate that the efficiency of RNA splicing is directly related to the degree of *GUS* expression and may at least partially explain intron-mediated enhanced expression.

III. RNA Transport

One additional parameter that must be considered is the transport of RNA from the nucleus to the cytoplasm. This process is not well understood, and it is very difficult to uncover or design an appropriate experimental system to examine the export of RNA from the nucleus. It is known that spliceosomal components are concentrated in discrete foci within the nucleus (61), and it is likely that splicing takes place at these loci. These observations are consistent with the likelihood that the spliceosomal assembly is compartmentalized within the nucleus and could be required for proficient RNA transport.

One may start by asking several questions: How closely are intron splicing and RNA transport coupled? Is intron splicing required for RNA to exit the nucleus? The answer to the first question is that they are closely linked processes. This is based on the observations that many of the mutations that affect RNA transport in yeast have been identified as components of the RNA-splicing machinery (1). The second question is a little more difficult to address. Obviously, there are RNAs (e.g., histone and heat-shock mRNAs) that lack introns, exit from the nucleus, and are subsequently translated into protein products. However, these mRNAs may depart via a less efficient and more passive route(s) than the intron-splicing pathway.

The (no-intron) heat-shock mRNAs may overcome this potential expression disadvantage by compensating through massive amounts of transcription. In the case of the histone mRNAs, which are abundant in dividing cells, the barrier between the nucleus and the cytoplasm is essentially removed by the repetitive dissolution of the nuclear membrane during mitosis. However, is it possible for pre-mRNA containing introns to move from the nucleus into the cytoplasm? We have presented data in this report that indicate that pre-mRNA, normal and splice-site-mutagenized, can be detected in our experimental maize system. This has also been observed in maize by other investigators (51), but where is this RNA localized? Utilizing yeast and a synthetic intron (inserted into a lacZ gene in a manner in which only pre-mRNA could be translated to produce β-galactosidase activity), other researchers (62) demonstrated that the pre-mRNA can be localized to the cytoplasm if either the 5' splice-site or branchpoint is deleted. In mutant yeast strains, which accumulate pre-mRNA (assayed at the nonpermissive temperature), splicing inhibition was observed to occur simultaneously with a large increase in pre-mRNA translation.

These results indicate that early factors interacting with the 5' splice-site and/or branchpoint sequence commit the precursor RNA to the splicing pathway, preventing transport to the cytoplasm. Such observations, and others, indicate a strong linkage or dependence of RNA transport on intron splicing and that pre-mRNA in yeast can only be found in the cytoplasm if the 5' splice-site or branchpoint is altered. Yost and Lindquist (55) also found small amounts of pre-mRNAs in the cytoplasm when Drosophila cells were subjected to a heat shock. If maize is comparable to these two systems, we would expect to find pre-mRNA in the cytoplasm only if the splice-sites have been altered. If maize cells subjected to a heat treatment react in the same manner as *Drosophila* cells, we may expect to detect some pre-mRNA in the cytoplasm.

Unlike yeast, the maize protoplast system lacks mutants that result in pre-mRNA accumulation. Furthermore, our experimental system has utilized predominately the 35-S promoter, and this limits our analysis to steady-state levels of mRNA and pre-mRNA. Therefore, we have recently turned to more extensive use of maize heat-shock promoters (63) with our reporter gene system. With appropriate induction, these promoters allow us to induce new transcription at a specific time. Preliminary results with the heat-shock promoter demonstrate that we can induce transcription of *GUS* pre-mRNA by a 39°C treatment without significantly inhibiting RNA splicing. This should permit a more accurate examination of the timing of induction of transcription, intron processing, and subsequent transport of the *GUS* mRNA. A more severe heat shock (41°C) inhibits RNA splicing, yet optimally induces new RNA transcription driven off the heat-shock promoter. We are investigating whether an even higher temperature treatment will still permit new *GUS* pre-mRNA transcription, but totally block any RNA splicing. This would enable the cells to build up large quantities of pre-mRNA, and when the cells are released from the high temperature block of splicing, we could examine the kinetics and timing of RNA processing and transport. We hope that the heat-shock system and other approaches will uncover more details of the mechanism by which introns mediate the enhanced expression of genes that lack introns in maize protoplasts. A better understanding of the important features of this mechanism will allow us to achieve more predictable levels of heterologous gene expression in maize.

IV. Other Observations

There are several other observations that should be mentioned and emphasized.

First, our survey of other promoters shows that intron-mediated enhanced expression can be obtained with almost any maize promoter. Generally, the weaker the promoter, the greater the enhancement mediated by the intron. Second, we have also observed that the degree of intron-mediated enhancement depends on the reporter gene utilized. For example, the enhancement with the *CAT* gene is usually greater than that obtained with the same intron with the *GUS* gene. Currently, we have no plausible explanation as to how the coding sequence of the reporter gene can affect the degree of intron-mediated enhanced expression. However, inherent mRNA stability, mRNA size, or codon preference could contribute to this phenomenon.

V. Concluding Remarks

In this essay, we have shown that the basic recognition sites (5', 3', and branchpoint) for intron splicing in plants do not differ significantly from those of vertebrates (see Table V for a comparison between the consensus sequences of monocots and dicots and the reported consensus sequences of vertebrates and plants). We have also demonstrated, by mutations of splice-site recognition sequences, that the 5' GT or 3' AG dinucleotides are essential for proper splicing in monocots. Our experiments have not addressed the role of the branchpoint sequence in efficient RNA splicing, although the observations by others (12) do not indicate an important function for the branchpoint in competent intron processing in higher plants.

We have also discussed the differences in base composition observed in monocot and dicot introns. These differences could explain some of the reports of inefficient splicing or nonsplicing observed in dicot cells with genes containing monocot introns. The reports of splicing difficulties between vertebrate and plant introns in heterologous systems may be attributed to the lack of a "good" polypyrimidine sequence adjacent to the 3' splice-site in the plant introns. Moreover, previous reports by other investigators have broadly generalized the observations of inefficient or incorrect splicing in dicot cells (with vertebrate introns) to be indicative of results in all plants.

We have demonstrated that the degree of enhanced *GUS* expression obtained in our assays is directly correlated with the extent of RNA splicing. Utilizing our transient *GUS* assay system as a measure of splicing efficiency, we find that maize cells are very proficient at processing introns from both monocot and dicot sources, whereas tobacco or carrot cells are not. In our view, it is reasonable to assume that maize cells can effectively process introns of vertebrate origin, and that it is likely that the lack of efficient splicing of introns (of vertebrate or monocot origin) may be specific to dicotyledonous cells, not of plant cells in general.

We have attempted to characterize and explain the mechanism by which introns enhance expression in maize cells, and several conclusions can be stated. Introns placed in the 5' untranslated leader of gene expression constructs enhance transient reporter gene activity in maize Black Mexican Sweet protoplasts. Similar enhancement is *not* observed when these constructs are electroporated into dicot (carrot or tobacco) protoplasts. While investigating this phenomenon, we have uncovered the following:

1. The relative degree of enhancement is variable. This variability appears to be dependent on the physiological condition of the protoplasts.

2. There is a minimum 3′ and 5′ exon length requirement for optimal enhancement. Two base-pairs of native 3′ exon does not allow for intron enhancement. There appears to be an optimal 5′ exon length of 60–90 bp.

3. The placement of any maize intron in the 5′ untranslated leader does not necessarily result in enhanced transient activity, even when the intron includes sufficient exon length, 5′ and 3′ splice junction consensus sequences, and an exon sequence highly homologous to that of an intron construct that does enhance. This indicates that there are internal sequences necessary for enhancement.

4. There are four observations that indicate that removal of the intron is necessary for enhanced transient expression:

   a. Disrupting the 5′ or 3′ splice consensus sequence decreases the reporter gene activity dramatically.

   b. Heat-shock experiments with intron-containing constructs result in lowered enhancement. It has been demonstrated in other experimental systems that a heat shock inhibits or reduces the efficiency of splicing.

   c. When placed in the opposite, or antisense, orientation in expression plasmids, introns strongly inhibit *GUS* expression.

   d. PCR experiments demonstrate that native introns are spliced correctly, but the 5′ and 3′ splice-site mutants are no longer spliced.

5. Steady-state mRNA levels are greatly enhanced by the introns.

6. The mechanism by which the introns enhance expression in maize protoplasts probably involves the efficiency of precursor RNA splicing and/or its transport to the cytoplasm.

ACKNOWLEDGMENTS

We acknowledge the contributions of E. Silva Casey, J. West, P. S. Dietrich, A. Semrau, and G. DiCola. We thank N. Sinibaldi and K. Marrs for reading the manuscript and making many useful suggestions.

REFERENCES

1. S. W. Ruby and J. Abelson, *TIG* **7**, 79 (1991).
2. I. W. Mattaj, *Curr. Opin. Cell Biol.* **2**, 528 (1990).
3. P. A. Sharp, *Science* **235**, 766 (1987).
4. M. R. Green, *Curr. Opin. Cell Biol.* **1**, 59 (1989).
5. R. A. Padgett, P. J. Grabowski, M. M. Konarska, S. Seiler and P. A. Sharp, *ARB* **55**, 1119 (1986).
6. T. R. Cech, *Science* **236**, 1532 (1987).

7. C. Gunthrie and B. Patterson, *ARGen* **22**, 387 (1988).
8. A. Bindereif and M. R. Green, in "Genetic Engineering" (J. K. Setlow, ed.), Vol. 12, p. 201. Plenum, New York, 1990.
9. D. W. Copertino and R. B. Hallick, *EMBO J.* **10**, 433 (1991).
10. J. D. Hawkins, *NARes* **16**, 9893 (1988).
11. J. W. S. Brown, *NARes* **14**, 9549 (1986).
12. G. J. Goodall and W. Filipowicz, *Cell* **58**, 473 (1989).
13. G. D. Zieve and R. A. Sauterer, *CRC Crit. Rev. Biochem. Mol. Biol.* **25**, 1 (1990).
14. U. Vijsyraghavan and J. Abelson, *Nucleic Acids Mol. Biol.* **3**, 197 (1989).
15. J. L. Woolford, *Yeast* **5**, 439 (1989).
16. J. A. Steiz, D. L. Black, V. Gerke, K. A. Parker, D. Frendewey and W. Keller, in "Structure and Function of Major and Minor Small Ribonucleoprotein Particles" (M. L. Birnstiel, ed.), p. 71. Springer-Verlag, Berlin, 1987.
17. R. Luhrman, *Mol. Biol. Rep.* **14**, 183 (1990).
18. T. Maniatis and R. Reed, *Nature* **325**, 673 (1987).
19. M. R. Green, *ARGen* **20**, 671 (1986).
20. C. W. J. Smith, J. G. Patton and B. Nadal-Ginard, *ARGen* **23**, 527 (1989).
21. T. Blumenthal and J. Thomas, *TIG* **4**, 305 (1988).
22. M. Hildebrand, R. B. Hallick, C. W. Passavant and D. P. Bourque, *PNAS* **85**, 372 (1988).
23. M.-C. Shih, P. Heinrich and H. Goodman, *Science* **242**, 1164 (1988).
24. M. McKeow, in "Genetic Engineering" (J. K. Setlow, ed.), Vol. 12, p. 139. Plenum, New York, 1990.
25. D. Latchman, *New Biologist* **2**, 297 (1990).
26. V. L. van Santen and A. Spritz, *Gene* **56**, 253 (1987).
27. K. Wiebauer, J. Herrero and W. Filipowicz, *MCBiol* **8**, 2042 (1988).
28. B. Keith and N.-H. Chua, *EMBO J.* **5**, 2419 (1986).
29. B. A. Hanley and M. A. Schuler, *NARes* **16**, 7159 (1988).
30. M. Kudo, Y. Iida and M. Shimbo, *CABIOS* **3**, 319 (1987).
31. M. Jacob and H. Gallinaro, *NARes* **17**, 2159 (1989).
32. D. H. Hammer and P. Leder, *Cell* **18**, 1299 (1979).
33. A. R. Buchman, Ph.D. thesis. Stanford University, Stanford, California, 1986.
34. A. R. Buchman and P. Berg, *MCBiol* **8**, 4395 (1988).
35. P. Gruss, C. J. Lai, R. Dhar and G. Khoury, *PNAS* **76**, 4317 (1979).
36. D. H. Hammer, K. D. Smith, S. H. Boyer and P. Leder, *Cell* **17**, 725 (1979).
37. C.-J. Lai and G. Khoury, *PNAS* **76**, 71 (1979).
38. C. S. Gasser, C. C. Simonsen, J. W. Schilling and R. T. Schimke, *PNAS* **79**, 6522 (1982).
39. R. Treisman, U. Novak, J. Favaloro and R. Kamen, *Nature* **292**, 595 (1981).
40. P. P. Chee, C. Klassy and J. Slighton, *Gene* **41**, 47 (1986).
41. J. Callis, M. Fromm and V. Walbot, *Genes Dev.* **1**, 1183 (1987).
42. E. M. Silva, I. J. Mettler, P. S. Dietrich and R. M. Sinibaldi, *Genome* **30**, 72 (1988).
43. A. C. Semrau, I. J. Mettler, P. S. Dietrich, E. M. Silva and R. M. Sinibaldi, *J. Cell Biol.* **109**, 39 (1989).
44. D. Mascarenhas, I. J. Mettler, D. A. Pierce and H. Lowe, *Plant Mol. Biol.* **15**, 913 (1990).
45. J. H. Oard, D. Paige and J. Dvorak, *Plant Cell Rep.* **8**, 156 (1989).
46. V. Vasil, M. Clancy, R. J. Ferl and L. C. Hannah, *Plant Physiol.* **91**, 1575 (1989).
47. T. Deng, Y. Li and L. F. Johnson, *NARes* **17**, 645 (1989).
48. I. Ottavio, C.-D. Chang, M.-G. Rizzo, S. Travali, C. Casadevall and R. Baserga, *MCBiol* **10**, 303 (1990).
49. A. Tanaka, S. Mita, S. Ohta, J. Kyozuka, K. Shimanoto and K. Nakamura, *NARes* **18**, 6767 (1990).

50. C. Maas, J. Laufs, S. Grant, C. Korfhage and W. Werr, *Plant Mol. Biol.* **16**, 199 (1991).
51. K. Luehrsen and V. Walbot, *MGG* **225**, 81 (1991).
52. R. A. Jefferson, *Plant Mol. Biol. Rep.* **5**, 387 (1987).
53. P. Chomczynski and N. Sacchi, *Anal. Biochem.* **162**, 156 (1987).
54. H. J. Yost and S. Lindquist, *Cell* **45**, 185 (1986).
55. H. J. Yost and S. Lindquist, *Science* **242**, 1544 (1988).
56. H. J. Yost and S. Lindquist, *MCBiol* **11**, 1062 (1991).
57. U. Bond, *EMBO J.* **7**, 3509 (1988).
58. A. L. Beyer and Y. N. Osheim, *Genes Dev.* **2**, 754 (1988).
59. R. R. Shukula, Z. Dominski, T. Zwierzynski and R. Kole, *JBC* **265**, 20377 (1990).
60. P. S. Dietrich and R. M. Sinibaldi, *J. Cell Biol.* **99**, 451 (1984).
61. X.-D. Fu and T. Maniatis, *Nature* **343**, 437 (1990).
62. P. Legrain and M. Roshbash, *Cell* **57**, 573 (1989).
63. P. S. Dietrich, R. A. Bouchard, E. S. Casey and R. M. Sinibaldi, *Plant Physiol.* **96**, 1268 (1991).
64. S. M. Mount, *NARes* **10**, 459 (1982).
65. E. B. Keller and W. A. Noon, *PNAS* **81**, 7417 (1984).

De Novo Purine Nucleotide Biosynthesis

HOWARD ZALKIN
AND JACK E. DIXON[1]

Department of Biochemistry
Purdue University
West Lafayette, Indiana 47907

Most organisms, with the exception of parasitic protozoa (*1*), have the capacity for *de novo* synthesis of purine nucleotides. The *de novo* synthesis of AMP and GMP proceeds by a 14-step branched pathway via IMP (see Fig. 1). A "salvage" reaction with PRPP to reutilize purine bases provides an alternative route for synthesis of AMP, IMP, and GMP. Although the *de novo* pathway is invariant, the genetic organization and regulation of expression differ among organisms. Genes for *de novo* purine nucleotide synthesis have been cloned and characterized from bacteria, lower eukaryotes, and invertebrates. Regulatory circuits have been worked out for the pathway

---

[1] Present affiliation: Department of Biological Chemistry, University of Michigan Medical School, Ann Arbor, Michigan 48109.

Progress in Nucleic Acid Research
and Molecular Biology, Vol. 42

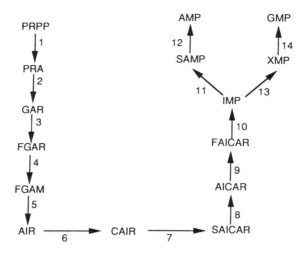

Abbreviations of Substrates

PRPP, 5-phosphoribosyl 1-pyrophosphate

PRA, 5'-phosphoribosylamine

GAR, 5'-phosphoribosylglycinamide

FGAR, 5'-phosphoribosyl N-formyglycinamide

FGAM, 5'-phosphoribosyl N-formyglycinamidine

AIR, 5'-phosphoribosylaminoimidazole

CAIR, 5'-phosphoribosyl-5-aminoimidazole carboxylate

SAICAR, 5'-phosphoribosyl 4-(N-succinocarboxamide)-5-aminoimidazole

AICAR, 5'-phosphoribosyl 4-carboxamide-5-aminoimidazole

FAICAR, 5'-phosphoribosyl 4-carboxamide-5-formamidoimidazole

IMP, inosine monophosphate

SAMP, adenylosuccinate

XMP, xanthosine monophosphate

(cont.)

	Enxymes	*E. coli* genes	Map Position
1.	glutamine PRPP-amidotransferase (EC 2.4.2.14)	*purF*	50.0
2.	GAR synthetase (EC 6.3.4.13)	*purD*	90.3
3.	GAR transformylase (EC 2.1.2.2)	*purN*	53.5
4.	FGAM synthetase (EC 6.3.5.3)	*purL*	55.2
5.	AIR synthetase (EC 6.3.3.1)	*purM*	53.5
6.	AIR carboxylase (EC 4.1.1.21)	*purEK*	12.2
7.	SAICAR synthetase (EC 6.3.2.6)	*purC*	53.3
8.	adenylosuccinate lyase (EC 4.3.2.2)	*purB*	25.2
9.	AICAR transformylase (EC 6.3.2.6)	*purH*	90.3
10.	IMP cyclohydrolase (EC 3.5.4.10)	*purH*	90.3
11.	adenylosuccinate synthetase (EC 6.3.4.4.)	*purA*	95.0
12.	adenylosuccinate lyase (EC 4.3.2.2)	*purB*	25.2
13.	IMP dehydrogenase (EC 1.1.1.205)	*guaB*	54.0
14.	GMP synthetase (EC 6.3.4.1)	*guaA*	54.0

FIG. 1. Outline of the pathway for *de novo* purine nucleotide synthesis. Commonly used abbreviations are defined, enzymes are named, and *E. coli* gene designations and map positions (in minutes) are given. Map positions are taken from 2 and 3.

in bacteria. More recently, cDNA clones have been isolated from vertebrates and gene cloning is in progress.

This article focuses on recent developments that have contributed to our current understanding of gene organization, gene regulation, and gene–enzyme relationships for purine nucleotide biosynthesis from selected organisms. It is not intended to be comprehensive, but rather to focus on developments that have guided our work.

I. *De Novo* Purine Nucleotide Biosynthesis in Prokaryotes

A. Gene Organization and Regulation in *Escherichia coli*

In *E. coli*, genes encoding enzymes for *de novo* purine nucleotide synthesis are scattered throughout the chromosome as monocistronic and small polycistronic operons (2, 3). The outline of the 14-step pathway in Fig. 1 gives *E. coli* gene designations, summarizes map positions, and gives gene–enzyme relationships. The map positions in Fig. 1 indicate that the 14 genes are organized into nine operons. Seven operons are required for synthesis of IMP (1, 2): *cvp purF dedF; purL; purMN; purEK; purHD; purC;* and *purB*. A *guaBA* operon is involved in converting IMP to GMP, and *purA* and *purB* are involved in the synthesis of AMP from IMP. The *purF* operon contains a gene, *cvp*, for colicin V production (4) and an uncharacterized gene, *dedF* (4a). All genes listed in Fig. 1, except *purA*, are coregulated by a *purR* regulatory gene and respond to the levels of purine bases. These and several other coregulated genes constitute a *pur* regulon. Gene *purA*, however, appears to be under separate regulation (5).

Gene cloning was instrumental in working out the regulatory mechanism. The first bacterial gene for *de novo* purine nucleotide synthesis to be cloned was *E. coli purF* (6). Deletion analysis of cloned *purF*, transcript mapping, and *in vitro* transcription (7), combined with sequence analysis of the coregulated *purM* control region (8), provided an initial description of a promoter and *cis*-acting control site for purine nucleotide biosynthesis. More recently, genes for the remaining steps of the pathway have been isolated from *E. coli* (9–20a). In addition, a second gene encoding GAR transformylase (step 3) has been cloned (J. M. Smith, unpublished).

The principal features that characterize the promoter and *cis*-acting control sites of the *E. coli pur* genes are summarized here. (i) The *pur* regulon genes contain a −10 promoter element having a good match to the TATAAT consensus (21) sequence. (ii) In these same genes, there are relatively poor matches to the consensus −35 promoter element. (iii) Coregulated genes *purF, purL, purMN, purEK, purHD, purC,* and *purB* contain a conserved 16-bp palindromic control site, designated the *pur* operator (20a, 22, 23). (iv) This operator site, to which the *purR*-encoded repressor binds, has a consensus sequence aCGCAAAC·GTTTtCNT.[2] With the exception of *purB* 'and *purR*, this control site is situated in the promoter region between positions

---

[2] Upper-case letters indicate highly conserved positions, lower-case letters indicate less conserved positions, and n represents any nucleotide. The center of symmetry is marked by a dot.

−46 and 10 relative to the start of transcription. As noted below, there are two operators in *purR*, one downstream from the promoter in the 5′ mRNA untranslated region, and one in the protein-coding sequence. In *purB*, there is a single *pur* operator in the protein-coding region. Mutations in either a *pur* operator or *purR* result in high-level constitutive expression, indicative of a single repressor–operator control mechanism to sense purine availability.

Regulatory mutations designated *purR* were described many years ago (*24, 25*). However, in all of these instances, the term *purR* was used to designate a regulatory phenotype, since the mutations were not characterized genetically. The genetic characterization of the PurR phenotype was limited by the high spontaneous mutation rate in the strains used. More recently, stable mutants were isolated and *purR* was cloned and mapped (*26, 27*) to coordinate kilobase-pair 17,755 on the *E. coli* restriction map (*28*), corresponding to minute 36 on the chromosome. Nucleotide sequence analysis indicates that *purR* encodes a 341-amino-acid protein (*26*) belonging to a class of regulatory proteins that bind to DNA with a helix–turn–helix motif (*29*). Pur repressor is homologous to the Rbs (C. A. Mauzy and M. A. Hermodson, unpublished), Lac (*30*), Gal (*31*), Cyt (*32*), Mal (*33*), Raf (*34*), and Fru (*35*) repressors. The *pur* repressor binds to the conserved 16-bp operator site in each of the *pur* regulon genes (*22*). As expected for homologous regulatory proteins, operator sites are also conserved in several positions (see *20a, 26*).

Gene *purR* is transcriptionally autoregulated (*23, 26*). Transcriptional regulation of *purR* is dependent on two operator sites, designated $purRO_1$ and $purRO_2$. These sites do not overlap the promoter. Operator O_1 is located in the region of DNA between the transcription start site and the site for translation initiation, and O_2 is in the protein-coding region. PurR binds noncooperatively to O_1 with a six-fold higher affinity than to O_2 (*36*). However, both O_1 and O_2 are required for the two- to three-fold *in vivo* autoregulation. Of all the genes thus far known to be regulated by the Pur repressor, only *purR* employs a two-operator mechanism.

Gene *purR* regulates the expression of several additional genes. These include *pyrC* (*37–39*) and *pyrD* (*38*), involved in pyrimidine biosynthesis, *codA* (*17*), required for pyrimidine salvage, as well as *glyA* (*40*), which encodes serine hydroxymethyltransferase and provides a one-carbon unit for purine biosynthesis. These circuits of cross-pathway regulation, outlined in Fig. 2, presumably function to integrate pathways for the biosynthesis and catabolism of purine and pyrimidine nucleotides.

Hypoxanthine and guanine have a particularly important role in the regulatory circuit shown in Fig. 2. A role for these two purines was initially recognized for repression of *pur* gene expression in *Salmonella typhimurium*

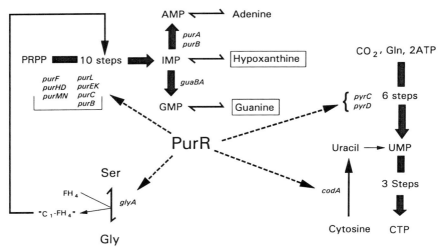

FIG. 2. Outline of the regulatory circuit in *E. coli* controlled by the purine repressor (PurR). PurR controls genes for *de novo* purine and pyrimidine nucleotide synthesis, synthesis of a one-carbon unit ("C_1–FH_4") and degradation of cytosine. The product C_1–FH_4 is 5,10-methylenetetrahydrofolate, which is subsequently converted to 10-formyltetrahydrofolate. Guanine and hypoxanthine are boxed to emphasize that they are the signal molecules that interact with PurR to form the active holorepressor.

(41). Their function as corepressors was recently confirmed by direct binding measurements to purified repressor (42). Binding of purified repressor to *pur* operator DNA depends on the presence of one of them; purine nucleotides are ineffective. Dissociation constants of 7.1 and 1.7 μM for hypoxanthine and guanine, respectively, have been reported (42) for interaction with purified repressor. More recent experiments using equilibrium dialysis indicate complex cooperative binding of them to the dimeric repressor (K. Y. Choi and H. Zalkin, unpublished). Hypoxanthine and guanine thus function to reflect the availability of purine nucleotides for biosynthesis in *E. coli* and *S. typhimurium*. (42, 43).

B. Gene Organization in *Bacillus subtilis*

There is a completely different picture for the organization and regulation of genes required for purine nucleotide synthesis in *B. subtilis*. Earlier studies had indicated that levels of enzymes involved in the synthesis of IMP in *B. subtilis* are repressed by addition of purine bases or nucleosides to the medium (44, 45). Gene cloning has provided an outline of *de novo* purine nucleotide synthesis in this organism. There is a 12-gene *pur* operon at 55° on the genetic map that encodes all of the enzymes for *de novo* synthesis of IMP. Expression of the operon is regulated independently by adenine and

guanine compounds. For convenience, the regulatory molecules are referred to as purines. However, the coregulators may be purines, purine
nucleosides, nucleotides, or metabolites of these molecules.

B. subtilis purF was initially cloned by functional complementation in E.
coli (46). Approximately 14 kb of 5' and 3' DNA flanking purF was subsequently cloned and sequenced (47). Contiguous genes flanking purF were
identified by complementation of E. coli pur mutants, and by sequence
comparisons to homologous genes from other bacteria, yeast, and Drosophila. By this analysis, an operon of 12 genes that spans 13,080 bp at
position 55° on the B. subtilis chromosome was identified. The pur operon
encodes all of the enzymes required for the *de novo* synthesis of IMP. The
pur operon gene order is purEKBC(orf)QLFMNHD. Transcription of the
operon is initiated from a σ43-dependent promoter 242 nucleotides upstream from purE, and is terminated approximately 38 nucleotides downstream from purD. Gene–enzyme relationships are similar to those given in
Fig. 1 for E. coli, with one exception. E. coli purL corresponds to a purL–
purQ fusion (Fig. 3). B. subtilis purL is related to codons 161–996 of the E.
coli gene. B. subtilis purQ is homologous with codons 1041–1295 of E. coli
purL. Gene purQ encodes the 227-amino-acid glutamine amide transfer
domain of FGAM synthetase. Several of the pur operon gene–enzyme assignments have been confirmed (48).

The B. subtilis pur operon is organized into three sets of overlapping
genes separated by intercistronic gaps: purEKB–(73 bp)–purC(orf)QLF–

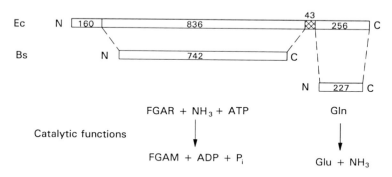

FIG. 3. Schematic representation of FGAM synthetase from *E. coli* and *B. subtilis*. The
figure is derived from alignments of the *purL*-encoded enzyme from *E. coli* (9, 10), with the
corresponding subunits encoded by *B. subtilis purL* and *purQ* (47). The number of amino acids
in each domain or subunit is indicated. The deduced structure–function relationship, NH_3-
dependent FGAM synthesis, and glutamine amide transfer/hydrolysis are shown below. The
active-site cysteine required for glutamine amide transfer is conserved at position 86 in *B.
subtilis* PurQ and position 1135 in *E. coli* PurL.

(101 bp)–*purMNH*–(15 bp)–*purD*. Overlaps of the 3′ end of one coding sequence with the 5′ end of the contiguous downstream coding sequence are as follows: *purE–purK*, 8 bp; *purK–purB*, 4 bp; *purC–orf*, 8 bp; *orf–purQ*, 4 bp; *purQ–purL*, 17 bp; *purL–purF*, 25 bp; *purM–purN*, 4 bp; and *purN–purH*, 4 bp. This pattern of gene overlaps is similar to that for the *B. subtilis trp*, *trpEDC*–(4 bp)–*trpFBA* (49) and *pyr*, pyr(orf1)–(145 bp)–*pyrBC(AA)* *(AB)(orf)DFE* (50) operons. Clusters of presumably contiguous genes are also found in bacilli for biosynthesis of arginine (51), cobalamin (52), isoleucine, valine, leucine (53), and menaquinone (54). It appears that biosynthetic pathways in bacilli utilize clustered overlapping genes to a greater extent than do those in Gram-negative enteric bacteria.

Gene overlaps are thought to be diagnostic for translational coupling (55). Translational coupling provides one mechanism for 1:1 stoichiometric synthesis of proteins. The *pur* operon gene overlaps provide the potential for 1:1 enzyme stoichiometry from each set of overlapping genes.

C. Dual Regulation of Transcription in *B. subtilis*

Nuclease-S1 mapping of the 5′ end of *pur* operon mRNA provided the initial evidence for dual regulation of this operon (47). Transcription initiation is repressed by addition of adenosine to the growth medium. Transcription is independently regulated by a termination–antitermination mechanism in the 242-nucleotide untranslated mRNA region preceding *purE*. Addition of guanosine to the growth medium promotes transcription termination at nucleotide ~200 in the leader mRNA immediately following a ρ-independent transcription-termination secondary structure.

Mutually exclusive formation of antiterminator ($\Delta G = -38$ kcal/mol) and terminator ($\Delta G = -32$ kcal/mol) secondary structures in the 242-nucleotide untranslated leader mRNA were proposed to regulate transcription. The working hypothesis for antitermination is based on the antitermination model for regulation of the *B. subtilis trp* operon (56), in which a *trans*-acting regulatory protein, the *mtr* gene product (57), binds to untranslated leader mRNA and promotes formation of an RNA secondary structure required for transcription termination. By analogy, a guanine-activated regulatory protein is visualized to bind to an mRNA site to inhibit formation of the antiterminator secondary structure, thus allowing the terminator to form (Fig. 4). When the guanine pool is insufficient to activate the regulatory protein, binding to mRNA does not occur. In this case, the antiterminator secondary structure forms and prevents formation of the transcription terminator. Evidence for a formally similar antitermination mechanism has been reported for other *E. coli* (58) and *B. subtilis* (59) genes.

Two lines of evidence support a model for regulation of transcription initiation in response to the pool of adenine (60). (i) A series of deletions

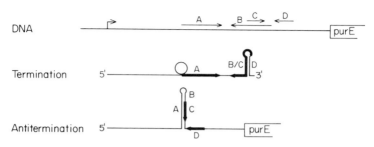

FIG. 4. Schematic representation of the termination–antitermination model for regulation of the *B. subtilis pur* operon. The first line shows the region of DNA between the promoter (⌐→) and the first structural gene. Dyad symmetries are indicated by arrows and letters. The second line shows the prematurely terminated mRNA. Hairpin C:D, followed by several uridylate residues, is the terminator. A hypothetical guanine-activated regulatory protein, shown as a circle, binds and obstructs segment A. The third line shows the antitermination secondary structure that leads to transcription of coding-length mRNA. (From 55 with permission.)

upstream from the promoter interfered with repression by adenine, but had little or no effect on expression or on guanine-dependent termination control. (ii) A protein having the capacity to bind to the *cis*-acting control region identified by deletion analysis was partially purified. The boundaries of the control region were mapped by gel mobility shift and DNase-I footprinting to positions −145 to −29 relative to the start of transcription at position 1. Based on the pattern of alternating protected and hypersensitive DNase-I sites, as well as an (A+T) sequence periodicity, a nucleosome-like interaction was proposed. According to this proposal, an extended control region between nucleotides −145 and −56 wraps around the protein. This interaction then extends to position −29, as shown by the DNase-I footprint, and blocks access of RNA polymerase to the −35 promoter sequence, resulting in repression of transcription initiation.

D. Enzyme Differences in *E. coli* and *B. subtilis*

Two enzymes in the pathway for *de novo* purine nucleotide synthesis differ significantly in *E. coli* and *B. subtilis*.

1. GLUTAMINE PRPP AMIDOTRANSFERASE

Catalytic properties and feedback inhibition by purine nucleotides are similar for the enzymes from *E. coli* and *B. subtilis* (61), reflecting the 41% identity in amino-acid sequence (46). However, the amidotransferase from *B. subtilis* has two unique structural components. The *B. subtilis* enzyme is synthesized with an 11-amino-acid NH_2-terminal pro-peptide that must be cleaved to expose an NH_2-terminal active-site cysteine residue. To understand the role of Cys[1] in the mature enzyme, it is helpful to describe the overall amidotransferase reaction in terms of two partial reactions [Eqs. (1) and (2)].

$$\text{Glutamine} + H_2O \rightarrow \text{glutamate} + NH_3 \qquad (1)$$
$$\text{PRPP} + NH_3 \rightarrow \text{PRA} + PP_i \qquad (2)$$
$$\text{Glutamine} + \text{PRPP} + H_2O \rightarrow \text{PRA} + \text{Glutamate} + PP_i \qquad (3)$$

Reaction (1) reflects a glutaminase activity; reaction (2), an NH_3-dependent synthesis of PRA; and reaction (3), the sum of these two reactions, the glutamine-dependent synthesis of PRA. For the normal glutamine-dependent reaction, the amide of glutamine is either transferred directly to PRPP or is sequestered as enzyme-bound NH_3 prior to reaction with PRPP. Cysteine-1 in the mature enzyme forms a covalent glutaminyl intermediate, which is required for the initial step of glutamine hydrolysis and/or amide transfer (62–65). Mutations that prevent pro-peptide cleavage abolish glutamine-dependent activity (66), leading to the conclusion that the NH_2-terminal position of the active-site cysteine residue is obligatory for glutamine amide transfer. In the E. coli enzyme, Met^{-1} is cleaved by methionine aminopeptidase to expose Cys[1].

Whereas the role of the 11-amino-acid pro-peptide is not understood, it is not peculiar to the B. subtilis enzyme. Recent cloning and analysis of avian and human glutamine PRPP amidotransferase cDNA (Section II,C) indicate conservation of an 11-amino-acid pro-peptide sequence. In addition, E. coli glutamate synthase, an Fe–S-containing glutamine amidotransferase, contains a comparable pro-peptide sequence (67, 68).

The second unique structural feature in the B. subtilis amidotransferase is a [4Fe–4S] cluster (69). This structural element does not appear to have a direct role in catalysis. Present evidence supports a role of the [4Fe–4S] cluster in a mechanism to shut down purine biosynthesis prior to sporulation (70). The [4Fe–4S] cluster serves as a site for oxidative inactivation of the amidotransferase, the rate-limiting step in enzyme degradation in nutrient-starved cells. The E. coli amidotransferase is not subject to oxidative inactivation and does not contain a [4Fe–4S] cluster.

Three observations forge a connection between the [4Fe–4S] cluster and pro-peptide processing. (i) Mutations that prevent assembly of a [4Fe–4S] cluster abolish pro-peptide processing (70, 71). (ii) E. coli glutamate synthase contains a pro-peptide sequence and [4Fe–4S] clusters (68, 72). (iii) Avian and human glutamine PRPP amidotransferases contain an uncharacterized Fe component (73, 74) and also have the conserved 11-amino-acid pro-peptide (Section II,C, and Fig. 5).

It is important to ask what possible rationale could explain a requirement for an Fe–S cluster in pro-peptide processing? An obvious explanation is not

```
                  -11              1                35    112
  Chicken        MELEELGIREECG----LQHRGQE---AHNG-
  B. subtilis    MLAEIKGLNEECG----LQHRGQE---AHNG-
  E. coli              MCG----LQHRGQD---AHNG-

                  427     479
  Chicken        PCY---IGHCTACLTG-- 8-CO₂H
  B. subtilis    PCF---CGQCLACFTG--22-CO₂H
  E. coli        PNV---QQFECSVFNG--41-CO₂H
```

FIG. 5. Alignment of glutamine PRPP amidotransferase segments. The alignment shows the conserved pro-peptide sequence (-11 to -1), active-site positions 1, 35, and 112 [positions numbered for chicken sequence (97)] and the regions containing the four cysteinyl ligands to the [4Fe–4S] cluster in the *B. subtilis* enzyme (46).

apparent. However, one possibility is that availability of Fe is a signal to indicate whether aerobic metabolism can occur. A functional Krebs cycle is dependent on aconitase, an Fe–S protein. A functional electron transport chain is dependent on cytochromes and succinate dehydrogenase, which contain heme Fe and Fe–S clusters, respectively. Glutamine PRPP amidotransferase is an early control point for synthesis of nucleotides, RNA, and DNA, and could provide an early switch to turn down biosynthesis when there is insufficient Fe for aerobic metabolism. Neither *E. coli* nor yeast, which can grow anaerobically, has an Fe–S-containing glutamine PRPP amidotransferase.

2. FGAM Synthetase

As noted in Section I,B, *E. coli purL* conforms to a fusion of genes *purL* and *purQ* from *B. subtilis*. The *E. coli purL*-encoded FGAM synthetase is a glutamine amidotransferase. Although FGAM synthetase and glutamine PRPP amidotransferase are members of different subfamilies, distinguished by the location of the active-site cysteine required for glutamine amide transfer, these enzymes have comparable structural domains that catalyze glutaminase, NH_3-dependent, and glutamine-dependent reactions [Eqs. (1)–(3), in Section I,D,1]. A schematic representation of the homologous domains is shown in Fig. 3. This relationship of separated versus fused domains for a glutamine amidotransferase is also found in carbamoyl-phosphate synthetase (EC 6.3.5.5) (75) and anthranilate synthase (EC 4.1.3.27) (76, 77). The functional significance, if any, is not known.

II. *De Novo* Purine Nucleotide Synthesis in Vertebrates

In this section, we summarize human chromosome localization for genes of *de novo* purine nucleotide synthesis and describe strategies for cDNA cloning. This is followed by information obtained from recently isolated cDNAs. Microbial sequences have been invaluable for the identification of functional domains. cDNA sequences have contributed insights into the organization of functional domains in the enzymes for purine nucleotide synthesis from higher eukaryotes. The emerging pattern is that, compared to prokaryotes, higher eukaryotic organisms place increased reliance on multifunctional enzymes in this pathway. We also draw attention to inferences provided by structural information and unsolved questions of enzyme and overall pathway regulation. Finally, relationships with genetic and neoplastic diseases are noted.

A. Chromosomal Localization

CHO-cell mutants deficient in each of the steps to AMP have been isolated (78) and human chromosome localizations have been derived from cytogenetic analysis of CHO/human hybrids (79). The CHO mutant cell lines, gene designations, and human chromosome assignments are summarized in Table I. Gene designations are based on abbreviations of common

TABLE I
CHO MUTANTS, GENE DESIGNATIONS, AND HUMAN CHROMOSOME ASSIGNMENTS

Step	Enzyme[a]	CHO mutant[b]	Gene[c]	Human chromosome[b]
1	Glutamine PRPP amidotransferase	Ade⁻A	GPAT	4
2	GAR synthetase	Ade⁻C[d]	GART	21
3	GAR transformylase	Ade⁻P_{CG}	GART	21
4	FGAM synthetase	Ade⁻B	FGAMS	14
5	AIR synthetase	Ade⁻G	GART	21
6	AIR carboxylase	Ade⁻D	AIRC	4
7	SAICAR synthetase	Ade⁻D	AIRC	4
8	Adenylosuccinate lyase	Ade⁻I	ASL	22
9	AICAR transformylase	Ade⁻F	IMPS	2
10	IMP cyclohydrolase	Ade⁻F	IMPS	2
11	Adenylosuccinate synthetase	Ade⁻H	ADSS	1
12	Adenylosuccinate lyase	Ade⁻I	ASL	22

[a]Abbreviations are defined in Fig. 1. Connections indicate covalent attachment in multifunctional enzymes or, in the case of adenylosuccinate lyase, a single activity for two steps.

[b]CHO mutants and human gene assignments are summarized in 78 and 79.

[c]A system for gene designation based on enzyme nomenclature was suggested by David Patterson. GART is chosen to designate the gene for steps 2, 3, and 5 because of previous use in Drosophila (80). Patterson has used the designation PRAT (phosphoribosylamidotransferase) instead of GPAT (glutamine PRPP amidotransferase). IMP cyclohydrolase (EC 3.5.4.10) is also known as IMP synthetase (IMPS).

[d]Mutations in the GART locus encoding trifunctional GAR synthetase/AIR synthetase/GAR transformylase give rise to different complex phenotypes, presumably depending on the site of mutation. Some ADE⁻G mutants are deficient not only in AIR synthetase, but also in GAR transformylase. ADE⁻P_{CG} lines are deficient in GAR synthetase and GAR transformylase.

enzyme names. With one exception, genes for *de novo* purine nucleotide synthesis are on different chromosomes. Only genes *GPAT* and *AIRC*, corresponding to Ade⁻A (step 1) and ADE⁻D (steps 6 and 7), respectively, have been located in an overlapping region of chromosome 4. Furthermore, precise mapping is required to examine the possibility of physical linkage. However, physical linkage is not required for coregulation. For example, a CHO mutant designated Ade⁻P_{AB} exhibited defective expression of *GPAT* (Ade⁻A) and *FGAMS* (Ade⁻B), which are likely on different chromosomes *(81)*. At present, mechanisms for coordinating expression of genes for *de novo* purine nucleotide synthesis remain to be described. Mechanisms should exist for ensuring developmental, tissue-specific, and cell-cycle coexpression.

B. Cloning Strategies

Cloning of genes for *de novo* purine nucleotide synthesis from vertebrates has been limited by the availability of purified enzymes for antibody preparation or for design of oligonucleotide probes using amino-acid sequence information. Prior to 1990, only the hamster and human IMP dehydrogenase cDNA (step 13, Fig. 1) had been cloned *(82)*. The cloning steps in this case were gene amplification in CHO cells to facilitate enzyme purification, preparation of polyclonal antibodies, and isolation of a partial cDNA by immunoscreening of a mouse λgt11 expression library, followed by isolation of full-length CHO and human cDNA clones by hybridization screening with the mouse cDNA probe *(82, 83)*. Clones for all steps except 4 and 13 (Fig. 1) have recently been isolated by more generally applicable and convenient methods. cDNA clones for steps 2, 3, 5–10, and 12 were isolated from an avian library by functional complementation of *E. coli pur* mutants *(84–87)*, step 13 from mouse by complementation in *E. coli (88)*, and steps 2, 3, and 5–7 by complementation of yeast purine mutants using an expression library prepared from human HepG2 RNA *(89, 90)*.

We chose initial cloning from an avian liver cDNA library because of increased enzyme activity and mRNA levels in birds relative to rat liver and human cells. Increased abundance in birds results from use of the *de novo* purine nucleotide pathway for synthesis and excretion of uric acid to dispose of excess nitrogen. A λ cDNA expression library was converted into a phagemid library by *in vivo* excision *(91)* and was used to transform *E. coli* purine auxotrophs. In this "Bluescript" phagemid vector, cDNA inserts are transcribed from the *lac* promoter. Heterologous expression is often limited by the capacity for protein synthesis. With this type of vector, translation is by one of two mechanisms: utilization of the *lacZ* translation initiation site to give in-frame fusion proteins or, alternatively, fortuitous internal reinitiation to give amino-terminally truncated enzymes. The probability for synthesis of a functional enzyme by internal translation reinitiation is enhanced, but is not restricted to multifunctional proteins. In our work, clones encoding all three multifunctional enzymes of the pathway were obtained by complementation, whereas DNA for only one of the five monofunctional enzymes was obtained by this procedure.

We have used polymerase-chain-reaction (PCR) cloning to isolate cDNA for steps not obtained by complementation. cDNA for steps 1 and 11 was cloned by PCR amplification of avian and human cDNA derived from poly(A)$^+$ RNA. Degenerate primers derived from conserved regions of homologous genes can provide a cDNA fragment for subsequent use as a hybridization probe. In two cases to be described, full-length coding cDNA subsequently isolated from the avian library was not functional in *E. coli*.

Avian cDNA clones have been useful in isolating the corresponding human cDNAs. We describe below (Section II,C–I) new information on *de novo* purine nucleotide synthesis obtained from the initial avian and human clones.

C. Step 1: Glutamine PRPP Amidotransferase

Glutamine PRPP amidotransferase (EC 2.4.2.14) catalyzes the first committed step in the *de novo* pathway: glutamine + PRPP → phosphoribosylamine → glutamate + PP$_i$. Similar to other glutamine amidotransferases, NH$_3$ can replace glutamine *in vitro* and *in vivo* (65). Structure–function analysis of the *E. coli* enzyme indicates two functional domains. Amino-acid residues 1 to ~200 function as a glutamine–amide transfer domain to bind glutamine and provide the amide as a source of endogenous NH$_3$ (92, 93). Amino-acid residues from ~200 to the carboxyl terminus encode a domain for the NH$_3$-dependent synthesis of phosphoribosylamine. The microbial (61) and mammalian (94) enzymes are subject to allosteric feedback regulation by adenine and guanine nucleotides, whereas feedback regulation of the avian enzyme is uncertain (95). Mechanisms for the regulation of *de novo* purine nucleotide synthesis in vertebrates are not understood, but feedback control of the amidotransferase is assumed (96).

A cDNA encoding glutamine PRPP amidotransferase was not obtained by functional complementation of an *E. coli purF* mutant with an avian liver library. Because of the expected importance of this amidotransferase in regulating *de novo* purine nucleotide synthesis in animals, a cloning approach based on PCR was used to isolate an avian cDNA (97). An intact coding sequence of 510 amino acids ($M_r = 56,309$) was derived from the longest (2971-bp) cDNA clone. The following structural information was obtained from the sequence analysis. (i) The amino-acid sequence of the avian enzyme is 40% and 31% identical to amidotransferase sequences from *B. subtilis* and

E. coli, respectively, indicative of homology. (ii) Two structural features initially found in the *B. subtilis* enzyme were identified in the avian amidotransferase sequence. First, the chicken enzyme contains an 11-amino-acid pro-peptide, numbered from -11 to -1 in Fig. 5. The mature avian enzyme starts at Cys^1, similar to the microbial enzymes. Second, three of the four cysteine residues that serve as ligands to the [4Fe–4S] cluster in the *B. subtilis* enzyme are conserved (Fig. 5). Recent experiments (summarized below) confirm that the avian amidotransferase is synthesized as a 510-amino-acid residue pro-enzyme that undergoes amino-terminal pro-peptide cleavage to generate a mature enzyme with an NH_2-terminal cysteine residue at position 1 (G. Zhou, H. Zalkin and J. E. Dixon, unpublished). The three conserved cysteine residues at positions 427, 482, and 485 are candidate ligands to an Fe component (73) of undetermined structure. (iii) Active-site residues Cys^1, an acidic residue at position 36, and His^{112} are conserved (Fig. 5).

Initial objectives were to determine the role of the amidotransferase pro-peptide, to identify the Fe component, and to specify its role. The results to date are summarized here. Analyses of function in animal and bacterial cells provide direct evidence for pro-peptide cleavage and indirect evidence for an Fe component. The avian amidotransferase cDNA is functional in CHO and HeLa cells, but not in *E. coli* (97). Western blot analysis with antibody to the pro-peptide demonstrates cleavage in HeLa cells, but not in *E. coli*. An engineered deletion of the pro-peptide restores limited function of the avian enzyme in *E. coli*. These results confirm that pro-peptide processing is essential for enzyme activity and demonstrate that the chicken amidotransferase pro-peptide is processed in animal cells, but not in *E. coli*. The summarized observations are compatible with the hypothesis that the avian amidotransferase Fe component is necessary for pro-peptide processing, and is not correctly assembled into the chicken enzyme in *E. coli*. Low activity of the chicken enzyme with an engineered pro-peptide deletion in *E. coli* may be a consequence of defective incorporation of the Fe component.

Recent analysis of a cloned human amidotransferase cDNA indicates conservation of the pro-peptide sequence and cysteine residues implicated with assembly of the Fe component (Z. Chen, G. Zhou, A. Gavalas, J. E. Dixon and H. Zalkin, unpublished). The efforts to characterize the pro-peptide and Fe component are founded on the premise that these conserved structural elements are essential for enzyme function and are possibly involved in regulation of the *de novo* pathway.

Another human glutamine PRPP amidotransferase has been isolated by functional complementation of a yeast amidotransferase-deficient mutant (97a). This cDNA restored enzyme activity and capacity for *de novo* purine nucleotide synthesis to CHO Ade⁻A cells, thus providing strong evidence for its capacity to encode the amidotransferase. Based on the reported content of $BglI$ and $SalI$ restriction sites, this cDNA would appear to be different from that obtained by Chen et $al.$ (unpublished).

D. Steps 2, 3, and 5: Trifunctional GAR Synthetase/GAR Transformylase/AIR Synthetase

An avian cDNA encoding GAR synthetase (step 2, Fig. 1), GAR transformylase (step 3), and AIR synthetase (step 5) was assembled from partial clones initially isolated by complementation of an $E.$ $coli$ AIR synthetase mutant (84). Nucleotide sequence and Northern blot analysis identified a 1003-amino-acid trifunctional enzyme product of a 4.0-kb poly(A)⁺ mRNA. Alignments with previously isolated monofunctional bacterial genes established the structure–function relationship, (NH₂)GAR synthetase/AIR synthetase/GAR transformylase(CO₂H) shown in Fig. 6. A second monofunctional GAR synthetase coding sequence of 433 amino acids was identified as the product of a 2.5-kb poly(A)⁺ mRNA. The nucleotide sequence of the monofunctional GAR synthetase coding region is identical to that in the trifunctional enzyme, but it is followed by a unique 3′ untranslated region and poly(A)⁺ tail. This situation is reminiscent of the $Drosophila$ $GART$

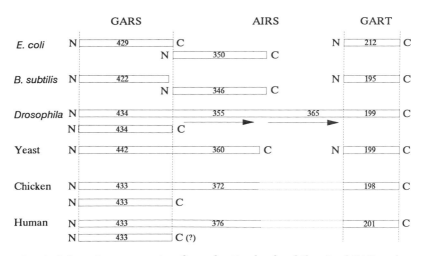

FIG. 6. Schematic representation of monofunctional and multifunctional GAR synthetase, AIR synthetase, and GAR transformylase. The number of amino-acid residues in each coding unit is derived from sequence alignments with the monofunctional bacterial enzymes. Arrows represent a gene duplication. The monofunctional human GAR synthetase was not isolated, but is inferred from mRNA. (Adapted from 99 with permission.)

locus (*80*). *Drosophila GART* encodes a trifunctional GAR synthetase/AIR synthetase/GAR transformylase and a monofunctional GAR synthetase. The monofunctional GAR synthetase likely results from alternative mRNA processing in an intron situated at the GAR synthetase/AIR synthetase boundary (*98*).

A corresponding human cDNA encoding the trifunctional enzyme was subsequently isolated from a HepG2 library by hybridization screening with avian DNA probes (*84*). The human and chicken coding sequences exhibit 76% identity at the amino-acid level. Poly(A)$^+$ RNAs of 3.7 and 1.9 kb from HepG2 cells correspond to the 4.0- and 2.5-kb mRNAs from chicken liver encoding trifunctional and monofunctional enzymes, respectively. However, the inferred 1.9-kb monofunctional GAR synthetase cDNA remains to be isolated. A human trifunctional GAR synthetase/AIR synthetase/GAR transformylase cDNA was also cloned by functional complementation of yeast mutants defective in each of the genes (*89*). This cDNA is functional in CHO cells (*89a*). The human *GART* gene has been isolated from a yeast artificial chromosome library and has been shown to span ~40 kb (*89b*). The cloned gene complemented the purine requirement of CHO cells lacking GAR synthetase and AIR synthetase.

It is appropriate to discuss here three issues regarding the trifunctional GAR synthetase/AIR synthetase/GAR transformylase. First, sequence identities between monofunctional and multifunctional genes provide evidence for homology; that is, the multifunctional genes have likely evolved by fusions of monofunctional ancestral genes. A single-nucleotide insertion in overlapping translation termination and initiation sequences of contiguous *E. coli* (*8*) and *B. subtilis* (*47*) *purMN* genes would generate an in-frame AIR synthetase/GAR transformylase fusion. A precisely positioned intron between *Drosophila* GAR synthetase and AIR synthetase domains (*98*) suggests a translocation or transposition that may have occurred for the purpose of gene fusion. In addition, as noted below, it is also attractive to think that this intron has retained an independent role in gene expression.

The second aspect of the structure–function relationship in Fig. 6 concerns the rationale for multifunctional GAR synthetase/AIR synthetase/GAR transformylase in higher eukaryotes in contrast to the three monofunctional enzymes in bacteria. What is the role of the multifunctional enzyme? The usual explanations for multifunctional proteins are increased catalytic efficiency by channeling of substrates, and a mechanism to coordinate synthesis of proteins that are required in 1:1 stoichiometry (*99*). Although these are reasonable ideas, there is no experimental evidence for increased catalytic efficiency by the trifunctional enzyme, nor for interaction of enzyme 4, FGAM synthetase, which is required to permit direct channeling of PRA to AIR (Fig. 1). An earlier report of copurification of multiple activities required for the overall conversion of PRPP to IMP (*100*) has yet to be confirmed. Therefore, there is no evidence at this time that points to a unique role for the trifunctional enzyme.

A third important point is that there are mechanisms to adjust the stoichiometry in multifunctional enzymes. The alignment in Fig. 6 clearly shows two such mechanisms. (i) In the *Drosophila* enzyme, a gene duplication provides two complete copies of the AIR synthetase domain. Although the basis for the AIR synthetase duplication in *Drosophila* is not known, the duplication clearly increases the AIR synthetase stoichiometry relative to GAR synthetase and GAR transformylase. (ii) The stoichiometry of GAR synthetase to GAR transformylase is likewise adjusted in *Drosophila*, chickens, and probably humans. Conservation of a monofunctional GAR synthetase in invertebrates and vertebrates implies an essential function. The requirement for increased GAR synthetase might be to maximize the capacity for utilization of 5-phosphoribosylamine, the labile product of step 1. It has a half-life of 38 sec at 37°C and pH 7.5 (*101*), and excess GAR synthetase may be required for its rapid conversion to GAR, a stable product. The intron between GAR synthetase and AIR synthetase in the *Drosophila* GART gene appears to provide the alternative splicing mechanism (*98*) that permits synthesis of monofunctional and trifunctional versions of GAR synthetase from a single gene. It is not known whether alternative splicing is regulated in *Drosophila*, nor whether this intron is conserved in the vertebrate genes.

The trifunctional GAR synthetase/AIR synthetase/GAR transformylase was initially purified from chicken liver (*102*) and more recently from HeLa cells, L1210 cells (*103*), and a murine lymphoma cell line (*104*). GAR transformylase is a target of antifolate drugs that inhibit *de novo* purine nucleotide synthesis (*105*). A putative site for 10-formyltetrahydrofolate binding has been identified by sequence alignment with a domain of rat 10-formyltetrahydrofolate dehydrogenase (*106*) and affinity labeling with the folate analog N^{10}-(bromoacetyl)-5,8-dideazafolate (*107*). Overproduction of the cloned avian and human trifunctional enzymes will permit analysis by site-directed mutagenesis of catalytic mechanisms, inhibitory drugs, and channeling.

E. Steps 6 and 7: Bifunctional AIR Carboxylase/SAICAR Synthetase

cDNA encoding AIR carboxylase and SAICAR synthetase has been cloned from chicken liver (*85*) and human cell (*89, 90*) libraries by complementation of *E. coli* and yeast purine mutants. Functional domains were identified by alignments with the homologous bacterial (*12, 13, 17, 47*) and yeast (*108, 109*) genes. A representation of these alignments in Fig. 7 illus-

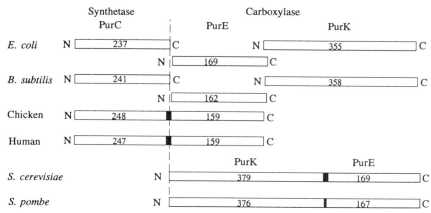

FIG. 7. Schematic representation of monofunctional and multifunctional SAICAR synthetase and AIR carboxylase. Bacterial SAICAR synthetase is designated PurC; bacterial AIR carboxylase, PurE and PurK. The solid boxes represent connector sequences, approximately 19 residues in chickens and humans, 23 residues in *Saccharomyces cerevisiae*, and nine residues in *Schizosaccharomyces pombe*, that join domains. The yeast AIR carboxylase is a PurK–PurE fusion.

trates several points. (i) The chicken and human amino-acid sequences, which are 85% identical, correspond to fusions of bacterial synthetase (PurC in bacterial nomenclature) and carboxylase (PurE) domains. The calculated M_r of 47,245 for the avian enzyme is close to the value of 50,000 estimated for the purified enzyme subunit (*110*). (ii) Because of low amino-acid conservation at the carboxyl terminus of PurC and the amino-terminus of PurE, the exact boundaries of the domains in the bifunctional enzymes are uncertain. Nevertheless, we estimate that the synthetase and carboxylase domains are joined by an approximately 19-amino-acid connector sequence not present in the microbial enzymes. This connector is conserved in 18 of 19 positions in the human and chicken enzymes. (iii) The cloned chicken and human cDNAs encode enzymes lacking the carboxylase PurK protein. Yet, as discussed below, these enzymes are functional in heterologous cells that normally utilize a PurK protein. The avian enzyme is functional in an *E. coli purK* mutant (*85*); the human enzyme, in a yeast *ade2* mutant (*89, 90*). (iv) The yeast carboxylase corresponds to a PurK–PurE fusion (*108, 109*) in which the two conserved carboxylase domains are joined by connector sequences of approximately 23 and nine amino acids in *Saccharomyces cerevisiae* and *Schizosaccharomyces pombe*, respectively.

Although the AIR carboxylase mechanism has not been studied, interesting implications can be derived from heterologous complementation experiments. *E. coli* AIR carboxylase is assumed to be a PurE–PurK oligomer (*12, 13*). The function of the *E. coli* PurK subunit is stated to be in CO_2 binding

(24), based on a requirement of elevated CO_2 for the growth of *purK* mutants. Thus, under normal growth conditions, PurE is thought to catalyze the carboxylation of AIR using CO_2 or HCO_3^- provided by PurK. The PurK subunit is essential since *purK* mutants are purine auxotrophs. However, since *purK* mutants can grow using elevated CO_2, it has been assumed that PurE can directly bind and utilize CO_2 (or HCO_3^-) only if the concentration is elevated.

The complementation of an *E. coli purK* mutant by chicken synthetase–carboxylase demonstrates that a PurK function is not needed for the AIR carboxylase reaction in *E. coli* at normal CO_2 levels. Carboxylase function, assayed by complementation of *purE* and *purK* mutants, was abolished by a series of point mutations and deletions in different regions of the PurE domain, but was not affected by mutations in the PurC synthetase domain (85). These results suggest that the chicken carboxylase differs from the microbial enzyme by having a lower K_m for CO_2/HCO_3^- or that *E. coli* PurK has a role other than binding CO_2. It appears possible that PurK may activate the PurE carboxylase subunit in some way.

To summarize, avian and human AIR carboxylase contains a PurE domain fused to a SAICAR synthetase domain. There is no evidence at present that a PurK function is required for the avian and human enzymes in birds, humans, or *E. coli*. The roles of the PurK subunit in *E. coli* and the PurK domain in the yeast carboxylase remain to be determined.

F. Steps 8 and 12: Adenylosuccinate Lyase

Avian adenylosuccinate lyase (EC 4.3.2.2) cDNA was isolated by functional complementation of an *E. coli purB* mutant (86). The derived amino-acid sequence of 459 residues exhibits 27% identity with the sequence of the *B. subtilis* enzyme, and 24% identity with that from *E. coli*. The avian and bacterial enzymes are homologous.

Based on the structural similarity of SAICAR and adenylosuccinate—substrates for steps 8 and 12, respectively—both compounds probably bind to the same active site; the enzyme is thus monofunctional, not bifunctional. The β-elimination reaction catalyzed by adenylosuccinate lyase is formally similar to that of argininosuccinate lyase (EC 4.3.2.1). Significant amino-acid sequence identity was noted between avian adenylosuccinate lyase and human argininosuccinate lyase, consistent with presumed similarities in their catalytic mechanisms (111). A block of amino-acid residues, GSSAM-PYKRHP, highly conserved in adenylosuccinate lyase, argininosuccinate lyase, and *E. coli* aspartase (EC 4.3.1.1) appears to be involved in β-elimination reactions that yield fumarate.

A deficiency of adenylosuccinate lyase in children has been implicated in a syndrome consisting of severe psychomotor retardation, muscle wasting, epilepsy, and autism (*112*, *113*). Patients with reduced adenylosuccinate lyase activity accumulate "succinylpurines" in cerebrospinal fluid, blood, and urine. These compounds are the dephosphorylated substrates of adenylosuccinate lyase. Decreased thermal stability was noted in the enzyme from lymphoblast cell lines of two siblings with infantile autism (*114*). Adenylosuccinate lyase cDNA from these cell lines as well as from normal human cells has been cloned and sequenced (R. Stone, J. Aimi, B. Barshop, H. Zalkin and J. E. Dixon, unpublished). A single-nucleotide change that results in a Ser^{413}-to-Pro replacement in the enzyme was identified. This nucleotide change also results in an *Hph*I restriction-fragment-length polymorphism. Introduction of a Ser^{413}-to-Pro replacement into the normal enzyme decreases thermal stability. It remains to be determined whether this change is responsible for the biochemical and clinical manifestations of the disease.

G. Steps 9 and 10: Bifunctional AICAR Transformylase/IMP Cyclohydrolase

Avian AICAR transformylase/IMP cyclohydrolase cDNA, isolated by complementation of an *E. coli purH* auxotroph, is the product of a single 2.3-kb mRNA (*87*). There is 36% identity between the sequences of the enzymes from chickens and bacteria. Definitive information is lacking on functional domains required for catalysis of the two sequential reactions. However, mouse FM3A-cell mutants deficient in AICAR transformylase have been classified into two complementation groups that are either IMP cyclohydrolase + or − (*115*). These mutations appear to define the two domains for steps 9 and 10 in the bifunctional enzyme.

The avian enzyme was initially purified by a six-step procedure, using affinity chromatography on AICAR–Sepharose (*116*). Recombinant avian AICAR transformylase/IMP cyclohydrolase, expressed in *E. coli* as a glutathione S-transferase fusion, can be purified in one step by affinity chromatography and isolated following cleavage of glutathione S-transferase. The V_{max} for this purified enzyme, which contains a 13-amino-acid NH_2-terminal extension, was one-tenth that of the enzyme purified from chicken liver, although K_m values for substrates were similar. The avian cDNA has been used to isolate the corresponding human cDNA. This should provide a source for preparation of large amounts of the human enzyme.

Both AICAR and GAR transformylase utilize N-10-formyltetrahydrofolate as a one-carbon donor. By sequence analysis, a "folate" site has been inferred in GAR transformylase (*106*), but a comparable site has not been noted in AICAR transformylase. To conclude that the sites for formyltetrahydrofolate binding in AICAR and GAR transformylases are structurally distinct would be consistent with the observed specificity for inhibition of these enzymes by antifolates (*117, 118*). The availability of human AICAR and GAR transformylase cDNAs should facilitate screening antifolates with specificity for inhibition of *de novo* purine nucleotide synthesis.

H. Steps 11 and 13: Adenylosuccinate Synthetase and IMP Dehydrogenase

The reactions catalyzed by adenylosuccinate synthetase (EC 6.3.4.4) and IMP dehydrogenase (EC 1.1.1.205) [Eqs. (4) and (5)] dictate the distribution of IMP into the AMP and GMP branches of the pathway. The reciprocal requirements of GTP for synthesis

$$IMP + aspartate + GTP \rightarrow suc\text{-}AMP + GDP + P_i \tag{4}$$

$$IMP + ATP + NAD^+ \rightarrow XMP + AMP + PP_i + NADPH \tag{5}$$

of AMP and ATP for synthesis of GMP presumably contribute to balanced production of the purine nucleotides. The effects of perturbations of the branch-point enzymes on the synthesis of adenine and guanine nucleotides have been determined (*119–122*). A murine lymphoma T-cell line deficient in adenylosuccinate lyase maintained a normal pool of ATP by increased *de novo* synthesis of IMP (*119, 120*). It is not known to what extent increased glutamine PRPP amidotransferase activity or amount contributed to enhanced *de novo* synthesis.

Two further consequences of increased synthesis of IMP were (i) a 10-fold increase in amount of GMP, but only a two-fold increase in GTP amount and (ii) massive excretion of inosine. Thus, the GMP pool has a limited capacity to regulate IMP dehydrogenase effectively. Yet there are unknown mechanisms to maintain the GTP pool and GTP/ATP ratio within a fairly narrow range. With a second transport mutation to limit efflux of inosine, the wild-type rate of *de novo* synthesis was restored, the ATP pool was maintained, and the GTP/ATP ratio remained two-fold greater than that of the wild type. Thus, *de novo* purine nucleotide synthesis in these cells is regulated by intracellular purine compounds and the GTP/ATP ratio is also maintained within a two-fold range. It appears likely that when efflux is limited, IMP regulates *de novo* synthesis by feedback inhibition of glutamine PRPP amidotransferase.

The biosynthetic role of adenylosuccinate synthetase is complicated by the existence of two species, acidic and basic isozymes, present in variable proportions in different tissues (reviewed in *123*). An acidic isozyme is considered to have a primary role in biosynthesis, while the basic isozyme may participate in a purine nucleotide cycle: AMP $\rightarrow$ IMP $\rightarrow$ adenylosuccinate $\rightarrow$ AMP. Multiple functions attributed to this cycle are controversial (*123*).

The possibility that both isozymes arise from a single gene is discussed below.

Adenylosuccinate synthetase cDNA has been cloned from *Dictyostelium discoideum* (*124*), mice (*124a*), and humans (S. M. Powell, H. Zalkin and J. E. Dixon, unpublished). The derived amino-acid sequences of these enzymes and that from *E. coli* are highly conserved (41–47% identity). The cloned mouse cDNA encodes the basic isozyme. The human adenylosuccinate cDNA encodes an enzyme with a calculated pI of 7.0. Sequence motifs attributed to nucleotide binding (*125*) have been identified and are conserved in all of the enzymes. These include the sequences GXXXXGK at positions 11–17 (numbering of the human sequence), DXXG at residues 283–286, and N/T KXD at 329–332.

Based on efforts to clone the human cDNA by functional complementation in *E. coli*, it is known that an intact NH_2 terminus is required for activity (S. M. Powell, H. Zalkin and J. E. Dixon, unpublished). Fusion of short *lacZ* and vector polylinker sequences abolishes enzyme activity and prevents functional complementation, whereas cDNA starting with Met^1 complements an *E. coli* *purA* mutant. One possibility is that a modified NH_2 terminus precludes folding and interaction of the NH_2-proximal GXXXXGK portion of the GTP site with internal elements of this site.

Northern blot analysis of RNA from human liver and HeLa cells has provided evidence for 2.3- and 2.8-kb transcripts that hybridize to the human adenylosuccinate synthetase cDNA probe. No evidence was obtained for RNAs encoding different isozymes. It is therefore necessary to consider that acidic and basic isozymes might be the products of a single gene. This would be consistent with genetic analyses in CHO cells. Mutation at a single locus, Ade⁻H, results in defective adenylosuccinate synthetase and a growth requirement for adenine (*126*, *127*). Furthermore, a single locus on human chromosome 1 encodes an adenylosuccinate synthetase that corrects the defect in Ade⁻H cells (*128*).

An IMP dehydrogenase clone was initially isolated from a mouse bone marrow expression library by the steps described in Section II,B (*82*). The mouse clone enabled isolation of intact coding sequences from CHO and human cells. Information from these sequences was subsequently used to isolate a second human IMP dehydrogenase cDNA (*83*) and the gene from *Leishmania* (*129*). Parasitic protoza are interesting because they are auxotrophic for purines. They scavenge purines from host cells and utilize the branch-point reactions 11–14 (Fig. 1) for synthesis of AMP and GMP.

IMP dehydrogenase isozymes type I and type II (84% amino-acid-sequence identity) are differently expressed in normal and neoplastic blood cells (*130*). A comparable level of 3.5-kb mRNA for type-I IMP dehydrogenase was present in normal lymphocytes and leukemic cells, whereas a 2.3-kb mRNA for type-II enzyme was selectively increased in leukemic cell lines, accounting for the eight- to nine-fold increase in enzyme activity. The functional significance of this selective gene expression remains to be determined.

I. Steps 4 and 14: FGAM Synthetase and GMP Synthetase

At this writing, clones for FGAM synthetase (step 4) and GMP synthetase (step 14) have not been isolated from higher eukaryotes. Avian FGAM synthetase is a large protein chain of M_r 133,000 (131), which may account for the lack of success in cloning by functional complementation. However, the availability of relatively large amounts of the avian enzyme (132) bodes well for near-term cloning. Mammalian GMP synthetase is a single protein chain of 78,000, which appears to interact with IMP dehydrogenase (133).

III. Summary and Perspective

We have outlined recent progress in understanding *de novo* purine nucleotide biosynthesis and its regulation in bacteria. A *purR*-encoded repressor–operator interaction plays a key role in the genetic regulation of purine biosynthesis in *E. coli* and also appears to be involved in coordinating the expression of genes in related metabolic pathways. The outline of a more complex regulatory system has been described for *de novo* purine nucleotide synthesis in *B. subtilis*. These advances have resulted from the cloning and analyses of structural genes encoding the biosynthetic enzymes and the *purR* regulatory gene from *E. coli*. Cloning of regulatory genes is essential for a further understanding of the regulation of purine nucleotide biosynthesis in *B. subtilis*.

Current work is aimed at isolating structural genes for purine synthesis from higher eukaryotes. The major recent development has been cDNA cloning for most of the steps in the purine pathway in birds and humans by interspecies functional complementation. Interspecies complementation has been used previously to isolate genes. The first genes from yeast were isolated by complementation of *E. coli* amino-acid auxotrophs (134). A *Drosophila GART* gene was isolated by complementation of a yeast *ade8* mutation (135). However, the extent to which avian cDNAs for a multistep pathway have been obtained by complementation of *E. coli* purine mutants is unprecedented. cDNA encoding eight of the 10 steps to IMP and two of the four steps in the branches to AMP and GMP have so far been obtained by functional complementation in *E. coli* and yeast. Development of improved expression vectors for isolation of genes by functional complementation in yeast and *E. coli* should further enhance this approach (*136*).

The isolation of avian and human cDNAs and genes for purine synthesis provides a starting point to address questions of catalysis, enzyme structure and function, and gene expression. Some of the questions are (i) What, if any, advantages do multifunctional enzymes confer to purine synthesis in animals relative to the corresponding monofunctional enzymes in bacteria? (ii) What are the relative contributions of enzyme regulation and gene regulation to *de novo* synthesis? (iii) How is the expression of genes for *de novo* purine nucleotide synthesis regulated? (iv) What determines the relative expression of genes for *de novo* and salvage synthesis in different tissues, with age, or during development, when requirements for RNA and DNA synthesis vary? (v) Is *de novo* purine nucleotide synthesis coordinated with the cell cycle? These are only some of the questions likely to be pursued.

There are two immediate applications for cloned cDNAs and genes. First, purine metabolism has been a fertile area for development of drugs against a variety of diseases (*137*). Folate antimetabolites have played an important role as antiproliferative drugs. There are straightforward approaches for screening antifolates against the two steps in purine biosynthesis, using *E. coli* mutants transformed with human GAR and/or AICAR transformylase. New inhibitors could be screened by a bacterial plate assay, using an *E. coli* strain in which the defective bacterial gene is replaced by a human cDNA. This strategy does not require the isolation and characterization of substrates and is not limited to the folate-utilizing enzymes in the pathway.

Second, the availability of the human cDNAs also offers the opportunity to identify and analyze new metabolic defects in *de novo* purine nucleotide synthesis. Although the loss of function of an enzyme in the pathway is expected to be lethal, subtle changes resulting from point mutations in a gene could have profound effects in pathophysiology. One such defect may be associated with alterations of adenylosuccinate lyase activity in a small number of autistic children (*112*, *113*). The availability of human cDNA generated from the work described here (*86*) offers the opportunity to evaluate this question in a manner not previously possible. Other enzymes in the pathway could be altered, and this in turn could be responsible for some idiopathic forms of gout.

ACKNOWLEDGMENTS

Work from our laboratories has been supported by USPHS Grants GM24658 (to H.Z.) and NIDDKD 18024 (to J.E.D.). Computer facilities were supported by NIH Grant AI27713. We thank Gaochao Zhou for help with sequence alignments and comments on the manuscript. We are grateful to Steven Henikoff and David Patterson for suggestions and corrections.

REFERENCES

1. J. J. Marr, R. L. Berens and D. J. Nelson, *BBA* **544**, 360 (1978).
2. B. Bachmann, *Microbiol. Rev.* **47**, 180 (1983).
3. M. Masters, *J. Bact.* **172**, 1173 (1990).
4. M. J. Fath, H. K. Mahanty and R. Kolter, *J. Bact.* **171**, 3158 (1989).
4a. M. J. Nonet, C. C. Marvel and D. R. Tolan, *JBC* **262**, 12209 (1987).
5. S. A. Wolf and J. M. Smith, *J. Bact.* **162**, 822 (1985).
6. J. Y. Tso, H. Zalkin, M. vanCleemput, C. Yanofsky and J. M. Smith, *JBC* **257**, 3525 (1982).
7. C. A. Makaroff and H. Zalkin, *JBC* **260**, 10378 (1985).
8. J. M. Smith and H. A. Daum III, *JBC* **262**, 10565 (1987).
9. G. Sampei and K. Mizobuchi, *JBC* **264**, 21230 (1989).
10. F. J. Schendel, E. Mueller, J. Stubbe, A. Shiau and J. M. Smith, *Bchem* **28**, 2459 (1989).
11. J. M. Smith and H. A. Daum III, *JBC* **262**, 10565 (1987).
12. W. Watanabe, G. Sampei, A. Aiba and K. Mizobuchi, *J. Bact.* **171**, 198 (1989).
13. A. A. Tiedeman, J. Keyhani, J. Kamholz, H. A. Daum III, J. S. Gots and J. M. Smith, *J. Bact.* **171**, 205 (1989).
14. A. Aiba and K. Mizobuchi, *JBC* **264**, 21239 (1989).
15. Y. Shen, J. Rudolph, M. Stern, J. M. Stubbe, K. A. Flannigan and J. M. Smith, *Bchem* **29**, 218 (1990).
16. K. A. Flannigan, S. H. Hennigan, H. H. Vogelbacker, J. S. Gots and J. M. Smith, *Mol. Microbiol.* **4**, 381 (1990).
17. A. A. Tiedeman, D. J. DeMarini, J. Parker and J. M. Smith, *J. Bact.* **172**, 6035 (1990).
18. S. A. Wolfe and J. M. Smith, *JBC* **263**, 19147 (1988).
19. A. A. Tiedeman, J. M. Smith and H. Zalkin, *JBC* **260**, 8676 (1985).
20. A. A. Tiedeman and J. M. Smith, *NARes* **13**, 1303 (1985).
20a. B. He, J. M. Smith and H. Zalkin, *J. Bact.* **174**, 130 (1992).
21. D. Hawley and W. McClure, *NARes* **11**, 2237 (1983).
22. B. He, A. Shiau, K. Y. Choi, H. Zalkin and J. M. Smith, *J. Bact.* **172**, 4555 (1990).
23. L. M. Meng, M. Kilstrup and P. Nygaard, *EJB* **187**, 373 (1990).
24. J. S. Gots, C. E. Benson, B. Jochimsen and K. R. Koduri, *Ciba Found. Symp.* **48**, 23 (1977).
25. R. A. Levine and M. W. Taylor, *MGG* **181**, 313 (1981).
26. R. J. Rolfes and H. Zalkin, *JBC* **263**, 19653 (1988).
27. M. Kilstrup, L. M. Meng, J. Neuhard and P. Nygaard, *J. Bact.* **171**, 2124 (1989).
28. Y. Kohara, K. Akiyama and K. Isono, *Cell* **50**, 495 (1987).
29. R. G. Brennan and B. W. Matthews, *JBC* **264**, 1903 (1989).
30. P. J. Farabaugh, *Nature* **274**, 765 (1978).
31. B. von Wilcken-Bergmann and B. Müller-Hill, *PNAS* **79**, 2427 (1982).
32. P. Valentin-Hansen, J. E. Løve Larsen, P. Højrup, S. A. Short and C. Barbier, *NARes* **14**, 2215 (1986).
33. J. K. Reidl, M. Römisch, M. Ehrmann and W. Boos, *J. Bact.* **171**, 4888 (1989).
34. C. Aslanidis and R. Schmitt, *J. Bact.* **172**, 2178 (1990).
35. K. Jahreis, P. W. Postma and J. W. Lengeler, *MGG* **226**, 332 (1991).
36. R. J. Rolfes and H. Zalkin, *J. Bact.* **172**, 5758 (1990).
37. K. Y. Choi and H. Zalkin, *J. Bact.* **172**, 3201 (1990).
38. H. R. Wilson and C. L. Turnbough, Jr., *J. Bact.* **172**, 3208 (1990).
39. J. Neuhard, L. M. Meng, K. I. Sprensen and R. A. Kelln, *Int. J. Purine Pyrimidine Res.* **1**, 61 (1990).
40. J. G. Steirt, R. J. Rolfes, H. Zalkin and G. V. Stauffer, *J. Bact.* **172**, 3799 (1990).
41. U. Houlberg and K. F. Jensen, *J. Bact.* **153**, 837 (1983).

42. R. J. Rolfes and H. Zalkin, *J. Bact.* **172**, 5637 (1990).
43. L. M. Meng and P. Nygaard, *Mol. Microbiol.* **4**, 2187 (1990).
44. H. Momose, H. Nishikawa and I. Shiio, *J. Biochem.* **59**, 325 (1966).
45. H. Nishikawa, H. Momose and I. Shiio, *J. Biochem.* **62**, 92 (1967).
46. C. A. Makaroff, H. Zalkin, R. L. Switzer and S. J. Vollmer, *JBC* **258**, 10586 (1983).
47. D. J. Ebbole and H. Zalkin, *JBC* **262**, 8274 (1987).
48. H. H. Saxild and P. Nygaard, *MGG* **211**, 160 (1988).
49. D. J. Henner, L. Band and H. Shimotsu, *Gene* **34**, 169 (1984).
50. C. L. Quinn, B. T. Stephenson and R. L. Switzer, *JBC* **266**, 9113 (1991).
51. A. Mountain, J. McChesney, M. C. M. Smith and S. Baumberg, *J. Bact.* **165**, 1026 (1986).
52. R. N. Brey, C. D. B. Banner and J. B. Wolf, *J. Bact.* **167**, 623 (1986).
53. C. J. Mackey, R. J. Warburg, H. O. Halvorson and S. A. Zahler, *Gene* **32**, 49 (1984).
54. P. Miller, A. Rabinowitz and H. Taber, *J. Bact.* **170**, 2735 (1988).
55. H. Zalkin and D. J. Ebbole, *JBC* **263**, 1595 (1988).
56. H. Shimotsu, M. Kuroda, C. Yanofsky and D. J. Henner, *J. Bact.* **166**, 461 (1986).
57. P. Gollnick, S. Ishino, M. I. Kuroda, D. J. Henner and C. Yanofsky, *PNAS* **87**, 8726 (1990).
58. F. Houman, M. R. Diaz-Torres and A. Wright, *Cell* **62**, 1153 (1990).
59. M. Debarboville, M. Arnaud, A. Fouet, A. Klier and G. Rapoport, *J. Bact.* **172**, 3966 (1990).
60. D. J. Ebbole and H. Zalkin, *JBC* **264**, 3553 (1989).
61. R. L. Switzer, *in* "Allosteric Enzymes" (G. Hervé, ed.), p. 129. CRC Press, Boca Raton, Florida, 1989.
62. L. J. Messenger and H. Zalkin, *JBC* **254**, 3382 (1979).
63. J. Y. Tso, M. A. Hermodson and H. Zalkin, *JBC* **257**, 3532 (1982).
64. S. J. Vollmer, R. L. Switzer, M. A. Hermodson, S. G. Bower and H. Zalkin, *JBC* **258**, 10582 (1983).
65. P. Mäntsälä and H. Zalkin, *JBC* **259**, 14230 (1984).
66. J.-L. Souciet, M. A. Hermodson and H. Zalkin, *JBC* **263**, 3323 (1988).
67. G. Oliver, G. Gosset, R. Sanchez-Pescador, E. Lozoya, L. M. Ku, N. Flores, B. Becerril, F. Valle and F. Bolivar, *Gene* **60**, 1 (1987).
68. L. Velázquez, L. Camarena, J. L. Reyes and F. Bastarrachea, *J. Bact.* **173**, 3261 (1991).
69. B. A. Averill, A. Dwivedi, P. Debrunner, S. J. Vollmer, J. Y. Wong and R. L. Switzer, *JBC* **255**, 6007 (1980).
70. J. A. Grandoni, R. L. Switzer, C. A. Makaroff and H. Zalkin, *JBC* **264**, 6058 (1989).
71. C. A. Makaroff, J. L. Paluh and H. Zalkin, *JBC* **261**, 11416 (1986).
72. R. E. Miller and E. R. Stadtman, *JBC* **247**, 7407 (1972).
73. P. B. Rowe and J. B. Wyngaarden, *JBC* **243**, 6373 (1968).
74. M. Itakura and E. W. Holmes, *JBC* **254**, 333 (1979).
75. J. P. Simmer, R. E. Kelly, A. G. Rinker, Jr., J. L. Scully and D. R. Evans, *JBC* **265**, 10395 (1990).
76. H. Zalkin, *in* "Multifunctional Proteins" (H. Bisswanger and E. Schmincke-Ott, eds.), p. 123. Wiley, New York, 1980.
77. Y. M. Bae, E. Holmgren and I. P. Crawford, *J. Bact.* **171**, 3471 (1989).
78. L. Lai, I. M. Hart and D. Patterson, *Genomics* **9**, 322 (1991).
79. D. Patterson, *in* "Molecular Cell Genetics" (M. Gottesman, ed.), p. 267. Wiley, New York, 1985.
80. S. Henikoff, M. A. Keene, J. S. Sloan, J. Bleskan, R. Hards and D. Patterson, *PNAS* **83**, 720 (1986).
81. D. C. Oates, D. Vannais and D. Patterson, *Cell* **20**, 799 (1980).
82. F. R. Collart and E. Huberman, *JBC* **263**, 15769 (1988).

83. Y. Natsumeda, S. Ohno, H. Kawasaki, Y. Konno, G. Weber and K. Suzuki, *JBC* **265**, 5992 (1990).

84. J. Aimi, H. Qiu, J. Williams, H. Zalkin and J. E. Dixon, *NARes* **18**, 6665 (1990).

85. Z. Chen. J. E. Dixon and H. Zalkin, *PNAS* **87**, 3097 (1990).

86. J. Aimi, J. Badylak, J. Williams, Z. Chen, H. Zalkin and J. E. Dixon, *JBC* **265**, 9011 (1990).

87. L. Ni, K. Guan, H. Zalkin and J. E. Dixon, *Gene* **106**, 197 (1991).

88. A. A. Tiedeman and J. M. Smith, *Gene* **97**, 289 (1991).

89. D. Schild, A. J. Brake, M. C. Kiefer, D. Young and P. J. Barr, *PNAS* **87**, 2916 (1990).

89a. F.-H. Chang, T. S. Barnes, D. Schild, A. Gnirke, J. Bleskan and D. Patterson, *Somatic Cell Mol. Genet.* **17**, 411 (1991).

89b. A. Gnirke, T. S. Barnes, D. Patterson, D. Schild, T. Featherstone and M. Olson, *EMBO J.* **10**, 1629 (1991).

90. M. Minet and F. Lacroute, *Curr. Genet.* **18**, 287 (1990).

91. J. M. Short, J. M. Fernandez, J. A. Sorge and W. D. Huse, *NARes* **16**, 7583 (1988).

92. B. Mei and H. Zalkin, *JBC* **264**, 16613 (1989).

93. B. Mei and H. Zalkin, *J. Bact.* **172**, 3512 (1990).

94. E. W. Holmes, *Adv. Enzyme Regul.* **19**, 215 (1981).

95. S. C. Hartman, *JBC* **238**, 3024 (1963).

96. M. A. Becker and M. Kim, *JBC* **262**, 14531 (1987).

97. G. Zhou, J. E. Dixon and H. Zalkin, *JBC* **265**, 21152 (1990).

97a. J. W. Barton, J. Bleskan, and D. Patterson, *Somatic Cell Mol. Genet.* **17**, 311 (1991).

98. S. Henikoff, J. S. Sloan and J. D. Kelly, *Cell* **34**, 405 (1983).

99. S. Henikoff, *BioEssays* **6**, 8 (1987).

100. P. B. Rowe, E. McCairns, G. Madsen, D. Sauer and H. Elliott, *JBC* **253**, 7711 (1978).

101. F. J. Schendel, Y. S. Cheng, J. D. Otvos, S. Wehrli and J. Stubbe, *Bchem* **27**, 2614 (1988).

102. S. C. Daubner, J. L. Schrimsher, F. J. Schendel, M. Young, S. Henikoff, D. Patterson, J. Stubbe and S. J. Benkovic, *Bchem* **24**, 7059 (1985).

103. S. C. Daubner, M. Young, R. D. Sammons, L. F. Courtney and S. J. Benkovic, *Bchem* **25**, 2951 (1986).

104. C. A. Caperelli, *Bchem* **24**, 1316 (1985).

105. S. W. Baldwin, A. Tse, L. S. Gossett, E. C. Taylor, A. Rosowsky, C. Shih and R. G. Moran, *Bchem* **30**, 1997 (1991).

106. R. J. Cook, R. S. Lloyd and C. Wagner, *JBC* **266**, 4965 (1991).

107. J. Inglese, J. M. Smith and S. J. Benkovic, *Bchem* **29**, 6678 (1990).

108. P. Szankasi, W. D. Heyer, P. Schuchert and J. Kohli, *JMB* **204**, 917 (1988).

109. A. Stotz and P. Linder, *Gene* **95**, 91 (1990).

110. C. A. H. Patey and G. Shaw, *BJ* **135**, 543 (1973).

111. E. Havir and K. Hanson, *in* "The Enzymes" (P. D. Boyer, ed.), 3rd Ed., Vol. 7, p. 75, Academic Press, New York, 1973.

112. J. Jaeken and G. van den Berghe, *Lancet* **2**, 1058 (1984).

113. J. Jaeken, S. K. Wadman, M. Duran, F. J. van Sprang, F. A. Beemer, R. A. Holl, P. M. Theunissen, P. de Cock, F. van den Bergh, M. F. Vincent and G. van den Berghe, *Eur. J. Pediatr.* **148**, 126 (1988).

114. B. Barshop, A. Alberts and H. Gruber, *BBA* **999**, 19 (1989).

115. Y. Matsake, D. Ayusawa, K. Shimizu, T. Seno and M. Matsuhashi, *Somatic Cell Mol. Genet.* **15**, 39 (1989).

116. W. T. Mueller and S. J. Benkovic, *Bchem* **20**, 337 (1981).

117. R. G. Moran, S. W. Baldwin, E. C. Taylor and C. Shih, *JBC* **264**, 21047 (1989).

118. R. Bertrand and J. Jolivet, *JBC* **264**, 8843 (1989).

119. B. Ullman, M. A. Wormsted, M. B. Cohen and D. W. Martin, Jr., *PNAS* **79**, 5127 (1982).

120. B. Ullman, K. Kaur and T. Watts, *MCBiol* **3**, 1187 (1983).

121. B. Ullman, *JBC* **258**, 523 (1983).

122. B. Ullman, *JBC* **258**, 9620 (1983).

123. M. M. Stayton, F. B. Rudolph and H. J. Fromm, *Curr. Top. Cell. Regul.* **22**, 103 (1983).

124. L. Wiesmüller, J. Wittbrodt, A. A. Noegel and M. Schleicher, *JBC* **266**, 2480 (1991).

124a. O. M. Guicherit, F. B. Rudolph, R. E. Kellems and B. F. Cooper, *JBC* **266**, 22582 (1991).

125. T. E. Dever, M. J. Glynia and W. C. Merrick, *PNAS* **84**, 1814 (1987).

126. D. Patterson, *Somatic Cell Genet.* **2**, 41 (1976).

127. A. S. Tu and D. Patterson, *BGen* **15**, 195 (1977).

128. L. Lai, I. M. Hart and D. Patterson, *Genomics* **9**, 322 (1991).

129. K. Wilson, F. R. Collart, E. Huberman, J. R. Stringer and B. Ullman, *JBC* **266**, 1665 (1991).

130. Y. Konno, Y. Natsumeda, M. Nagai, Y. Yamaji, S. Ohno, K. Suzuki and G. Weber, *JBC* **266**, 506 (1991).

131. J. M. Buchanan, S. Ohnoki and B. S. Hong, *in* "Methods in Enzymology" (P. A. Hoffee and M. E. Jones, eds.), Vol. 51, p. 193. (1978).

132. F. J. Schendel and J. Stubbe, *Bchem* **25**, 2256 (1986).

133. K. Hirai, Y. Matsuda and H. Nakagawa, *J. Biochem.* **102**, 893 (1987).

134. B. Ratzkin and J. Carbon, *PNAS* **74**, 487 (1977).

135. S. Henikoff, T. Tachell, B. D. Hall and K. A. Nasmyth, *Nature* **289**, 33 (1981).

136. S. J. Elledge, J. T. Mulligan, S. W. Ramer, M. Spottswood and R. W. Davis, *PNAS* **88**, 1731 (1991).

137. G. B. Elion, *Science* **244**, 41 (1989).

Index